Psychological Treatment of Health Anxiety and Hypochondriasis

A Biopsychosocial Approach

To Stacy, Emily, and Miriam with all my love.
— J.S.A.

To Eric, the love of my life.
— A.E.B.

Psychological Treatment of Health Anxiety and Hypochondriasis

A Biopsychosocial Approach

Jonathan S. Abramowitz, PhD
University of North Carolina

Autumn E. Braddock, PhD
VA Greater Los Angeles Healthcare System

HOGREFE

Library of Congress Cataloging in Publication

is available via the Library of Congress Marc Database under the
LC Control Number 2008923642.

Library and Archives Canada Cataloguing in Publication

Abramowitz, Jonathan S.
Psychological treatment of health anxiety and hypochondriasis : a biopsychosocial
approach / Jonathan S. Abramowitz, Autumn E. Braddock.
Includes bibliographical references.
ISBN 978-0-88937-347-1
1. Hypochondria. I. Braddock, Autumn E. II. Title.
RC552.H8A27   2008   616.85'25   C2008-903557-7

© 2008 by Hogrefe & Huber Publishers

PUBLISHING OFFICES
USA: Hogrefe & Huber Publishers, 875 Massachusetts Avenue, 7th Floor,
                Cambridge, MA 02139
                Phone (866) 823-4726, Fax (617) 354-6875; E-mail info@hhpub.com
EUROPE: Hogrefe & Huber Publishers, Rohnsweg 25, 37085 Göttingen, Germany
                Phone +49 551 49609-0, Fax +49 551 49609-88, E-mail hh@hhpub.com

SALES & DISTRIBUTION
USA: Hogrefe & Huber Publishers, Customer Services Department,
                30 Amberwood Parkway, Ashland, OH 44805
                Phone (800) 228-3749, Fax (419) 281-6883, E-mail custserv@hhpub.com
EUROPE: Hogrefe & Huber Publishers, Rohnsweg 25, 37085 Göttingen, Germany
                Phone +49 551 49609-0, Fax +49 551 49609-88, E-mail hh@hhpub.com

OTHER OFFICES
CANADA: Hogrefe & Huber Publishers, 1543 Bayview Avenue, Toronto,
                Ontario M4G 3B5
SWITZERLAND: Hogrefe & Huber Publishers, Länggass-Strasse 76, CH-3000 Bern 9

Hogrefe & Huber Publishers. Incorporated and registered in the State of Washington,
USA, and in Göttingen, Lower Saxony, Germany.

Printed and bound in the USA
ISBN: 978-0-88937-347-1

About the Authors

Jonathan S. Abramowitz, PhD, ABPP is Associate Professor and Associate Chair of Psychology as well as Research Associate Professor of Psychiatry, at the University of North Carolina (UNC) at Chapel Hill. He also serves as Director of the Anxiety and Stress Disorders Clinic at UNC. From 2000 to 2006 he was Director of the OCD/Anxiety Disorders Treatment and Research Program at the Mayo Clinic in Rochester, Minnesota. Dr. Abramowitz conducts research on the psychopathology and treatment of anxiety disorders and has authored or edited 5 books and over 100 peer-reviewed research articles and book chapters on these topics. He currently serves as Associate Editor of two professional journals, *Behavior Research and Therapy* and *Journal of Cognitive Psychotherapy*, as well as serving on the editorial boards of a number of other professional journals. Dr. Abramowitz is a member of the Obsessive Compulsive Foundation's Scientific Advisory Board and a member of the Anxiety Disorders Association of America's Clinical Advisory Board. In 2005 he was elected to the Board of Directors of the Association for Behavioral and Cognitive Therapies (formerly AABT). He also served on the DSM-IV-TR Anxiety Disorders Work Group. In 2003, Dr. Abramowitz received the Outstanding Contributions to Research Award from the Mayo Clinic Department of Psychiatry and Psychology, and in 2004 he received the David Shakow Early Career Award for Outstanding Contributions to Clinical Psychology from Division 12 (Clinical Psychology) of the American Psychological Association. He currently lives in Chapel Hill, North Carolina with his wife, Stacy, and their daughters Emily and Miriam.

Autumn E. Braddock, PhD, is a primary care psychologist within the Veterans Affairs Greater Los Angeles Healthcare System, specializing in behavioral medicine and cognitive-behavioral therapy for anxiety. She is the former Codirector of the Anxiety Disorders Clinic at Mayo Clinic (2006–2008), where she served as a staff clinical health psychologist in the Department of Psychiatry and Psychology and an Instructor in the Mayo Medical School. Dr. Braddock received her B.A. in Psychology from Yale University and her Ph.D. in Clinical Psychology with a minor in Sport Psychology from UCLA. She completed an APA-Accredited internship at the VA Greater Los Angeles Healthcare System (West Los Angeles) and a 2-year APA-Accredited postdoctoral fellowship in Clinical Health Psychology at Mayo Clinic. She has received numerous awards and grants including the Howard R. Rome Fellow Grand Rounds Award at Mayo Clinic, Distinguished Teaching Award at UCLA, and the Mead Prize for Leadership and Character at Yale University. Dr. Braddock has presented her research, primarily addressing anxiety within medical populations, at national and international conferences. She enjoys visiting with her loving parents and brothers in Colorado. Currently, she lives in Santa Maria, California with her partner and best friend, Eric.

Table of Contents

About the Authors v

Table of Contents vii

Preface ix

Acknowledgments xii

Part 1
What Do We Know About Health Anxiety?

 1 The Clinical Picture: Health Anxiety in Their Own Words   3

 2 The Nature of Health Anxiety 13

 3 Causes of Health Anxiety: Nature, Notion, and Nurture 41

 4 The Persistence of Health Anxiety 67

 5 Treating Health Anxiety: Overview and Evidence 85

Part 2
Effective Assessment and Treatment of Health Anxiety

 6 Initial Assessment and Diagnosis 103

 7 Enhancing Motivation and Communication 123

 8 Functional Assessment 145

 9 Case Formulation and Treatment Planning 167

10 Psychoeducation 181

11 Cognitive Therapy 203

12 Exposure Therapy and Response Prevention 233

13 Overcoming Common Obstacles and Maintaining Treatment Gains 257

References 275

Appendix 289

Index 317

Preface

Despite a rich 2000-year history, hypochondriasis remains a controversial topic in the fields of mental health and medicine. Some experts consider it a primary mental disorder; others view it as secondary to more prominent psychological conditions such as depression; still others view it as a personality trait or disorder – a Freudian defence mechanism, an abnormal perceptual style, a means of nonverbal communication, or a response to stress, trauma, or abuse. Not surprisingly, throughout the millennia, hypochondriasis has been a much misunderstood, criticized, and scorned condition. Even today, at the beginning of the 21st century, hypochondriasis evokes mostly a bewildered sigh from many clinicians, who often view those with this and related conditions as little more than a nuisance. But what sufferers of this and related problems truly need is for their treatment providers to listen more carefully to their complaints – and to listen in a *different* way. The focus of this book thus reflects recent advances in the understanding of hypochondriasis and related problems as *health anxiety*.

Our collaboration began at the Mayo Clinic in Rochester, Minnesota. Mayo Clinic is one of the best places in the world to study health anxiety because it attracts medical patients from around the United States (and indeed from around the world) who have been referred from primary care and specialty physicians in their local areas who were unable to successfully diagnose or treat the individual. Once at Mayo, most of these patients receive consultation and, often, helpful treatment for their medical problems. A significant minority, however, are examined thoroughly yet found to have no organic basis for their physical complaints. A proportion of such individuals are relieved to receive the news that they are in fact medically healthy. Yet, there remains one last group of patients who appear unsatisfied when test after test, exam after exam, yields nothing but negative results. It is as if such individuals simply cannot accept their being told they are healthy.

That's where we, the clinical psychologists, come in! Our colleagues in internal medicine, cardiology and cardiovascular diseases, neurology, and gastroenterology (among other specialties) rely on our expertise in anxiety and behavioral medicine to provide proper evaluation and consultation for patients with persistent but medically unexplained (or undiagnosed) physical symptoms who do not respond to what would otherwise be a convincing reassurance of good health. There is but one further difficulty: Many individuals in this position do not appreciate being told by their physicians that they need to see a mental-health professional. They often perceive this as akin to being told that "it's all in your head." Thus, the initial hurdle in working with such individuals is engaging them in consultation or treatment.

As the reader can gather, the task of helping individuals with medically unexplained symptoms to view their problem as one involving psychological factors such as anxiety and fear (as opposed to a serious or rare medical condition that requires even further evaluation) is a difficult one indeed. After much training and practice (and much trial and error), we have, often on the basis of existing theoretical and empirical work, developed a conceptual framework that helps us understand these patients as suffering from *health anxiety* – characterized by excessive fear and worry that they *might* have a terrible disease. We have also adapted techniques for assessing, consulting for, and treating individuals with health anxiety using empirically supported techniques. We share this information in the present volume.

Part 1 of the book presents the scientifically based theoretical framework for understanding health anxiety and related phenomena. The opening chapters help clinicians form a conceptualization of the problem to guide them through the use of treatment procedures described in Part 2 of the book. Chapter 1 presents a case example illustrating the symptoms of health anxiety from the perspective of the patient and his treatment providers. In Chapter 2, we explore the nature of health anxiety; in Chapter 3, we examine various explanations of the causes of health anxiety; and in Chapter 4, we outline a biopsychosocial model to explain how the problem persists despite medical evidence to the contrary. Part 1 concludes with Chapter 5, which presents a review of the health-anxiety treatment literature.

Part 2 illustrates how to conduct assessment, consultation, and psychological treatment for health-related anxiety. The treatment procedures described have a solid scientific foundation, yet applying them is still very much an art that requires a blend of sensitivity and ingenuity. Effective treatment relies on thorough assessment, motivating the patient for change, and includes a strong educational component. The emphasis is on helping patients (1) to correct mistaken beliefs and interpretations about relatively benign body sensations and other health-relevant stimuli, and (2) to stop performing behaviors that interfere with the correction of these mistaken beliefs. Thus, an implied goal of therapy is to increase tolerance for acceptable levels of uncertainty when it comes to one's health.

Within Part 2, Chapter 6 describes the initial assessment of health anxiety using interview and self-report questionnaire techniques. The aim of Chapter 7 is to give the clinician techniques for engaging the patient in psychological treatment, which is often a very challenging task. Chapters 8 and 9 describe how to build on the diagnostic assessment and gather information about the patient's difficulties in a way that guides the construction of an individualized case formulation and treatment plan. Chapter 10 (psychoeducation), Chapter 11 (cognitive therapy), and Chapter 12 (exposure and response prevention) constitute a flexible manual for implementing empirically supported cognitive and behavioral treatment as informed by the conceptual model presented in the first part of the book. Finally, Chapter 13 provides solutions to a number of common obstacles in treatment as well as describes a maintenance program to be implemented following termination of treatment. Case examples illustrating phenomenology, assessment, and treatment are abundant throughout the book (the names of patients have been changed to protect confidentiality), and worksheets to be used in therapy are provided in many of the chapters.

Let us offer some words about treatment manuals in general, especially manuals for the treatment of health anxiety. Psychological treatment manuals are intended to standardize therapy procedures across clinicians and patients. Optimally, such documents should specify the essential principles of assessment and treatment, and provide respective guidelines for implementation. The challenge in writing such a manual is to describe the principles of treatment in sufficient detail that they can be applied to a variety of patients, but not in so much detail that the manual becomes overly cumbersome. Striking this balance is difficult in the case of health anxiety, since this constellation of problems is heterogeneous: Each patient presents with his or her particular health concerns. Indeed, no manual could adequately address the implementation of treatment across the countless personal variations of health anxiety. Our solution, therefore, is to present numerous case examples and emphasize the need for thorough assessment, flexibility, and creativity in dealing with the symptom variations one is likely to be come across in clinical practice. In general, any manifestations of health anxiety we do not address in this volume can be managed by relying on the cognitive-behavioral conceptualization that forms the basis of successful treatment.

Acknowledgments

This volume reflects how we conceptualize, provide consultation for, and treat the constellation of problems known as health anxiety. The theoretical model and intervention strategies elucidated herein are based on a firm foundation of scientific literature of which we are both consumers and contributors; we would like to thank all those who have helped us learn from and add to this knowledge. This includes the countless patients we have evaluated and treated, and whose treatment we have supervised; as well as our teachers who have taught us so much about the clinical and research methods described in this book.

We have been very fortunate to have formed many collaborative relationships with fine researchers, clinicians, and teachers in the field of anxiety. We would especially like to thank those with whom we have worked most closely, including Michelle Craske, Brett Deacon, Kristi Dahlman, Sarah Kalsy, Dean McKay, Katherine Moore, Bunmi Olatunji, Mary Sheeran, Jill Snuggerud, and Steven Taylor: They have helped us refine our thinking about the concepts and treatment techniques discussed herein. Thanks also to Rob Dimbleby from Hogrefe & Huber Publishers for his enthusiastic support and assistance throughout the writing process.

PART 1

What Do We Know About Health Anxiety?

1

The Clinical Picture: Health Anxiety in Their Own Words

This opening chapter gives the reader an example of the experience of health anxiety from the perspective of the patient and his or her treatment providers. Health anxiety involves physiologic, cognitive, and behavioral processes that exert influence on one another. Although the three factors might not have an equal impact on dysfunction in any given individual (e.g., a person's health anxiety might be determined primarily by physiological factors rather than by behavioral factors at any particular time), most often it is important to attend to all three domains in assessment and therapy. The following case example illustrates the complex interplay of the factors in one man's struggle with intense health anxiety.

Background

Gabriel is a 42-year-old married man with two school-aged children. He is employed as a computer security analyst at a regional airport and describes this job as "often pretty stressful." An avid soccer player in high school and college, Gabriel had always taken good care of his body and had always been particularly conscientious about his health – habits that he continued even after the birth of his children. For instance, he consumes alcohol only rarely and maintains a healthy diet. He also has a full gym in the basement of his home where he and his wife work out several times each week. Sleep is very important to Gabriel, and he is careful to get at least 7 hours of rest each night. He says he notices a difference in how his body feels after only 6 hours of sleep as compared to when he has a "full 7-hour" night of sleep.

Gabriel takes his personal health seriously, perhaps in part because of the fact that he has always been athletic. Yet another possible explanation is that several members of his family had suffered medical problems and died somewhat early in life, making Gabriel feel somewhat vulnerable to illnesses. When Gabriel was 17, his grandfather developed heart problems and passed away suddenly. Later, when Gabriel was 27, his father developed a serious case of liver cancer and died within several months. The death of his father was particularly distressing to Gabriel since the two had been very close. Gabriel had spent lots of time tending to his ill father's needs and providing care. When his father was given just 6 months to live, it made Gabriel put his own life into perspective. Although he began to show greater concern with his own health after witnessing his father's illness and eventual death, significant problems involving health anxiety – under which Gabriel now suffers – did not begin until a decade later. Below, in his own words, is Gabriel's story . . .

Gabriel's Perspective

Since my father died I had always felt like it was only a matter of time before *I* got ill; and finally, 6 months ago, it struck. I remember the exact moment. I was walking up the stairs to my office at work and I felt my heart beating more rapidly than normal. I had trouble breathing. I felt lightheaded for a few minutes. My fingers and toes started to feel cold and numb *like I was dying*. It was awful – I'd never felt that way before in my life. I wondered what could be wrong with me since I climb those three flights of stairs every day without any problem. I remember breaking out into a cold sweat and my head spinning as if my brain had become detached from the rest of my body and was just swimming around in my head. I'd heard about people – even those who never smoked – developing lung cancer at my age, and for a few days I couldn't get the idea out of my head that *that's what I had*. After that incident, my health start going down hill. One sign was when I got on the treadmill, my heart would start to race and I would feel short of breath. "I must be putting too much strain on my lungs," I said to myself. So, I figured it was a good idea for me not to exercise until I saw a doctor. I also stopped sexual relations with my wife because that increased the strain on my heart and lungs, too.

I had to know just what was going on and couldn't wait until my doctor's appointment later that week. I spent lots of time researching my symptoms on the internet; and sure enough, I read that shortness of breath, lightheadedness, and tachycardia could be signs of lung cancer. So, when I went to see my primary care physician, Dr. Watson, I explained to him what had been happening to me. When I mentioned my concerns about lung cancer, to my surprise he didn't seem very alarmed. He only asked me how work was going and if everything was all right at home. When I said that everything had been going fine, he physically examined me by listening to my heart and lungs, feeling my neck and throat, taking my blood pressure, and doing a few other tests and asking a few more questions. During that appointment, I remember feeling worried that he was about to tell me I was in big trouble; but again, *he* didn't seem concerned.

At the end of the exam I asked Dr. Watson, "So, how do I look?" He confirmed that my heart was beating rapidly and that my breathing seemed a little strained, but said that nothing serious had come up during my physical exam. Still, he said he would get to the bottom of it and he asked me to have some other blood tests which would help reveal what was wrong. When I went back to Dr. Watson a week later to get the test results, he said they didn't show anything serious. At that point, I objected and suggested a second opinion. That's when Dr. Watson sent me to a heart and lung specialist, Dr. Singleton.

A week later I met Dr. Singleton, who looked over my medical records and examined me. During my consultation he ran some tests on my heart and lungs, but when these came up negative he rather quickly concluded that my heart and lungs were healthy, and that my problems were due to "stress." I disagreed with him, but he reiterated that he thought everything was OK, and that I should "go home and rest," and feel reassured that I was in fine health. I didn't like this kind of treatment; my problems were not caused by *stress* – there was something *seriously wrong* with my heart and lungs. I had hoped Dr. Singleton would help me figure out what was happening to me and start me on the road to recovery. Instead, I left his office feeling *worse*. All I could think about was what could be wrong.

More trouble came my way a few days later when I woke up one morning (it was a Tuesday). As I was getting out of bed, I started feeling dizzy and lightheaded again. I think I almost fainted on my way into the bathroom. This was especially disconcerting because I had just had 8 full hours of sleep, so my body should have been in top condition and ready for the day. That's how I knew there must be something seriously wrong. I stayed home from work that day and it seemed the only thing I could do to keep from getting dizzy and passing out was to just lay in bed. After some persistence with Dr. Singleton's office, I was given a referral to see a specialist in hematology. I made an appointment for the following week and proceeded to read all the information I could about blood diseases so that I would be prepared for my visit.

Meanwhile I ended up missing work the rest of the week because of my illness. Every time I tried getting up from the bed I felt lightheaded. Going to the bathroom became an adventure. Even while I was in bed I would notice my heart rate speeding up and my breath becoming shallow from time to time (I prayed to God not to take me before I could at least figure out what was wrong with me). My fingers, toes, and lips sometimes felt numb and tingly, my mouth and eyes felt dry, and I occasionally felt chest pains. I was also weak and unable to deal with anything. My wife even had to bring me my food. On one of my internet searches, I read that all of these physical symptoms could be signs of diseases I hadn't even considered: multiple sclerosis, diabetes, and even amyotrophic lateral sclerosis (ALS or Lou Gehrig's disease). I remember reading the book *Tuesday's with Morrie*, which is about a man who died of ALS. It was an awful demise. I worried that this was in store for me as well. I thought about

Dad a lot that week. Like him, I had quickly gone from feeling very healthy to feeling very sick. I suppose it's in our genes.

My much-anticipated visit with Dr. Brody, the hematology specialist, was not exactly what I'd expected. I had been very hopeful, but she didn't have any answers for me. She read over my medical records, interviewed me about my symptoms, physically examined me, ran a few tests on my blood and urine. But in the end, she told me she thought I was in good health. When I ask about Lou Gehrig's disease and M.S., she chuckled at me and tried to reassure me that I didn't have these diseases. It took several times restating my symptoms before I could get her to recommend some extra lab tests just to be sure she wasn't missing anything. This scared the hell out of me. Why would she refer me for more tests if she didn't think anything was wrong?

So, I had some lab work done on my blood to check for lupus, anemia, lymphoma, Hodgkin's disease, and other diseases. But these all came up negative. Perhaps, I thought, I was suffering from an extremely rare condition that no tests could detect. Dr. Body tried to reassure me one day on the phone, "You have no serious medical history, you've taken good care of yourself, and you're young. When I consider all of this along with the results from all of these tests, my experience and judgment tells me that you are a healthy man." But I disagreed – she *had* to be missing something. After two visits with more specialists to get additional opinions, I met again with Dr. Watson (the primary-care doctor) who reviewed all of my records and said he was referring me to the Mayo Clinic for a complete work-up. "Now we're getting somewhere," I thought. Surely the doctors at the Mayo would be able to figure out what was wrong with me.

One month later I was in Rochester, Minnesota, at the Mayo Clinic. I started out with a general internal medicine specialist, Dr. Newman, who read my medical history and arranged for me to see five different doctors in four days. Each of these specialists conducted various tests which were fed back to Dr. Newman to review with me at the end of my visit. I was curious as to why one of the doctors on my list was a clinical psychologist. After all, I was here for a medical work-up, not a psychiatric problem. When I met with her, the psychologist, Dr. Davis, said most Mayo patients see a psychologist since Mayo's philosophy is that mind and body are interrelated. Dr. Davis asked me about my experiences feeling frustrated with not having a good explanation for my medical symptoms. She never said I was making up my symptoms, but she *did* give me the name of another psychologist in my hometown. She recommended I call this person if I don't get a satisfactory explanation for my medical problems and continue to feel frustrated.

Unfortunately, my frustration continued since even the "world-famous" Mayo Clinic couldn't give me a straight answer. At the end of my stay in Rochester, Dr. Newman reviewed each test result with me. But all of the tests were negative, and all of the doctors had indicated that they considered me generally healthy. Although this uniform conclusion put me at ease temporarily, I wondered why the doctors had also suggested I keep an eye on my symptoms. Some had even recommended one or two further tests that *could* be done to rule out possible problems, which they said were "unlikely." Puzzled and uncertain, I asked Dr. Newman why I was having all of these physical symptoms if I was medically healthy. He again suggested that it could be due to "stress." But, I didn't like that answer: I was not going crazy, and I was not making up these symptoms! Then something made me start to wonder whether the Mayo doctors had all discounted me as a hypochondriac. Maybe I would never get a straight answer. Part of me wanted to believe there was nothing wrong, but deep inside I couldn't stand not knowing for sure.

When I returned home things started getting worse. I was missing more work and wasn't socializing very much since all I could think of was my health. I avoided certain places where I might encounter second-hand smoke and other dangerous airborne chemicals; and I restricted my diet based on advice I had read on various medical websites. I didn't do anything I thought might put unnecessary strain on my body. I bought a stethoscope, blood pressure cuff, and lung capacity meter so that I could keep track of my symptoms and report this to my doctors, who I called and visited every few weeks. I was referred to five or six different specialists to get more opinions, but no two physicians had the same impressions. After a number of MRIs, EKGs, and stress tests came up negative I was beginning to feel suicidal. I had invested so much time and money in trying to find out what was wrong with me, but I had literally nothing to show for it.

My wife was becoming more and more upset with me. She wanted our life back. She was sick and tired of how much time and energy I was spending on trying to get a grip on my illness. She was also infuriated by the financial costs I had incurred. Finally, she pleaded with me to see the psychologist I was referred to while at the Mayo Clinic. She was right. Things were getting out of control. Perhaps the psychologist could at least help me cope with my illness. So, I decided to give it a try. I went and saw Dr. Moore for a consultation. She seemed to understand how frustrated I was feeling, although I wonder whether she really believed I was sick (a few times she interrupted me rather than listening to all of my symptoms). Anyway, I am going back for a second visit to see what therapy is all about. I have my doubts, but I've caused so much upheaval in my family that I owe this to my wife.

The Physician's Perspective

Dr. Watson (Gabriel's Primary-Care Physician)

When Gabriel first came to see me I thought there might be some sort of serious medical illness present. After all, he was very persistent, and his complaints sounded serious. When a thorough physical exam didn't show anything, I even ordered some comprehensive lab tests. I remember sending him home from that first visit by reassuring him that we would get to the bottom of things. I thought the tests would reveal something definitive, but when they came back unremarkable, I decided he needed to be referred to see a specialist. Perhaps I was missing something important.

When I saw Gabriel a few months later he had been evaluated by a number of specialty doctors – experts in their field – who had run numerous tests, all of which had come back negative. The specialists had unanimously concluded that Gabriel was not ill. Instead, they suggested he was suffering from stress and hypochondriasis. I agreed that Gabriel's somatic complaints were probably caused by a psychological problem such as stress, anxiety, or depression, but not a medical illness. I found this interesting since I'd had a hunch Gabriel was a hypochondriac the first time I saw him. I noticed the way he described vague symptoms and was preoccupied with having terrible and very rare illnesses. It raised a red flag for me. Things just didn't seem to add up when he told his story. Still, I wasn't absolutely sure; and because you have to practice defensive medicine these days, I didn't want to take any chances. After all, how could I tell someone they are a hypochondriac?

But now we had lots of evidence of good health. Still, when I confronted Gabriel with this reality, he was quite displeased. He wanted more tests and was not ready to accept that his problems were all in his head. I tried very hard to reassure him that everything was fine, but each time he kept calling my office asking about more and more possible problems that he might have. It's almost as if he was trying to *stump* me. What would it take to make him happy? Once when I suggested he see a psychiatrist he became very angry and hung up the phone on me. What was I to do? I think he wanted me to show concern for him, but that was hard to do when he was being so intrusive and disrespectful. He would call my secretary every few days trying to speak to me. So, I finally gave in and told him he could be right – something *could* be wrong that was not caught despite all of the testing. That's when I made the referral to the Mayo Clinic. They would either find something wrong or reassure Gabriel once and for all that he was healthy. Gabriel liked the idea of going to Mayo.

Dr. Newman (Department of Internal Medicine, Mayo Clinic Rochester)

The Mayo Clinic Department of Internal Medicine serves a regional and national patient base. Most of our clientele is referred from primary-care and specialty physicians who either desire a second (or third or fourth) opinion or who feel unable or unequipped to handle cases of very serious illnesses. Our department is the first stop when most people come to Mayo. From here, they are commonly referred for consultation (and perhaps treatment) in other specialty areas at the clinic. Before going home, most patients meet again with us to put closure to their visit.

We see our share of patients with unexplained physical complaints. These patients are not satisfied with their medical care at home – not that their care is actually deficient in any way, but the patient is not satisfied with the feedback (the *results*) they receive from their doctors. When all referral options are exhausted in the patient's region, they might then be referred to Mayo for our expertise. In the words of many of our patients, we are their "last hope" of finding a diagnosis.

In the case of Gabriel it was not surprising that medical tests were not helpful in determining a definitive diagnosis, since there did not appear to be anything seriously medically wrong with him. It is our job, however, to provide a comprehensive workup and rule out all possible medical explanations: We don't want to leave any stone unturned. That said, I ordered a consultation with a psychologist for Gabriel since there were notes in his medical record indicating that he seemed to be preoccupied with his health. The behavioral medicine psychologists at Mayo are adept at recognizing the role that stress can play in influencing medical symptoms, even if these symptoms are not part of a serious disease. Patients like Gabriel often feel cast off when told they will be seeing a psychologist, yet I try to explain the importance of a thorough workup that includes mental as well as physical health. It is important for them to see the links between the two. In the end, what Gabriel really needs is a psychologist who can give him reassurance that he is well and teach him strategies for relaxing when he is feeling stressed.

The Psychologist's Perspective

Dr. Davis, Behavioral Medicine Section, Mayo Clinic

Our section is part of the Psychiatry and Psychology Department at Mayo, and we generally serve the other medical practices. For example, we conduct consultations and short-term therapy for patients with serious diseases (e.g., cancer, diabetes, and those in need of organ transplants) who are also having problems with depression, anxiety, or with issues related to the self-management of their medical conditions. Another population we serve includes patients with somatic complaints but no organic pathology. Often, these individuals present as overly preoccupied with concerns about having serious illnesses and have seen many physicians and undergone many tests, the results of which are generally negative. Nevertheless, they seem determined to find a medical diagnosis for their suspected problem and often do not (and are unwilling to) consider the possibility that psychological factors are playing a role in their difficulties. My job is to determine what role such factors might be playing and to recommend getting help from this perspective along with (if not in lieu of) continuing the search for a proper medical diagnosis (which usually does not bear fruit).

Like many patients the physicians from Internal Medicine refer to us for consultation, Gabriel appeared perturbed that he was in a psychologist's office. He must have told me that he wasn't "stressed or crazy" at least 10 times during the 90 minutes I spent meeting with him. It wasn't exactly clear where Gabriel got the message that he is stressed or mentally ill, but it is unfortunate he feels he has to deny this so vehemently. After all, I wouldn't refer to his problems as "mental illness." I don't think he is making up his symptoms; nor do I think he has a personality disorder and is trying to gain attention. Instead, I fully accept that Gabriel is experiencing the physical sensations he reports. The question is, however, whether these sensations are really as serious as Gabriel thinks they are. I had reviewed Gabriel's medical records before his visit, but took the time to ask him about them during our session. Although his physicians aren't finding anything wrong, Gabriel is having a very hard time accepting that perhaps he is not as sick as he thinks. That is, he appears to be misinterpreting his bodily sensations as more serious than they really are. The following interaction took place during the consultation:

Dr. Davis: So, what have your doctors told you about your physical complaints?
Gabriel: They don't seem to find anything wrong with me. None of the tests are positive.
Dr. Davis: I see; that's what I read in your medical records, too. I wonder what that's like for you. You know, to be told that you aren't ill even though you have all of these symptoms.
Gabriel: It makes me very upset . . . and worried. First, they say that they can't find anything wrong, but then the doctor usually wants to rule something out, so he tells me to get another test. What am I supposed to think?
Dr. Davis: I can understand your frustration. It would be nice to have a straight answer, wouldn't it?
Gabriel: Well, I'm going to keep searching until I get one. I have one more test in hematology later today. That's my last hope.
Dr. Davis: Hmm. Let me ask you a question. How many tests have you had since you started feeling sick?

Gabriel: Oh God, probably between 15 and 20 for different sorts of problems.

Dr. Davis: Can I ask you, then, given what the previous test results have shown, would you bet that this afternoon's test is going to give you a definitive answer or not?

Gabriel: Probably not, but I need to know anyway. I just know there is something wrong with me. We just have to get to the bottom of this.

Sometimes in trying to helpful, physicians inadvertently reinforce somatization, illness behavior, and problems involving health anxiety. For example, by suggesting that there are more and more problems to "rule out," doctors perpetuate concerns that something *could* be seriously wrong. This also reinforces the patient's mistaken belief that any and all bodily symptoms must be accounted for with a medical explanation. In other words, it would be impossible to feel something in your body without being sick. Suggesting "one more test" also keeps patients in the sick role and puts them on an emotional roller coaster of mixed messages ("she said I was healthy, but suggested one more diagnostic test"). Even suggesting that Gabriel "keep an eye on" his symptoms reinforces paying attention to bodily sensations that don't seem to be serious, but that evoke excessive illness concerns.

How would I help Gabriel? *Not* by trying to reassure him that he is fine! This approach clearly hasn't worked when his other doctors have tried, and he already spends lots of time trying to gain assurances about his health from textbooks and the internet. What good would it do for one more person (a nonphysician) to try to convince him that he's healthy? Instead, I would help him develop alternate, less threatening, explanations for his bodily sensations by closely exploring with him and helping him challenge his own logic about what these symptoms mean. For example, there are a lot of relevant facts that Gabriel ignores when he gets concerned about his health. I would also explore with him how he responds when he notices certain bodily symptoms, and how such responses might actually be making his problems worse. For example, monitoring his vital signs only makes him more aware of body symptoms. He should learn new techniques for dealing with such symptoms so that they do not lead to preoccupation and illness worry. Of course, the first step would be helping Gabriel to buy into the possibility that examining behavioral and psychological factors could be helpful. Engaging him in therapy will not be an easy task, but there are nonconfrontational strategies that can help motivate people like him to more carefully consider the advantages and disadvantages of trying out this new approach. We wrapped up the consultation by having the following exchange:

Dr. Davis: So, if you had to decide on the percentage of your symptoms that is due to a medical illness versus the percentage that might be due to psychological factors, what would your estimates be? Is it 50–50? 60–40?

Gabriel: No, I'd say it's more like 90–10. No offense, but my problems are 90%
   medical. Maybe 10% is psychological.
Dr. Davis: Hmm. So, what kind of a role do you think psychological factors
   might be playing, even if they are only 10% of the problem?
Gabriel: Well, I guess I do get pretty stressed out by not having an answer. But,
   I don't understand how that makes my symptoms worse.
Dr. Davis: So, if I recommended that you get some help for managing stress –
   even if this is only 10% of the problem – would you consider it? I mean,
   you've got nothing to lose, and perhaps it could be helpful, don't you think?
Gabriel: Maybe . . . sure. I'll think about it.

As the chapters to follow will reveal in greater detail, health anxiety is a complex
problem involving the perception that somatic complaints are always evidence
of a serious medical condition. In order to prevent a catastrophic health outcome, patients typically seek excessive medical evaluations from multiple providers despite the absence of any findings suggestive of a medical problem. Patients commonly present first to their primary-care doctor complaining of
vague, diffuse symptoms. Only after all medical avenues have been exhausted –
if ever – do these patients present to mental health providers. Such patients can
present to psychologists extremely frustrated with their medical providers, em-
phatically stating that their doctors have "missed something," and that they are
truly suffering from a serious medical illness, often believed to be chronic and
terminal in nature. As Gabriel's case illustrates, these patients are typically ret-
icent to embrace a psychological conceptualization of their symptoms. In addition, the medical providers can be equally frustrated with individuals constantly
complaining of symptoms despite their consistently negative test results. Un-
knowingly, the physicians may be maintaining the individual's health anxiety
through ordering unnecessary tests and offering reassurance. Thus, health anxiety involves not only distressed and frustrated patients, but also perplexed and
annoyed medical providers. We have opened this volume with a case example
illustrating in anecdotal fashion the experience of health anxiety from personal,
medical, and psychological perspectives. Next, we consider the perspective of a
growing body of clinical observations and research literature.

2

The Nature of Health Anxiety

What are the main features of health anxiety? What are the similarities and differences across the various conditions that involve fears related to one's own health? Does health anxiety stand alone as a clinical disorder in its own right, or is it a part of other psychological disorders? This chapter addresses these and other issues related to the nature of intense health anxiety with the aim of providing the clinician with information to be used during the assessment and treatment of individuals with the condition. The more solid the clinician's foundation of basic knowledge about this problem, the better he or she will be able to evaluate patients diagnostically, to assess key features that may affect treatment outcome, and to respond knowledgeably to patients' questions about their symptoms and prognosis. In Chapters 3 and 4 we discuss perspectives on the development of problems with severe health anxiety (Chapter 3) and how they are maintained despite reassurance and other valid forms of evidence of good health (Chapter 4).

Defining Health Anxiety

Anxiety occurs as a normal response to the perception that a situation or stimulus is threatening, while doubting one's ability to cope with this perceived threat (Beck & Emery, 1985). Thus, *health anxiety* refers to inappropriate or excessive health-related fears based on misperceptions of bodily sensations as dangerous and indicative of a medical problem (Lucock & Morley, 1996; Warwick, 1989). Concurrently, the individual perceives him- or herself as being incapable of coping with the perceived health-related threat.

Although this book focuses on problematic and maladaptive health anxiety, it is important to keep in mind that anxiety is inherently an *adaptive* response that serves to protect us from danger. Often termed the *fight or flight response*, anxiety prepares us to take action against perceived threats. In this manner, some degree of health-related anxiety can be considered constructive if in the end it motivates us to take the appropriate measures or seek medical attention. Apprehension about shortness of breath in a person with asthma, for example, can lead the individual to promptly take corticosteroids or inhalant bronchodilator medication to prevent respiratory fatigue or even death by suffocation.

Maladaptive health anxiety, on the other hand, is extreme in relation to the actual degree of physical threat, if in fact any objective threat even exists. The frequency, intensity, and duration of the signs and symptoms of pathological health anxiety cause personal distress and interfere with multiple domains of functioning, such as relationships, self-care, work or school, home life, and leisure activities. Similarly, *too little* concern about one's own health can be maladaptive: If the person with asthma described above does not pay enough attention to the risks associated with his or her condition (e.g., highly pollinated air, leaving home without one's medication or inhaler), the effects on personal well-being and functioning could be quite serious. The nature and treatment of problems related to substandard chronic disease self-management such as this are not a focus of this book, however.

Hypochondriasis

Mental health professionals have traditionally used the diagnostic label *hypochondriasis* to refer to what contemporary theorists (ourselves included) identify as severe health anxiety. This is likely because hypochondriasis is the psychiatric disorder that best corresponds to the psychological experiences and observed behavior among people with this set of difficulties. Although we will generally refrain from using the term hypochondriasis in this volume, most (but not all) of what we know about severe forms of health anxiety comes from the study of people with hypochondriasis. Therefore, we now turn to a discussion of this condition.

The main feature of hypochondriasis as defined in the *Diagnostic and Statistical Manual of Mental Disorders* (DSM-IV-TR; American Psychiatric Association, 2000) is a preoccupation with fears of having – or the idea that one has – a serious medical condition such as a chronic, life-threatening (or life-altering) sickness (see Table 2.1). This "disease conviction" is essentially a strongly held belief based on a misinterpretation of bodily sensations. Moreover, it persists despite appropriate medical evaluation and reassurance of good health. That is, a thorough work-up has not identified a medical condition to account for the individual's health-related concerns. The disease conviction also results in clinically significant personal distress or interferes with important areas of functioning such as social, occupational, and family life. Hypochondriasis is categorized as a somatoform disorder in DSM-IV-TR.

For people with hypochondriasis, the health-related preoccupation might concern specific bodily functions such as peristalsis or heart beat; slight benign

---

Table 2.1. Summary of the DSM-IV-TR diagnostic criteria for hypochondriasis

A. Preoccupation with fears of having, or the idea that one has, a serious disease based on the person's misinterpretation of bodily symptoms.

B. The preoccupation persists despite appropriate medical evaluation and reassurance.

C. The belief in criterion A is not a delusion and is not restricted to a circumscribed concern about appearance (as in Body Dysmorphic Disorder).

D. The preoccupation causes clinically significant distress or impairment in social, occupational, or other important areas of functioning.

E. The duration of the disturbance is at least 6 months.

F. The preoccupation is not better accounted for by another Axis I disorder such as Generalized Anxiety Disorder, Obsessive-Compulsive Disorder, Panic Disorder, a Major Depressive Episode, Separation Anxiety, or another Somatoform Disorder.

Case Example: Sarah – "I have a brain tumor"

Sarah was a 45-year-old librarian with hypochondriasis; she was preoccupied with the notion that she had a brain tumor. Her concerns were based on a misinterpretation of chronic tension headaches and occasional feelings of dizziness (e.g., when awakening or when quickly turning her head). Sarah had been to numerous doctors in her city and had obtained several MRIs of her head and neck. However, there was no evidence of any tumors. Sarah spent a good deal of time researching brain tumors on the internet and looking up other symptoms that can accompany cancer. Whenever she noticed any bodily sensations that mimicked the symptoms of cancer, her concern would peak and she would call her primary doctor or a relative. Sarah also frequently "checked" herself to see whether her dizziness symptoms were still present. This included rolling her eyes and shaking her head to see if she had any feelings of vertigo (which might have been leading to her headaches!). If she felt any such sensations, she would have the need to report this to a physician of relative.

---

abnormalities, signs, and sensations such as an occasional cough, pulled muscle, mole, or small bruise; or vague and ambiguous physical complaints such as "a hollow head" or "weak spine." These individuals are often highly concerned with the cause, meaning, and authenticity of the feared bodily sensations and imagined disease state. In some instances, they describe a preoccupation with a specific organ (e.g., stomach, prostate gland) or disease (e.g., rabies, cancer). Despite these perceptions of illness, repeated medical tests for such complaints consistently turn up negative (i.e., no organic basis), though that provides only short-lived reassurance, if any at all.

Whereas some individuals with hypochondriasis recognize their health-related fears and preoccupations are excessive, many do not. The diagnostic specifier *with poor insight* is reserved for those who, for most of the time during the current episode of symptoms, do not realize that their concerns about serious illnesses are unreasonable. Nevertheless, despite their sometimes all-consuming health worries, people with hypochondriasis generally have no better health habits (e.g., diet, exercise, smoking, seat-belt use) than those without this disorder (Taylor & Asmundson, 2004).

Beyond DSM

Many clinicians now recognize the limitations of diagnostic criteria such as those of the DSM-IV-TR, including that they are largely atheoretical, superficial, and assume a nomothetic approach to conditions characterized by highly idiosyncratic (i.e., patient-specific) symptoms and controlling variables (e.g., Follette, Naugle, & Linerooth, 2000; Follette & Houts, 1996). As such, diagnostic criteria such as those present in the DSM classification system lead merely to an understanding of the form or topography of the problem (i.e., via a checklist of signs and symptoms that might or might not be present). Diagnostic criteria do not provide a solid conceptual framework for assessing and treating psychological problems. Proponents of the diagnostic criteria, on the other hand, argue that they serve to maintain a standardized definition assisting clinicians and researchers in communicating with each other, identifying etiologic models, and providing a prognosis (e.g., Barrios, 1988). In this book we take a *functional* approach to understanding and treating health anxiety. The goal of the functional approach is to operationalize and conceptualize clinically relevant problems for the purpose of identifying interventions that will produce the desired change. This is accomplished through adequately examining relevant antecedents, consequences, and conditions under which health anxiety most often occurs. This type of fine-grained analysis is not afforded by DSM classification alone.

In contrast to the diagnostic entity *hypochondriasis*, health anxiety itself is more broadly defined as a psychological process characterized by fears and worries focused upon a perceived threat to one's own health. The frequency, intensity, and duration of health-anxiety episodes vary considerably from person to person in the general population (Salkovskis & Warwick, 1986). Put another way, health-related concerns are universal. Most of us have had the experience of becoming uneasy or alarmed about some seemingly inexplicable bodily perturbation: a mysterious sensation in the abdomen; a racing heart beat; an especially painful headache. That health concerns are present in the general population should not be surprising since most people consider their physical well-being as vitally important. For many people, such concerns are short-lived and either get dismissed as illogical or are simply replaced by other more pressing thoughts. Thus, health anxiety that creates clinical levels of distress or functional impairment (e.g., hypochondriasis) represents the severe end of a continuum.

Research bears out the fact that health concerns are relatively common among the general population. In one study, 61% of college students reported intrusive thoughts about their own health (Freeston et al., 1994). In another study, 6% of adults sampled from a multicultural inner-city population reported health worry (Looper & Kirmeyer, 2001). In most people, these health worries and intrusions are short-lived, do not interfere with functioning, and are easily put to rest by reassurance in one form or another. To the extent that such concerns become more severe and impair daily life, the person might meet the criteria for a diagnosis of hypochondriasis. Chapters 3 and 4 show how and why some innocent health concerns balloon into clinical hypochondriasis.

Hypochondriasis vs. Health Anxiety

More and more experts in the field are using the term *health anxiety* in place of hypochondriasis to describe this phenomenon (e.g., Taylor & Asmundson, 2004; Asmundson, Taylor, & Cox, 2001). We advocate the term health anxiety for three reasons. First, it provides a clear and meaningful description of the psychological experiences and observed behavior of individuals with this problem. In contrast, the term hypochondriasis actually derives from the Greek *hypo* (below) and *chondros* (cartilage of the breast bone) and was originally used to describe unexplained stomach pains. It was thought by ancient Greek physicians that such pains were caused by the movement of the spleen, an organ located in the upper region of the abdomen just below the ribs (i.e., the hypochondrium). During the 19th century, the term evolved to be the male counterpart to hysteria.

The second reason we prefer health anxiety to hypochondriasis is that – as will become clear later in this chapter – hypochondriasis is but one of several clinical disorders that have as their main features health-related fears and worries. Thus, health anxiety is not a clinical diagnosis per se, but rather a phenomenon that can be present in a number of psychiatric conditions listed in the DSM, as well as in some medical diagnoses that often present with overlapping psychological symptoms (e.g., aerophagia, rumination syndrome). We describe these conditions, and the role that health anxiety plays in maintaining them later in this chapter.

Third and finally, whereas the term health anxiety is more or less value neutral, hypochondriasis has now acquired pejorative connotations and is associated with malingering and an underlying character disorder. Sadly, many medical and mental-health providers treat individuals with health anxiety in ways that are consistent with this association, passing them off as attention-seekers and ignoring their complaints. This might account for the tendency of such patients to feel that their doctors do not take their complaints seriously, leading to an even more aggressive search for medical services, which might appear to confirm the stereotype.

Consistent with the points raised above, this volume assumes a concept-driven approach to understanding and treating the problem of health anxiety as opposed to a diagnosis-driven approach. Moreover, throughout this book our use of the term *hypochondriasis* is reserved for references to specific clinical observations or research findings regarding this particular clinical syndrome, whereas *health anxiety* is used when referring to the broader range of unfounded conviction-based illness worry.

Essential Features of Health Anxiety: Form and Function

Our broad definition of health anxiety necessitates an appreciation of the form and function of the essential features of this problem. Four components are key to understanding health anxiety in a way that leads to effective treatment: (1) trigger stimuli, (2) cognitive phenomena, (3) behaviors, and (4) insight. While overlap exists among individuals, patients present with highly personalized variations within each parameter. The aim of this section is therefore to help the clinician recognize and develop an approach to thinking about the symptoms of health anxiety leading to effective treatment conceptualization. In Chapter 4, we place these components into a theoretical model of the development and maintenance of health anxiety.

Triggers

Internal Stimuli

Episodes of health anxiety are most commonly precipitated by innocuous non-illness-related physical sensations such as normal bodily variations (e.g., changes in the color and smell of urine), trivial physical complaints (e.g., a stiff neck), and naturally occurring sensations associated with emotional arousal (i.e., physical manifestations of anxiety such as tachycardia), or the use of certain substances (e.g., feeling keyed up from using caffeine). Table 2.2 presents examples of the sorts of physical sensations that evoke health anxiety. As can be seen, these stimuli can be acute (e.g., an abrupt, unexplained pain) or persistent (e.g., headache). In addition, they can be novel experiences, or recurrent and chronic. Some individuals report that "new" or "unexplained" internal stimuli evoke health worries, whereas others report being concerned with a certain body part (e.g., head), organ (brain), or system (digestive). Still others describe symptoms that are vague, varied, and generalized (e.g., "pain all over").

Table 2.2. Examples of physical sensations that trigger health anxiety

Normal bodily variations

– Hot/cold flash, or cold extremities

– Slight variations in visual acuity

– Itching

– Occasional feeling of dizziness

– Slight tremor

– Varied form and color of stools (and color or smell of urine)

– Stiff neck

– Ringing in the ears

– Dry mouth

– Tiredness/fatigue

Trivial physical complaints

– Bruises, sores, moles, discolorations

– Rash

– Joint, back, or muscle pain, & noncardiac chest pain

– Headache

– Soreness or dryness in throat

– Frequent urination

– Chronic belching

– Constipation

– Difficulty swallowing

Sensations related to emotional arousal

– Racing heart

– Shortness of breath

– Sweating

– Chest tightness

– Lightheadedness/confusion

– Blurred vision

– Nausea

– Tingling sensations

Because many of the bodily sensations in Table 2.2 often accompany actual, yet minor, medical problems such as colds, infections, allergies, and muscle pulls, such ordinary ailments can trigger episodes of health anxiety. In these instances, affected individuals come to doubt the more benign diagnosis and worry that a more serious condition is the true cause of the feared bodily sensations (e.g., shortness of breath due to flu-like symptoms are instead interpreted as representing lung cancer). Similarly, pregnant women with histories of health anxiety sometimes report that the many new and irregular physical sensations associated with pregnancy trigger episodes of health-related worry.

Episodes of health anxiety can also be triggered by negative thoughts and images. For example, vivid images of cancer "taking over the body," a "collapsed" lung, a "ruptured" spleen, "perforated" colon, or blood hemorrhaging ("gushing") from the brain. Mental pictures of certain bodily systems "giving out" or malfunctioning are also reported. Such thoughts and images are commonly evoked by external stimuli as described next.

External Stimuli

Exposure to health- and illness-relevant stimuli in the environment can also trigger health anxiety. Examples include hospitals and doctors' offices, seeing someone who has the feared illness, reading magazine stories pertaining to health and disease, viewing television shows and internet sites featuring stories about illnesses (e.g., cancer), and news coverage of feared diseases. In addition, health anxiety can increase when a friend or loved one is diagnosed or is already receiving treatment for a serious medical condition. Such experiences might make health-anxious individuals give pause to ponder their own susceptibility to such problems.

Whereas the sorts of triggers mentioned above are more or less patient-specific (e.g., one person might fear stories about cancer whereas another fears stories about multiple sclerosis), other stimuli seem to have a more widespread effect on health-anxious people in general. Well-known examples include extensive media coverage of serious disease outbreaks (e.g., West Nile virus, SARS). This effect is magnified when the publicized disease is described as involving symptoms that might be difficult to distinguish from less serious problems such as a cold or a viral infection. We observed, for instance, an increase in the number of health-anxiety referrals (even among people who do not typically worry about their health) during the much-publicized anthrax attacks and hoaxes following the September 11, 2001, terror attacks in the United States. The first signs of anthrax infection include cold and flu-like symptoms, although the disease can be fatal if not treated immediately. We evaluated and treated a number of individuals with routine colds and other minor illnesses

Table 2.3. Examples of external stimuli that trigger health anxiety

– Hospitals

– People with serious illnesses

– TV

– Doctors

– Medical equipment (e.g., needles)

– Knowledge of an outbreak (or threat of outbreak) of a serious disease

– Hearing about one's relative with a serious illness

– Helping a friend or relative cope with a serious disease

– Finding out that a certain illness (e.g., cancer) runs in the family

who were worried they had in fact been infected with anthrax and were not being taken seriously enough by their doctors. Table 2.3 presents specific examples of external stimuli known to trigger episodes of health anxiety.

Cognition

As we have discussed, dysfunctional cognitions (i.e., disease conviction) are a defining feature of health anxiety. It is important to distinguish between three types of cognitive phenomena in health anxiety:
1) Dysfunctional core beliefs,
2) Erroneous automatic appraisals, and
3) Intrusive thoughts, doubts, and images.

As we describe next, the first two types of cognitions are mistaken ideas and assumptions that the person holds regarding health, illness, and specific health-relevant stimuli. Cognitive intrusions, on the other hand, are stimuli that may occur spontaneously and sometimes precipitate episodes of health anxiety.

Dysfunctional Core Beliefs

Certain types of general, trait-like beliefs and assumptions regarding medicine, health, and illness are characteristic of people with health anxiety (e.g., "any change in my body is a sign of a serious disease"). For the most part, these beliefs are inconsistent with reality because they contain rigid or exaggerated estimates of (1) the nature of serious illnesses (e.g., prevalence, severity, course, and com-

Table 2.4. Examples of dysfunctional core beliefs among individuals with health anxiety

DOMAIN

The nature of serious illnesses

- Serious diseases are lurking everywhere.
- I am especially vulnerable to _____ (insert illness).
- Because _____ (insert serious illness) runs in my family, it is only a matter of time until I have it also.
- People don't recover from serious illnesses.
- I must be especially careful because I am at great risk of becoming ill.

Meaning of bodily symptoms

- If something hurts, there must be a problem or disease.
- Good health means being 100% symptom free.
- My _____ (insert specific organ or system) is defective.
- I have the body of an 80-year-old (spoken by a 25-year-old man).
- Real bodily symptoms require medical explanations; they cannot be produced by emotional states such as anxiety
- If my symptoms cannot be explained, I must have a very serious and unrecognized illness.

Inability to cope with illness or death

- I could never cope with having a serious disease.
- I am weak and unable to tolerate any stress.
- If I got _____ (insert illness) it would be the end of me.
- It will be cold and lonely in the grave.
- I can live forever if only I avoid serious illnesses.
- No one would be there to help me if I were ill.
- I will miss out so much after I am dead.

Dysfunctional beliefs about doctors, medical tests, and treatment

- Doctors should be able to explain all of my symptoms.
- If a doctor simply listens to me and concludes that I am healthy, he or she cannot be trusted.
- The only way a doctor can know if I am in good health is to review all the details of my medical history and conduct lab tests to rule out any possible problem.
- If different doctors disagree even slightly, or if the same doctor gives even a slightly different impression on different occasions, it means they can't figure me out and cannot detect my serious illness.
- Medical tests are generally unreliable and cannot be trusted.
- It is possible to be absolutely certain about my health.
- Doctors just think I am crazy and they discount whatever I say.
- If a treatment is going to work at all, it will be immediately apparent.
- I should always check my body so that I can catch the first sign of illness.
- If the doctor sends me for more tests, he or she thinks I am seriously ill.

municability), (2) the meaning of bodily symptoms, (3) the inability to cope with illness or death, or (4) the ineptitude of doctors, medical tests, and treatment (e.g., Abramowitz, Schwartz, & Whiteside, 2002[in refs 2001]; Taylor & Asmundson, 2004; Warwick & Salkovskis, 1990). Table 2.4 presents examples of core beliefs reported by patients with health anxiety. Where do such beliefs come from? Why do they affect some people but not others? In Chapter 3 we will explore the factors that give rise to core beliefs in health anxiety.

Automatic Appraisals

Erroneous appraisals of ostensibly benign bodily sensations, perturbations, and other health-relevant stimuli as threatening or indicative of a serious medical problem play a central role in health anxiety. These misinterpretations are considered *automatic* in that they occur reliably and seemingly without much forethought or reflection. Mistaken appraisals of mild, ambiguous, chronic, and diffuse sensations such as weakness, fatigue, nausea, and dull pain vary widely from person to person and can also vary across time within the same person (Barsky & Klerman, 1983). These types of vague symptoms could be misinterpreted as signs of well-known maladies (e.g., multiple sclerosis, Lyme disease) or of new, rare, or undetected diseases about which doctors presumably know little. Interpretations of acute and identifiable sensations, on the other hand, tend to be restricted to illnesses that affect certain parts of the body. In our clinics, we have observed patients misinterpreting:
– Headaches as brain tumors,
– A scratchy or painful throat as throat cancer,
– Tingling or cold extremities as a neurological disease such as Lou Gehrig's Disease (ALS),
– Mild fatigue or tremulousness as multiple sclerosis,
– Dizziness as indicating a brain disease or inner ear (vestibular) illness,
– Occasional forgetfulness as Alzheimer's or Pick's disease,
– Constipation or diarrhea as Crohn's disease, and
– A rash as Lyme disease.

Intrusive Thoughts, Doubts, and Images

The third types of cognitive phenomena in health anxiety are intrusive thoughts. These are distinct, identifiable cognitions that are unwanted, unintended, and recurrent (Clark & Rhyno, 2006). Such intrusions interrupt the flow of routine thought and might interfere with task performance. Moreover, the person experiences the thoughts as upsetting and difficult to control or suppress. Unlike core beliefs and automatic appraisals, intrusive thoughts are not an expression of the person's beliefs system, although in some cases they might reflect aspects of core beliefs. Intrusions might be triggered by external or internal events (e.g., bodily sensations), although this is not *always* the case. As discussed earlier, intrusions can themselves serve as triggers of health-anxiety episodes. Research indicates that both medically ill and healthy individuals commonly experience intrusive thoughts regarding health (Freeston et al., 1994).

Examples include the following:

- *Thought* – "Someone once told me that appendicitis usually starts off as a stomach ache that the person dismisses as 'nothing serious'."
- *Doubt* – "What if I could 'catch' cancer from being around my grandfather with cancer?"
- *Image* – Laying all alone in my cold, dark grave
- *Thought* – "It seems like people pity those with serious illnesses."
- *Doubt* – "Will my wife and children miss me after I die?"
- *Image* – Distorted impression of what one's own brain looks like inside the head.

Behavior

Anxiety is often termed the "fight-or-flight" response because, from a biological standpoint, a primary aim of this emotional experience is to prepare the person for dealing with threatening situations, usually by fighting them off or by fleeing. As we will discuss in subsequent chapters, these biological effects have much to do with the persistence of health anxiety, which involves an *unsubstantiated* threat. However, it is this urge to attack or, more likely in the case of health-anxious persons, to *escape* from perceived threat that motivates the behavioral manifestations of health anxiety. Classes or health-anxious behavior include (1) repetitious body-checking and reassurance-seeking regarding health status, (2) situation-specific behaviors ("safety behaviors") and active avoidance to make one feel safer, and (3) covert, passive avoidance of cues and triggers. These behaviors can be overt or covert, as well as occasional or routine. Regardless of their form and frequency, such strategies are consequences of illness fear and illness suspicion, and they are performed in attempt to manage, reduce, or prevent distress and doubt.

Checking and Reassurance-Seeking

The top portion of Table 2.5 lists common examples of checking and attempts to obtain reassurance about health status. As discussed above, such behavior is

Table 2.5. **Examples of health-anxiety behaviors**

Checking and assurance-seeking

- Repeated visits to doctors to have "symptoms" checked
- "Doctor-shopping" to check that the diagnosis (or nondiagnosis) is correct
- Repeatedly measuring heart rate, blood pressure, body temperature, etc.
- Constantly monitoring levels of "throat tightness," dizziness, or pain
- Frequently palpating one's throat or abdomen for lumps
- Checking urine and stool for blood, changes in color, or changes in consistency (stool)
- Frequent inspections of sores and moles on the skin
- Repeatedly discussing or asking questions about the feared problem
- Repeated internet searches to find information about a certain "symptom"
- Comparing actual moles on one's body to those plotted on a "map" of the body
- Reviewing test results and notes taken during doctor visits
- Persistently mentioning and describing symptoms to others
- Repeatedly reviewing medical texts or journal articles for information about illnesses or body symptoms

Situational safety behaviors and safety signals

- Keep cell phone on hand just in case an episode occurs
- Remain within a certain distance of the doctor's office, hospital, or medical center
- Keep medications on hand at all times
- Swallowing until it feels "normal"
- Keep head elevated above the heart
- Use a cane or wheelchair
- Sleep on one's back or without pillows (to prevent suffocation)
- Rigid adherence to a strict diet

Passive avoidance of:

- Hospitals
- People with illnesses
- Television shows, movies, news articles, and other stories about sick people, illnesses, or death
- Physical exertion or other activities that could "make things worse"
- Routine physicals
- Self-examinations (e.g., breast, testicles)
- Funerals and cemeteries

a defining and decidedly prominent feature of health-anxiety disorders (e.g., hypochondriasis). The specific functions – purposes – of these behaviors include obtaining an "adequate" explanation for feared bodily sensations and attempting to determine the exact risk of having the suspected illness. In some cases, patients believe repeated checking serves to prevent the feared illness (e.g., "If I continually check myself, I will catch the disease in its earliest stages").

One especially conspicuous form of checking and reassurance-seeking is repeated visits to medical professionals. Healthy patients sometimes undergo excessive physical examinations and diagnostic tests, some of which may even be invasive. For example, it is not unusual for a patient with the fear of having Lou Gehrig's disease to request and receive multiple uncomfortable electromyographies (EMG) or nerve conduction studies solely to quell health anxiety. Indeed, research indicates increased physician visits, emergency medical visits, and hospitalizations among health-anxious individuals (i.e., Noyes, Kathol, Fisher, Phillips, Suelzer, & Holt, 1993). Individuals with health anxiety tend also to spend extreme amounts of time researching their perceived symptoms and feared illnesses, pouring over their doctors' reports, and examining medical textbooks, internet websites, and encyclopedias. Relatives and close friends are frequently asked for clarification or assurances as well. Research demonstrates that health-anxious individuals continue to seek additional information about the results of medical tests regardless of whether they receive a positive or negative result (Hadjistavropolous, Craig, & Hadjistavropolous, 1998).

Other types of checking involve self-examination, where the person repeatedly scans or overly scrutinizes aspects of his or her body. Body checking usually consists of making repeated subjective appraisals of perceived symptoms. Common self-examinations take the form of routinely inspecting sores or moles for signs of malignancy and possible cancer; examining urine and feces for changes in odor, color, or texture; and flexing muscles to assure that they are functioning properly. Sometimes individuals excessively palpate or probe themselves to check for lumps (e.g., breasts, lymph nodes, stomach) or other signs of internal problems. In one example, a patient who believed her anal sphincter muscle was "too weak" routinely probed her anus with her finger to determine the extent of this imagined flaw and the likelihood of having embarrassing incontinence problems. In other instances, patients rely on more objective measures of functioning (e.g., heart beats per minute, blood glucose levels) and might use medical devices to aid in such checking. Examples include the use of thermometers to measure body temperature, ph-paper to measure the acidity of urine, stethoscopes and ambulatory blood pressure monitors, blood glucose meters, and lung-capacity meters. The frequency of such body-checking varies along a continuum from occasional to constant, with some individuals engaging in seemingly automatic monitoring of these processes.

Situational Safety Behaviors and Safety Signals

Many health-anxious patients utilize and rely on particular strategies aimed at remaining "safe," or intended to reduce the risk of future illness. These behaviors are excessive in that they are not medically necessary for the particular individual. Always carrying medication, taking aspirin everyday, carrying a cell phone *just in case*, and remaining nearby a hospital even though there is no medical need to do so are common examples of safety behaviors (others are listed in Table 2.5). Although the individual uses such strategies to reduce the perceived probability and severity of a supposed physical catastrophe, these maneuvers paradoxically in fact serve to perpetuate the vicious cycle of health anxiety, as we will explain in Chapter 4.

Passive Avoidance

Safety behaviors, as described above, can be considered *active avoidance strategies* since they involve taking action to reduce the perceived risk of illness. Individuals with health anxiety also commonly use *passive avoidance strategies*, whereby they simply steer clear of illness-related situations and stimuli to manage distress and reduce the probability and severity of the perceived threat. Avoidance may be of certain activities, including those involving "risky" behaviors such as strenuous physical exertion or walking though a building known to have asbestos. It might also be focused on situations and stimuli that evoke illness-related thoughts and images, such as staying away from hospitals, funerals, and sick people; and refraining from reading, viewing, or listening to stories about people with illnesses. Whereas some individuals check their bodies excessively because they fear they might miss a serious disease, others actually *avoid* administering self-examinations (e.g., self breast or testicular exams) because they *fear* discovering that they have a terrible disease. Additional examples of common avoidance behavior in health anxiety are listed in Table 2.5.

It might seem paradoxical that some health-related situations, activities, and stimuli may at once be avoided and also engaged in excessively. For example, avoidance of doctors and hospitals is common, yet one of the defining characteristics of health anxiety is *excessive* doctor visits. Similarly, as mentioned above, some patients avoid examining themselves, whereas others clearly overindulge in such activities. This point highlights the heterogeneity of health anxiety: The triggers, cognitive phenomena, and behavioral manifestations that clinicians are likely to encounter are as diverse as the patients presenting with these complaints. In addition, it illustrates the links between thinking and behavior that are part of the essential psychopathology of health anxiety. That is, whether one avoids or overindulges in a given behavior is motivated by patient-specific beliefs and assumptions (e.g., "If I do not give myself a breast exam, I will avoid having to cope with breast cancer"; "I had better examine my breasts everyday to make sure I do not have breast cancer"). We will return to this point in subsequent chapters as it forms a basis for the conceptual framework most helpful in understanding, assessing, and treating health anxiety.

One final point about the various behavioral manifestations of health anxiety is that these phenomena account for the bulk of functional impairment observed in hypochondriasis and other health-anxiety disorders. Family and other acquaintances in the patient's life often have difficulty tolerating avoidance patterns, frequent requests for reassurance, seemingly selfish health-related preoccupation, and repeated trips to the doctor. Occupational and academic performance often suffers because of time-consuming health-related checking, avoidance, and reassurance-seeking.

Insight

Individuals with health anxiety vary with respect to how well they recognize the senselessness and excessiveness of their illness-related fears and preoccupation. Initially, many patients have strong disease conviction that persists despite what would appear to be good evidence to the contrary, i.e., numerous negative test results and multiple reassurances from doctors. In some individuals, this conviction persists indefinitely, whereas in others the disease conviction weakens as time passes and the evidence accumulates refuting the likelihood of having the feared medical condition. Nevertheless, there usually exists some degree of ambivalence and uncertainty that causes considerable distress and interference in functioning.

The strength of disease conviction might also vary over time. Whereas at some point in time the person might seem completely convinced of being medically ill, at other times, he or she might be able to think critically about the gap between his or her beliefs and the medical evidence – and acknowledge the possibility that they are, in fact, not ill. At such a point, the patient is probably in the best position to seek psychological treatment, being open to alternative explanations for perceived symptoms. In our clinical experience, the desire to seek psychological treatment is associated with having better insight into the senselessness of their health concerns.

Clinical Conditions Characterized by Health Anxiety

Health anxiety is not an official DSM-IV-TR diagnosis; rather, it is a collection of signs and symptoms featuring medically unexplained physical complaints, disproportionate fears, concerns, and preoccupation with health and illness, and excessive behaviors such as avoidance, checking, and other types of reassurance-seeking. As described previously, hypochondriasis can be considered the quintessential "health-anxiety disorder." It is, however, only one of an array of conditions characterized by health anxiety. In this section we briefly describe a number of other psychological conditions that feature the prominent signs and symptoms of health anxiety.

We should note here that health-anxiety-related disorders are wholly different from either malingering – faking a disorder to achieve some goal, such as attention or an insurance settlement – or the factitious disorders, in which symptoms are feigned or induced with not apparent incentive. People with health anxiety believe that a medical condition actually exists or is imminent.

Somatization Disorder

Somatization refers to the tendency (1) to experience and communicate physical distress and "symptoms" that are unaccounted for by medical explanations, (2) to attribute these symptoms to physical illness, and (3) to seek out medical help for these symptoms (Lipowsky, 1988). Importantly, there are instances in which somatization is appropriate, as in the case of physical complaints associated with high levels of stress (e.g., headaches, backaches). *Somatization disorder* is a DSM-IV-TR somatoform disorder involving a persistent pattern of chronic, medically unexplained physical complaints beginning before age 30. These complaints result in excessive treatment-seeking and substantial impairment in social, occupational, or other important areas of functioning (APA, 2000). The physical complaints tend to shift over the course of the disorder. To meet DSM-IV-TR criteria, the individual must have experienced pain symptoms, gastrointestinal symptoms, sexual symptoms, and at least one pseudoneurological symptom. Common complaints associated with somatization disorder are listed in Table 2.6.

Health anxiety and preoccupation in somatization disorder is typically focused on the sorts of phenomena listed in Table 2.6. In particular, the individual is preoccupied with the nature and origin of the symptom, with its authenticity, and with finding a medical cause and obtaining a medical diagnosis, (as opposed to accepting the label "somatization"). Repeated doctor visits and "shopping around" for new doctors are the norm, and patients frequently feel disparaged and misunderstood when medical tests repeatedly come up negative. Consistent with our view of health anxiety as a set of signs and symptoms, it is not entirely clear whether somatization disorder and hypochondriasis form discreet categories. A comprehensive review of research on the clustering of these two disorders found evidence of much overlap between them (Creed & Barksy, 2004).

Table 2.6. Common physical complains observed in individuals with somatization disorder
Pain symptoms
– Headaches
– Joint pain
– Backaches
– Gait disturbance (abnormal walking often due to pain)
– Painful urination or sexual intercourse
Gastrointestinal symptoms
– Rumination syndrome (medically unexplained nausea/vomiting)
– Aerophagia (bloating, chronic belching)
– Intolerance of certain foods
Sexual symptoms
– Sexual indifference
– Excessive menstrual bleeding
Pseudoneurological symptoms
– Conversion symptoms
– Nonepileptic seizures
– Chronic dizziness
– Tinnitus (ringing in the ears)

Case Example: Rick – Chronic Fatigue

Rick was a 28-year-old with a 7-year history of body aches, fatigue, fevers, headaches, diarrhea, nausea, disinterest in sex, and joint pain. He lived at home with his mother, who stated that Rick had "chronic fatigue syndrome." Rick had graduated from high school and begun college, but dropped out and returned home when he became severely depressed. Most days, Rick remained in his room (often in bed) in the dark. He was receiving disability, and his mother was doing all of his cooking and cleaning. During multiple medical clinic visits, Rick repeatedly had normal examinations, although he and his mother were upset with his doctors, who appeared to be discounting Rick's condition as psychological rather than medical. Rick repeatedly denied stressors, psychological trauma, and victimization.

Somatic Delusions

Somatic delusions are included in the DSM-IV-TR (APA, 2000) under "Delusional Disorder, Somatic Type." Individuals with this condition experience extremely fixed, unshakable, and unfounded beliefs that they have a serious medical condition. The most common forms of somatic delusions include beliefs that

1) One is emitting a foul odor from the skin or a bodily orifice,
2) One is infested with insects or parasites,
3) Certain parts of the body, contrary to objective observation, are misshapen or ugly, and
4) Parts of the body (e.g., the autonomic nervous system) are not functioning properly despite evidence to the contrary.

People with somatic delusions might seek medical attention for their suspected problem, and sometimes take additional measures, such as abusing the services of pest-control agencies and exterminators for their supposed infestation. Taylor and Asmundson (2004) describe how some individuals even contact university zoology departments in the hopes of classifying and exterminating the suspected vermin. It remains unclear whether somatic delusions are best considered symptoms of hypochondriasis with poor insight, or whether they are indeed psychotic symptoms. We include somatic delusions in the present discussion of health-anxiety conditions on the basis of research demonstrating that delusions occur on a continuum with other beliefs, differing quantitatively rather than qualitatively (e.g., Morrison, 2001).

Case Example: Larry – "I have AIDS"

Larry was 45 years old and lived alone. He had a history of depression and panic attacks, and had been hospitalized in residential psychiatric facilities on two occasions. He had worked as a janitor for several years, but recently stopped when he began feeling "sick all over." Larry had no dating or sexual history. He was, however, convinced that he was HIV positive and developing AIDS despite the numerous tests and medical examinations that revealed otherwise. Larry had developed an extremely fixed belief that his immune system was not working properly. Upon being interviewed at our clinic (where he presented as extremely skeptical of psychiatry and psychology), he disclosed the belief that the U.S. government was trying to cover up the problem of AIDS in this country, and therefore was paying doctors large amounts of money to tell patients who were HIV positive that they were, in fact, healthy. Larry believed he was very sick, and that his physicians, including our own team, had been influenced by the government in this way.

Illness or Disease Phobia

Illness phobia (or disease phobia) appears in the DSM-IV-TR under the heading of "Specific Phobia, Other Type" (APA, 2000) and is defined as an unreasonable fear of contracting a disease. Core features include distress, apprehension, and avoidance of situations that, in the mind of the individual, may lead to contracting the feared illness. It is distinguished from hypochondriasis in that illness phobia involves fear of *developing* a disease, whereas hypochondriasis involves the conviction that the feared disease is *already present*. Whereas hypochondriasis is characterized by somatic complaints, such complaints are not always present in illness phobia. Moreover, illness phobia typically involves fears of acutely life-threatening conditions (e.g., choking, heart attack, stroke), whereas the feared health consequences in hypochondriasis are typically long-term and progressive (e.g., slow physical or mental decline). Consequently, and similar to other anxiety states, individuals with illness phobia typically avoid situations in which help might not be available, and seek proximity to medical facilities. In contrast, the primary behavioral manifestation of hypochondriasis is the seeking of reassurance regarding health status.

It is important to note that the distinctions between hypochondriasis and illness phobia are based primarily on clinical observations; little empirical research has been conducted to substantiate them (Noyes, Carney, & Langbehn, 2004). Perhaps for this reason, the distinction remains a source of controversy. Some authors consider illness phobia as a subtype of hypochondriasis (e.g., Marks, 1987). According to this view, individuals with illness phobia are concerned with a single bodily symptom or illness, whereas those with hypochondriasis are concerned with multiple bodily symptoms and illnesses. Others assert that illness phobia and illness conviction represent two subtypes of hypo-

---

Case Example: Sheila – Fear of Lyme disease

Sheila was a 29-year-old secretary who was extremely fearful of Lyme disease, and this concern permeated just about every area of her life. For example, she avoided wooded areas, zoos, and even people she knew who enjoyed camping. She also asked just about everyone she knew whether they had recently found tics on them, and how long the tic had been there. Answers to these questions dictated whether Sheila felt comfortable in such persons' presence. Sheila also spent over an hour each evening checking her body for tics using a flashlight and tweezers, and had even cut her hair very short to make this task easier. She also carried insect repellent everywhere she went (including to work) and frequently researched the disease on the internet to stay abreast of the latest prevention and treatment strategies. Although Sheila did not feel that she *had* Lyme disease, "suspicious" symptoms such as chills and headaches occasionally triggered acute episodes of intense health anxiety.

---

chondriasis: the former presenting as an anxiety disorder and the latter as depression over being ill.

Panic Disorder

Individuals with *panic disorder* typically report intense somatic sensations during their panic attacks, such as accelerated heart rate, shortness of breath, dizziness, and tingling sensations. They tend to attribute these sensations to organic causes, such as a heart attack, stroke, or other serious medical condition (Barlow, 2002). Accordingly, panic patients often seek extensive medical examinations and consult numerous specialists (especially cardiologists) in hopes of finding the organic cause of their intense and seemingly unpredictable physical symptoms. Typically, they resort to avoidance strategies (strenuous activity, caffeine) and safety-seeking behaviors (keeping medication, cell phone, or water bottle on-hand at all times) to help manage health-related worries. Many individuals with hypochondriasis also experience panic attacks (Warwick & Salkovskis, 1990). Thus, clinical observations suggest a large degree of phenomenological overlap between panic disorder and health anxiety (Noyes, 1999).

Three lines of research evidence support the notion that both panic and health anxiety involve exaggerated perceptions of health status. First, panic disorder patients score as highly on measures of severity of health anxiety as do those with hypochondriasis (Abramowitz, Olatunji, & Deacon, 2007; Noyes, Reich, Clancy, & O'Gorman, 1986). Second, panic and health-anxiety symptoms both demonstrate moderate to strong relationships with measures of the tendency to catastrophically misinterpret the meaning of normally internal bodily sensations, such as those associated with normal anxious arousal (e.g.,

---

Case Example: Donald – "My heart is stopping!"

Donald was a 55-year-old lawyer with panic disorder. He experienced recurrent episodes of extreme anxiety accompanied by intense body sensations and feelings of doom that occurred seemingly from "out of the blue." In particular, Donald was focused on his racing heart. He was afraid that during a panic attack, he would suffer a heart attack and die. Donald had started to mentally monitor his heart beat and had become very sensitive to even slight changes in its rate and strength. Because of the threat attached to it, he developed anticipatory anxiety over whether he might have a panic attack and require immediate medical help. This led to avoidance of certain situations, such as public transportation, where escape would be difficult. When in crowded areas, Donald tried to stay close to exits "just in case he needed to get to a hospital." He also felt more comfortable knowing exactly how far he was from the nearest hospital emergency room.

anxiety sensitivity; Abramowitz et al., 2007; Cox, Borger, & Enns, 1999). Third, patients with panic disorder and those with hypochondriasis evidence similarly high levels of *body vigilance* or the tendency to consciously attend to and monitor internal bodily sensations (Olatunji, Deacon, Abramowitz, & Valentiner, 2007; Schmidt, Lerew, & Trakowski, 1997).

Despite the similarities discussed above, clinical and empirical evidence exists suggesting that hypochondriasis and panic disorder are distinct disorders (Noyes, 1999). Panic patients' sense of doom during panic attacks, for example, arises from fears of immediate and irrevocable or life-threatening physical catastrophe (e.g., a heart attack, aneurysm). Moreover, the types of somatic sensations that cue such fears are typically "arousal-reactive", i.e., immediately exacerbated by anxious arousal (e.g., palpitations, dizziness). Conversely, as mentioned previously, individuals with hypochondriasis experience an insipid fear of delayed or protracted consequences (e.g., "I am slowly dying from lung cancer"). The sorts of bodily sensations and variations that cue such concerns may be arousal-reactive or arousal-nonreactive, i.e., not immediately exacerbated by anxious arousal (e.g., rashes, frequent urination). Put another way, panic patients fear *they are dying* whereas hypochondriacal patients fear *they will die*.

Consistent with the notion discussed above, individuals with panic disorder experience episodic attacks of fear that are triggered and rapidly exacerbated by autonomic arousal (i.e., panic attacks), whereas those with hypochondriasis experience both panic attacks as well as ongoing anxiety that is not necessarily triggered by autonomic arousal (Hiller, Leibbrand, Rief, & Fichter, 2005). Research also indicates that, compared to panic patients, those with hypochondriasis evidence more somatic complaints, functional disability, and help-seeking behavior (Barsky, Barnett, & Cleary, 1994). Accordingly, clinicians were able to distinguish between these groups of patients on the basis of increased demands for unnecessary medical evaluation and treatment among those with hypochondriasis (Hiller et al., 2005). Thus, panic disorder and health anxiety (hypochondriasis, in particular) clearly share a tendency to catastrophize about the meaning of somatic sensations, such as fearing that such sensations will result in death. The fact that these conditions are frequently comorbid (e.g., Barsky et al., 1994) raises the possibility that fears of arousal-reactive and arousal nonreactive bodily cues constitute a common dimension (Stewart & Watt, 2000).

Obsessive-Compulsive Disorder

Obsessive-compulsive disorder (OCD), also an anxiety disorder, is characterized
a) By recurrent intrusive, unacceptable, and somewhat bizarre or senseless thoughts, ideas, or images (obsessions) that evoke anxiety; and

b) By efforts to resist or neutralize obsessional anxiety by ritualistically engaging in some other thought or action (compulsive rituals; APA, 2000).

Common obsessions include excessive fears of making mistakes, unwanted sexual, violent, or sacrilegious images and impulses, ideas of causing harm or bad luck to others, thoughts that objects are not arranged or ordered "just right" (i.e., obsessions of incompleteness), and thoughts about germs and contamination that could lead to illnesses. Common compulsive rituals include excessive washing and cleaning, checking, repeating routine behaviors (e.g., turning off the light switch), reordering, counting, seeking reassurance that obsessionally feared outcomes will not materialize, and mentally replacing unacceptable obsessional thoughts with "good" or "safe" thoughts.

Some authors have classified hypochondriasis as belonging to a putative group of obsessive-compulsive spectrum disorders (e.g., Hollander, Friedberg, Wasserman, Yeh, & Iyengar, 2005; Abramowitz & Deacon, 2005). In particular, the persistent preoccupation with illness observed in hypochondriasis and other forms of health anxiety has been likened to obsessions in OCD, and the repetitive reassurance-seeking and checking with doctors has been described as being similar to compulsive rituals (e.g., Fallon, Javitch, Hollander, & Liebowitz, 1991). An experimental study of hypochondriacal symptoms confirmed that personally relevant health and illness-related stimuli provoke anxiety and the urge to engage in checking as well as other situational safety behaviors, which, if performed, engender an immediate reduction in anxiety and distress (Abramowitz & Moore, 2007). Thus, health preoccupation and checking behaviors in hypochondriasis share important functional characteristics with obsessions and compulsions in OCD.

Studies of OCD patients (e.g., Foa & Kozak, 1995; Savron et al., 1996) indicate that they report obsessions focused on fears of illnesses and diseases ac-

---

Case Example: David – Schizophrenia Obsessions

David was diagnosed with OCD in his early 20s. Now, at 35, he reports being consumed with the fear that he might develop schizophrenia. He has never met criteria for this condition, yet once he read on an OCD-related website that it is possible for obsessions to morph into psychotic delusions as found in schizophrenics. David avoided reminders of schizophrenia, including reading about people with this condition and driving past a local psychiatric hospital. He feared being around anyone with this condition. These external stimuli triggered doubts and discomfort over the possibility that he could develop schizophrenia. In response to these intrusions, David researched OCD and schizophrenia on the internet and in the library to reassure himself of the differences between the two conditions. He also routinely e-mailed and telephoned experts on OCD to repeatedly ask their opinions about the probability of obsessions turning into psychotic delusions.

companied by compulsive washing and checking rituals, which function as efforts to avoid or prevent injury and illness (e.g., avoidance of driving, washing to prevent contamination from germs). In addition, individuals with OCD evidence elevated scores on measures of health anxiety (Abramowitz et al., 2007). Whereas the presence of health-related obsessions does not necessarily increase the severity of OCD symptoms, it has been associated with poorer insight into the senselessness of the symptoms and greater fear and avoidance in response to bodily sensations (Abramowitz, Brigidi, & Foa, 1999; Neziroglu, Mckay, & Yaryura-Tobias, 2000).

Generalized Anxiety Disorder

Persistent and uncontrollable worrying, which is a main symptom of *generalized anxiety disorder* (GAD), is also a prominent feature of health anxiety. Individuals with GAD worry excessively about interpersonal relationships, work or school, finances, the future, and their own and significant others' health (APA, 2000). Research and clinical observations suggest, however, that health-related worries in GAD are less frequent and less intrusive than those observed in hypochondriasis. Individuals with GAD also report fewer somatic symptoms, fewer fears and misinterpretations of specific bodily sensations, and less fear of death relative to those with hypochondriasis (Abramowitz et al., 2007; Starcevic, Fallon, Ulenhuth, & Pathak, 1994).

Case Example: Lloyd – Health Worries

Lloyd, a 40-year-old married father of two young children, met criteria for GAD as he spent much time worrying uncontrollably about topics such as his finances, his marriage, his job performance, his own health, as well as the health of his wife and children. Although his marriage, occupational functioning, and finances were all generally going well, he was worried about when "the shoe would drop." His health worries were especially severe during the cold and flu season when he worried about whether his children would be exposed to viruses and bacteria while at school. What if other children were sick and passed along their germs to his kids? What if another child hadn't wash his or her hands after using the bathroom and spread the flu bug to Lloyd's family. Lloyd worried his children would end up missing too many days of school because of sickness, putting them behind the rest of their class. This, he feared in turn, would result in poor grades, which would then haunt them when they applied for college (his children were currently 10 and 8 years old), etc. Lloyd also had irritable bowel syndrome, problems with chronic headaches and muscle aches, and sleep loss.

Pain Disorder

The predominant feature of *pain disorder*, which is classified in the DSM-IV-TR (APA, 2000) as a somatoform disorder, is the complaint of severe pain at one or more anatomic sites. The reported pain might or might not occur along with a medical condition; but it is not explained by physiologic or neurological factors, and is reported as more severe than would typically be observed in patients with a medical condition. In some individuals with this problem, the pain is reported to linger long after an actual physical injury or disease has healed. The person often becomes preoccupied with the pain and subsequently develops patterns of accommodating behaviors, such as using a wheelchair, relying on others' help, and staying home from work. Such accommodations are extreme and result in a disruption of social, occupational, or other important areas of functioning. In addition, the individual frequently seeks out medical attention for the pain. Psychological factors are judged to play a significant role in the pain's onset and maintenance, yet the pain is neither intentionally produced, feigned, or better accounted for by another DSM disorder.

Two subtypes of pain disorder have been described. In the subtype *pain disorder associated with psychological factors*, general medical conditions play little or no role in the onset or persistence of the pain. In the subtype *pain disorder associated with both psychological factors and a general medical condition*, a general medical condition is present and is, along with psychological factors, judged to have an important role in the development and maintenance of the pain.

Case Example: Shirlene – It Hurts Here

Shirlene was receiving inpatient treatment for chronic pain in a residential occupational therapy setting. She was 42 and reported feeling as if she had the body of an 80-year-old. In particular, Shirlene's complaints focused on unrelenting lower back and leg pain. Interestingly, none of the numerous physicians who had evaluated Shirlene, however, had ever detected any organic basis for her pain. Shirlene continued to demand second opinions until she was given the diagnosis of fibromyalgia, which is how she referred to her problem. Speaking with Shirlene was somewhat arduous since she always found a way to bring the conversation to focus on her difficulties with pain. She had several canes, a wheelchair, and a sister who visited everyday and brought Shirlene food and other articles from "the outside." As long as Shirlene could remain in her wheelchair or in bed, her mood was good. Although Shirlene was having problems adhering to her occupational therapy, she was negotiating with the director of the program to allow her to stay hospitalized in the facility for several more weeks as she found the setting "therapeutic."

Associated Features of Health Anxiety

Prevalence, Onset, and Course

Estimates of the prevalence of health anxiety vary across settings and according to how the construct is defined (Creed & Barsky, 2004). The prevalence of hypochondriasis (based on DSM-III, DSM-IV-TR, or ICD-10 criteria) in the general population has been assessed in four studies, with estimates ranging from 0.02% to 7.7%. Seven studies have examined its prevalence in primary care samples, with estimates ranging from 0.8% to 8.5%. Estimates from specialty medical settings are consistently lower than those drawn from primary-care patients. For example, a 1.2% point prevalence was observed among cardiology outpatients (Aydemir et al., 1997); and a 1.0% rate was observed among chronic pain patients (Gatchell, Polatin, Meyer, Garcy, 1994). The available research suggests hypochondriasis is about as prevalent as other psychiatric disorders such as depression, panic disorder, and OCD, and that both genders are equally likely to be affected (Barsky et al., 1990b; Gureje et al., 1997; Kellner, 1985).

Estimates of the prevalence of somatization disorder in the general population range from 0.03% to 0.84% across 10 studies (Creed & Barsky, 2004). In contrast to hypochondriasis, somatization disorder is more common in females than males. In addition, ethnic minority status and fewer years of education were associated with higher rates of this disorder (Creed & Barsky, 2004).

Little is known about the average age of onset in health anxiety or its prevalence among children, although clinical observations indicate that such problems may begin at any age. As with many other psychological disorders, onset appears especially likely in early adulthood when the individual first faces increased responsibility, including the maintenance of his or her own health. Other potential onset triggers include increased life stress, a personal experience with illness, illness or death of a loved one, and exposure to mass-media coverage of illnesses. We discuss the causes of health anxiety in greater detail in the next chapter.

In a large ($N = 120$) longitudinal study of individuals with hypochondriasis recruited from a medical outpatient setting, Barsky, Fama, Bailey, and Ahern (1998) found that 63.5% ($n = 54$) still met diagnostic criteria 4 to 5 years later. Although these patients evidenced some improvement in their functional status, level of fear, disease conviction, and bodily preoccupations, they remained significantly more symptomatic and functionally impaired compared to a control group of nonhypochondriacal individuals at follow-up. Thus, despite some statistical regression toward the mean, health-anxiety patients appear to endure a long-term burden of morbidity, functional impairment, and personal distress.

Cross-Cultural Issues

Cultural factors can influence the frequency, expression, and interpretation of bodily sensations. Physical complaints often occur in reaction to stress among Asian-Americans (Sue & Sue, 1999). In fact, Asian-Indian children who were referred for psychiatric services had three times the somatoform disorder diagnoses of a control sample of Caucasian children (Jawed, 1991). Among some African groups, somatic complaints (e.g., hot flashes, numbness and tingling sensations) differ from those expressed in Western cultures (Ohaeri & Odejide, 1994). These differences may reflect variability in cultural views of the relationship between body and mind. In Western culture, the predominant view is the *psychosomatic* perspective, whereby psychological distress is expressed through physical complaints. In most other cultures, however, the dominant view is a *somatopsychic* perspective, whereby physical problems are thought to produce emotional and psychological symptoms.

Cultural differences also exist in the propensity to seek medical attention for bodily concerns. Compared to other groups of people, Asians, Africans, and Latin-Americans show a stronger tendency to report medically unexplained symptoms to their physicians (Escobar, Rubio, Canino, & Karno, 1989; Gureje, Ustun, & Simon, 1997). In addition, culture appears to influence the presentation of somatization and health anxiety (i.e., the types of bodily concerns; Escobar, 1995). Germanic cultures, for example, emphasize cardiopulmonary symptoms such as low blood sugar and poor circulation, whereas in the United Kingdom, health concerns often focus on constipation and other gastrointestinal concerns. In the United States and Canada, concerns about environmental viruses and diseases (e.g., AIDS, SARS) are highly prominent.

Not surprisingly, the rates of diagnosis of health anxiety problems such as hypochondriasis and somatization disorder vary systematically by culture. In a cross-cultural study including 14 countries (Gureje, 2004), the prevalence of somatization disorder was quite low (0.6%). Yet, the highest rates were found in cities such as Rio de Janero, Santiago, Berlin, and Paris, and the lowest rates were found in Tiwan, Ibadân, Manchester, Nagasaki, and Verona. These cultural variations highlight the importance of paying close attention to individual and contextual factors when working with health-anxious individuals from diverse ethnic and cultural backgrounds. Physical complaints expressed by persons of ethnic minority groups may have to be interpreted differently than similar complaints made by members of the majority culture.

Costs

As touched on previously, health anxiety can result in chronic and serious impairment in social and occupational functioning, as well as in activities of daily living (Robbins & Kirmeyer, 1996). Individuals with hypochondriasis, for example, are less likely to be employed outside the home (Barsky et al., 1993a) and more likely to receive disability compensation compared to individuals without this condition (Noyes et al., 1993). Women with hypochondriasis have higher rates of sick leave, pregnancy complications, divorce rates, and lower occupational status compared to nonaffected women (Cloninger, Sigvardsson, von Korring, & Bohman, 1984).

Health anxiety represents a public health concern in that it is associated with exorbitant medical expenses. One study, for example, estimated that 10%–20% of the annual United States medical budget is spent on individuals with hypochondriasis (Smith, 1987). Despite equivalent numbers of actual medical problems among health-anxious and non-health-anxious people, those with this condition utilize substantially more medical services (Smith, 1987). Frequent unfounded doctor visits escalate costs to patients and to physicians, and expose ostensibly healthy individuals to the iatrogenic risks that often accompany invasive diagnostic and treatment procedures.

3

Causes of Health Anxiety: Nature, Notion, and Nurture

Why do some people develop the problems described in the previous chapter, whereas others seem to be resilient to the ubiquitous stream of bodily sensations, variations, and other health-relevant information that we as humans regularly encounter? In this chapter we explore the possible answers to this question, with an emphasis on factors that have the greatest relevance to psychological treatment. Understanding etiologic factors is of importance to clinicians and researchers alike. Clinicians need a knowledge of causal mechanisms when educating patients about health anxiety and when providing a rationale for treatment. Etiologic factors might also (at least in part) influence the choice of treatment strategies and how such techniques will be implemented. For researchers, knowledge of etiologic factors is one key to developing more effective treatment and prevention programs. As with many psychological disorders, we do not know the exact causal mechanisms present in health anxiety. The existing research, however, does allow us to draw some conclusions regarding the relative contributions of biological, genetic, and environmental factors. We present below a biopsychosocial model that explains how physiology (nature), beliefs (notions), and the environment (nurture) interact to give rise to the phenomenon of severe health anxiety.

Somatosensory Amplification

The only well-elucidated and well-studied biological model of health anxiety (i.e., hypochondriasis) posits that individuals with this problem suffer from *somatosensory amplification* – a biologically determined predisposition to experience bodily sensations as intense, noxious, and disturbing (Barsky, Goodson, Lane, & Cleary, 1988a; Barsky, 1992). Somatosensory amplification is thought to involve three components:

a) Hypervigilance to bodily cues, including heightened self-scrutiny and attention toward bodily sensations;

b) The tendency to focus selectively on diffuse or infrequent sensations; and
c) The tendency to appraise visceral and somatic sensations as abnormal, pathological, and symptomatic of disease, rather than appraising them as benign.

A number of studies have examined somatosensory amplification as a possible underlying factor in the etiology of health anxiety problems (e.g., Barsky & Wyshak, 1990; Kirmayer et al., 1994). Many of these investigations used the Somatosensory Amplification Scale (SSAS; Barsky et al., 1990a), a 10-item self-report instrument, to assess this tendency. Although scores on the SSAS correlate with symptoms and attitudes characteristic of health anxiety (Barsky & Wyshak, 1990), physiological studies report equivocal evidence for the amplification hypothesis. Whereas some studies yield support (e.g., Gramling, Clawson, & McDonald, 1996), others failed to find correlations between somatosensory amplification scores and sensitivity to internal body sensations (e.g., Aronson, Barrett, & Quigley, 2001; Mailloux & Brenner, 2002).

Research on the somatosensory amplification hypothesis also indicates that this predisposition is neither sensitive nor specific to health anxiety. While some evidence supports the view that the three factors involved in somatosensory amplification play a role in health anxiety, additional factors (such as trait anxiety, which are not part of somatosensory amplification) also appear to play a role. Finally, elevated scores on the SSAS have also been found in non-health-anxious samples, such as medical outpatients and individuals with urinary tract infections (Duddu, Issac, & Chaturvedi, 2006). Thus, this model does not adequately explain the development of health anxiety.

Genetics and Heritability of Health Anxiety

Overview of Behavioral Genetics

Behavioral genetics is the area of psychology that examines the role of genetic influence over human (and animal) behavior. Researchers in this area have studied the *heritability* of behavioral and psychological characteristics such as shyness, aggression, IQ, attitudes, as well as the signs and symptoms of psychological disorders. Heritability, technically defined as the proportion of phenotypic variation (i.e., observed characteristics) in a population which is attributable to genetic variation among individuals; may be thought of as the extent to which genetics (as opposed to the environment) contribute to individual differences in observable characteristics and traits. In order to establish estimates of heritability, research designs are used in which the genetic variation in a sample is known and the environmental variation can be estimated.

Twin studies, which provide such an opportunity, are among the most common ways of estimating heritability. Identical (or monozygotic, MZ) twins share 100% of their genes whereas fraternal (or dizygotic, DZ) twins share, on average, only 50% of their genetic material (much like nontwin siblings). In twin research, data on the characteristic(s) of interest are collected from large groups of MZ and DZ twin pairs. Data from the MZ pairs can then be statistically compared to the data from the DZ pairs in order to assess the relative contributions of genetic and environmental factors to the characteristic(s) of interest. Given that MZ twins share twice the amount of genetic material as DZ twins, a greater similarity found among MZ twins compared to DZ twins indicates *genetic influence*. If, however, DZ twins are as similar on a particular characteristic as are MZ twins, shared *environmental influences* (factors shared by all members of a family that make them seem alike) would be indicated. Finally, if MZ and DZ twins did not look similar on the characteristic of interest, non-shared environmental influences (factors unique to the individual members of a family which serve to make them different from each other) would be indicated. Importantly, these conclusions can only be drawn if it is assumed

a) That MZ and DZ twins have equal environments (i.e., MZ and DZ twins are treated similarly), and

b) That there is nothing unusual about twins per se that would make their data on a particular characteristic markedly different from data from nontwin siblings (singletons).

Heritability of Health Anxiety and Related Phenomena

A number of behavioral genetics studies have provided estimates of the heritability of health anxiety, somatization, and related symptoms. Two investigations suggest that scores on the Hs (Hypochondriasis) scale of the Minnesota Multiphasic Personality Inventory (MMPI) are moderately heritable, with genetic factors accounting for up to 35% of the variance in scores (DiLilla, Carey, Gottesman, & Bouchard, 1996; Gottesman, 1962). A caveat of these studies, however, is that the MMPI Hs scale assesses awareness of bodily sensations, as opposed to fears of illness based on mistaken interpretations of such sensations. As such, the Hs scale is not a true measure of hypochondriasis nor of health anxiety. Thus, these studies are probably best interpreted as indicating that one facet of health anxiety – the propensity to report bodily sensations – is moderately heritable.

Torgerson (1986) used a structured interview to assess the lifetime prevalence of somatoform disorders in MZ and DZ twins. The concordance rate for hypochondriasis among MZ twins was not significantly higher than among DZ twins, suggesting that hypochondriasis is not heritable. Results also indicated no genetic links between hypochondriasis and other somatoform disorders. One problem with interpreting the results of this study, however, is the very small sample size (35 twin pairs), which along with the relatively low base rate of hypochondriasis renders estimates of concordance in this study highly unreliable.

As hypochondriasis has been linked to OCD (see Chapter 2), studies assessing the heritability of OCD and obsessive-compulsive symptoms could shed light on the etiology of health anxiety. Several twin studies of OCD have been conducted, with the earliest suggesting that about half the variation in such symptoms is accounted for by genetic factors (e.g., Clifford, Murray, & Fulker, 1984). More recently, Jonnal, Gardner, Prescott, and Kendler (2000) found that the heritability of obsessions was 33% and that of compulsions 26%, with a total aggregation of 53%. A caveat in interpreting the results of heritability research on OCD, however, is that, because of this disorder's heterogeneity (e.g., McKay et al., 2004), research samples tend to include different presentations of obsessions and compulsions. Thus, if the degree of genetic contribution differs systematically across symptom presentations (e.g., contamination obsessions vs. checking compulsions), it would be difficult to glean much meaningful information about the heritability of OCD – much less that of health anxiety – from the existing research. Future studies examining the heritability of individual OCD symptom dimensions (e.g., contamination, checking) is needed.

Larger scale twin studies, however, have improved what we know of how phenomena associated with health anxiety are transmitted through families. For example, Kendler et al. (1995) assessed the lifetime history of phobias, generalized anxiety disorder, and panic disorder (as well as bulimia, alcoholism, and major depression) among 1030 female-female twin pairs in the eastern United States. Results were consistent with the view that the development of these anxiety disorders is influenced in part by genetics, in part by environmental factors specific to a particular disorder, and in part by environmental factors common to a number of different disorders (e.g., nonspecific factors).

A large Australian study of the heritability of somatic complaints (Gillespie, Zhu, Heath, Hickie, & Martin, 2000) examined 3,469 twin pairs using measures of anxiety, depression, and somatization. Results revealed that genetic factors and nonshared (specific) environmental factors best explained individual differences in depressive and anxious symptoms. Genetic factors explained approximately 30% of the variation in somatization scores. Furthermore, approximately 33% of the genetic variance in somatization was attributable to specific genetic factors unrelated to depression and anxiety, and 74% of the individual environmental influence on somatization was unrelated to depression or anxiety. Thus, somatic symptoms appear somewhat etiologically distinct (both genetically and environmentally) from anxiety and depression.

Given the previous findings that somatization and the tendency to experience bodily sensations are moderately heritable (indeed many medical conditions are highly heritable), it would be desirable to know the role of genetic and environmental factors in the etiology of health anxiety while statistically controlling for the tendency to experience bodily symptoms. In the only study to address this question, Taylor, Thordarson, Jang, and Asmundson (2006) found that common genetic influences accounted for between 10% and 37% of the variability (a modest degree of heritability) in

a) Fears of illness, disease, pain, and death,
b) Interference in functioning due to bodily sensations,
c) Frequency of treatment-seeking, and
d) Disease conviction.

In contrast, environmental factors accounted for between 60% and 90% of the variability in these four dimensions, with most of the environmental factors being dimension-specific. These results suggest that health anxiety is largely a learned phenomenon, and that its various symptoms arise from particular sorts of environmental factors.

Heritability of Illness-Related Beliefs

Interest in the contributions of genetics to somatoform, anxiety, and depressive disorders stems from disease models that view these symptoms as arising from structural and functional abnormalities in neurochemistry and neurocircuitry (Emilien, Durlach, Lepola, & Dinan, 2002). Other conceptual models, however, view these sorts of psychological symptoms as arising from psychological processes such as early experiences and dysfunctional beliefs (e.g., Beck, 1976). Could psychological phenomena such as dysfunctional beliefs be heritable? To address this possibility, Stein, Jang, and Livesley (1999) investigated the heritability of dysfunctional beliefs about the dangerousness of certain bodily sensations (i.e., anxiety sensitivity; e.g., "When my heart pounds I believe I am having a heart attack") and found that such beliefs were highly heritable; genetics accounting for nearly half of the variance. Thus, whereas it is generally assumed that the heritable nature of problems such as hypochondriasis, panic disorder, and other disorders involving health anxiety reflect the genetic transmission of neurological disease processes, Stein et al.'s findings suggest this formulation may be overly simplistic.

Summary of Behavioral Genetics Research

In summary, although genetic factors appear to contribute to some degree to the development of hypochondriasis and other forms of health anxiety, specific and nonspecific environmental and psychosocial factors clearly play a more substantial role in the etiology of such problems. The influence of nonspecific factors may explain the overlaps between health anxiety and other anxiety and mood disorders as discussed in Chapter 2. In addition, the finding that beliefs about bodily sensations (i.e., anxiety sensitivity) are heritable indicates that consideration should be given to the possibility that psychological or cognitive risk factors are somehow heritable.

A Biopsychosocial Model of the Etiology of Health Anxiety

Given that biological and genetic factors cannot fully explain the development of health anxiety, we next consider a *biopsychosocial* model that incorporates physiologic as well as psychological and environmental/social factors. This model, synthesized from the work of authors such as Paul Salkovskis, Hillary Warwick, Steven Taylor, Gordon Asmundson, and others, explains health anxiety as arising from essentially normal physiological, psychological, and environmental processes. According to the model, health anxiety arises when one's learning history fosters the development of certain dysfunctional beliefs about health and illness which are activated by the perception of benign bodily sensations and variations. The dysfunctional beliefs underlie the misinterpretation of these benign bodily cues as indicative of serious illness. In the remainder of this chapter we elaborate on each of these processes, along with supporting empirical evidence.

Nature: Our "Noisy Bodies"

If people with health anxiety don't actually have the medical illnesses they are worried about, where do their uncomfortable and unexplained bodily sensations come from? It turns out there are many benign explanations for such physical experiences. The human body, for example, is an everchanging sea of activity, receptive and responsive to incalculable external and internal stimuli with millions of interrelated parts that constantly influence one another. Some of this "body noise" is perceptible if we "listen" carefully enough (and the perception of some of it doesn't require careful listening at all). People with health anxiety, as we explore in greater detail in Chapter 4, have an unfortunate propensity to do *too much* listening to their bodies. Such "body vigilance" develops subsequent to health anxiety and is part of the normal response to threat (which indeed involves vigilance and scanning). Thus, people with health anxiety become exquisitely sensitive to the even the most subtle bodily variations that most people simply miss or ignore.

There is a popular axiom that goes as follows: "The only constant is change." Although, we tend to think of this maxim as applying to changes in the external world (e.g., gas prices, cultural norms), it is equally true for the internal environment. Our bodies are highly variable, and they generate a steady stream of more or less benign sensations. An important point to be made here is that the physiological cues that trigger episodes of health anxiety are not necessarily psychiatric or medical *disease processes;* rather, they are often mundane and innocent physiologic processes that cause vague, diffuse, and ambiguous bodily sensations, perturbations, and variations.

Homeostatic Functions

As with all living organisms, a fundamental characteristic of the human body is that it maintains its own internal environment. This self-regulatory process, known as *homeostasis*, accounts for bodily noise since different systems must be activated and deactivated (e.g., by the release of hormones) depending upon the particular needs of the body. For example, the body must maintain its temperature, oxygen levels, rate of blood flow, and vestibular functioning. Thus, healthy people invariably experience normal fluctuations in their heart rate, breathing rate, body temperature, and level of alertness throughout the day. Even visual and auditory acuity are (slightly) variable depending on the occurrence of completely normal bodily functions.

Effects of Diet

Other more or less subtle bodily sensations and variations also have well-established "noncatastrophic" explanations. For example, even healthy people can have odorous or discolored urine. This might be caused by reduced fluid intake, the side effects of medication, or the recent consumption of certain foods such as beets, blackberries, or artificial food coloring. It is also common for healthy people to experience changes in the smell, color, and texture of their stool. Such variations are related to changes in diet, such as adding (or subtracting) fat, fiber, or iron. Changes in diet can also produce gastrointestinal discomfort, bloating, and mild hypoglycemia, which can be associated with sweating, tachycardia, and feelings of faintness (Airola, 1977).

Sympathetic Arousal

Emotional responses such as anxiety, fear, worry, elation, excitement, anger, and rage are all accompanied by activation of the body's sympathetic nervous system and the release of adrenaline (also known as epinephrine). This activity produces a set of perceptible internal changes including (but not limited to):
- Increased heart rate,
- Increased strength of heart beat,
- Increased and speed and depth of breathing,
- Increased muscle tension,
- Increased vigilance and startle response,
- Dilation of the pupils,
- Perspiration,
- Decreased salivation,
- Decreased activity in the digestive system,
- Changes in urinary frequency and bowel urgency.

Although they can seem intense and uncomfortable, these effects are in fact benign and harmless. As part of the body's natural fight-or-flight response, their purpose is to make the organism mentally and physically alert, i.e., prepared to take action to defend itself from potential danger. It is as if this response serves as the body's natural alarm reaction. The obvious increase in heart rate and depth of breathing, for example, is akin to flashing lights and a loud internal siren. This response also serves to enrich the supply of energy-giving oxygen and glucose for the body's muscles. Moreover, only vital bodily processes occur during fight-or-flight; thus digestion, for example, ceases.

   Every action, however, has a *reaction*; thus, prolonged sympathetic nervous system activity can also be associated with additional unpleasant (yet again, benign) sensations. These sensations might be considered the "side effects" of sympathetic arousal:
- Exhaustion and fatigue (from the increase in activity within the body),
- Faintness and feelings of unreality (from hyperventilation and the body's conversion of oxygen to carbon dioxide),
- Blurred vision and spots (from pupil dilation),
- Numbness and tingling in the extremities (from blood vessel constriction),
- Breathlessness and feelings of choking or smothering (from the increased rate and depth of breathing),
- Aches, pains, tightness, trembling, and twitching (from muscle tension),
- Hot or cold flashes (from sweating),
- Dry mouth (from the increased rate and depth of breathing and reduced digestive system activity),
- Nausea and constipation (from reduced digestive system activity).

So, it is not surprising that people with health anxiety commonly misinterpret sympathetic arousal (and its sequelae) as indicating a serious medical problem. This is probably due to the fact that most people are unaware of the effects of adrenaline and the function of the sympathetic nervous system. Thus, the sensations described above might seem to occur "from out of the blue" or, worse, just when the individual is becoming worried about his or her health. We discuss this point further in Chapter 4, as the physiology of anxious arousal is an important contributor to the persistence of health anxiety.

Benign Medical Conditions

Many minor medical conditions can produce vague and diffuse bodily signs and sensations that health-anxious people misinterpret as symptoms of serious or degenerative diseases. Aerophagia (which literally means "eating air"), as exemplified in the case of Aron presented below, involves chronic belching, gas, and distention of the stomach. It has no organic basis and is conceptualized as arising from habits such as eating and drinking rapidly, chewing gum, and smoking. As Aron's case shows, it is quite common for health-anxious people to misinterpret the complications of aerophagia as indicators of gastrointestinal disease. Similarly, rumination syndrome – which also has no known organic cause – is characterized by the effortless regurgitation and rechewing of partially digested food. The regurgitation does not involve nausea and is often preceded by a belching sensation. The most typical complications include indigestion, bad breath, and chapped lips.

Irritable bowel syndrome (IBS) is characterized by abdominal pain, bowel cramps and urgency, diarrhea, bloating, constipation, and intestinal gas. It is

---

Case Example

Aron was a 35-year-old accountant who had become worried that he was slowly dying of a serious gastrointestinal disorder which his doctors could not identify or treat. His physical signs included chronic constipation, diarrhea, and belching which he attributed to his medical condition. On examination, Aron reported drinking several cans of soda each day and eating and drinking very rapidly, especially when anxious about his stomach problems. In the absence of evidence for a medical condition, Aron's gastrointestinal symptoms were considered to be those of aerophagia resulting from his high daily intake of carbonated beverages and rapid eating and drinking. He was referred to a behavioral medicine specialist who worked with him to (a) correctly understand the origins of his gastrointestinal complaints and (b) modify his unhealthy eating habits.

exacerbated by consumption of foods that produce bowel motility, such as to-mato products, certain spices, red meats, and fatty foods. Caused by a problem with bowel muscle contraction, IBS is known to be associated with anxiety and can be managed by altering one's eating habits (e.g., avoiding spicy foods) and learning stress management techniques. Nevertheless, people with health anxi-ety often misinterpret the symptoms of IBS, and those of hemorrhoids (which also produce pain and bloody stools), as signs of bowel or colorectal cancer (Taylor & Asmundson, 2004). Like IBS, common colds, sore throats, headaches, minor allergies, asthma, pyrosis ("heartburn"), acid reflux, moles, pulled mus-cles, and contusions (bruises) are all generally low-risk or fairly easily managed conditions that can produce health anxiety if their symptoms are misinterpret-ed as indicating the presence of a more serious medical disease.

Orthostatic intolerance or *postural orthostatic tachycardia syndrome* (often referred to as POTS) is a condition of unknown origin characterized by the body's inability to make the necessary adjustments to counteract gravity (Grubb, 2002). Orthostatic hypotension occurs when blood pressure drops as a result of moving from a sitting or supine position to a standing position. People with POTS, upon standing up (and sometimes when engaged in vigorous phys-ical activity), experience a cadre of uncomfortable internal sensations that might include a substantial increase in heart rate, feelings of nausea, faintness (although actually fainting is rare), headaches, and fatigue. Although POTS is not associated with any serious diseases, people with health anxiety often mis-take the tachycardia symptoms for a serious cardiovascular disease and the lightheadedness and dizzy spells for a dangerous neurological condition.

Many transient (or not so transient) episodes of vertigo (which might involve unreality, confusion, faintness, dizziness, or imbalance) are associated with or-thostatic hypotension and are normal and harmless. Even fainting (termed "syncope"), although rare, is usually not a need for concern. These experiences, however, can be misconstrued as medical conditions because they are uncom-fortable and ubiquitous symptoms in descriptions of serious illnesses such as anemia, many types of cancer, various neurological conditions, diabetes, and thyroid problems.

People with health anxiety are also prone to misinterpret *nonepileptic seizures* as serious neurological symptoms. Nonepileptic seizures (aka pseudoseizures or psychogenic seizures) appear to resemble epileptic seizures because they involve subjectively uncontrollable episodes of simple movement (e.g., shaking), gross motor or vocal behaviors (e.g., flailing of the arms), and physical sensations (e.g., tingling, blind spots). The resemblance to epilepsy, however, is only super-ficial since nonepileptic events do not have a neurological basis (i.e., they are not associated with epilepsy or any other forms of cortical output), nor are they associated with other medical conditions (Alsaadi & Marquez, 2005). Research indicates that such nonepileptic events are typically evoked by emotional states such as stress and anxiety (e.g., Chalder, 1996). In addition, they are responsive to cognitive and behavioral treatment techniques that teach the individual how to gain control over the seemingly uncontrollable behaviors.

Floaters are tiny deposits of protein and other cell debris that become suspended within the eye's normally transparent vitreous humor – the gel-like substance that fills the eye. They typically appear as translucent shadow-like shapes, spots, fragments, or threads that slowly drift through the visual field. Floaters are a very common occurrence in adults, but can also occur in children, and typically amount to only a minor nuisance if they cannot be ignored altogether. They might appear following eye trauma or cataract surgery, but as a rule do not indicate the presence of any medical problem. Nevertheless, some individuals with health anxiety are known to misinterpret the presence of floaters as indicating a serious eye condition or visual disturbance.

Lipomas are fatty growths situated just under the skin and muscle layer. They typically protrude gently from the body in the neck and shoulder region and are doughy to the touch and easily movable. They are typically painless. Although the term lipoma suggests a tumor (indeed, it literally means "fatty tumor"), these are not cancerous and are usually harmless. Nevertheless, some people become very anxious upon noticing lipomas, fearing they are malignant.

Finally, a number of *benign dermatological symptoms* (for which no medical cause has been determined) can become the focus of preoccupation and fear among individuals with health anxiety. These symptoms are collectively referred to as "the unexplained cutaneous sensory syndrome," and can include pain, rash, numbness, and pruritus (an itching sensation that evokes the urge

---

Case Example

Stuart was approaching his 38th birthday when his wife noticed a lump on the back of his neck, just above his shirt collar and below his hairline. Stuart had felt the lump weeks earlier but had thought nothing of it. This time, however, his wife had noticed it and seemed mildly concerned. This triggered health anxiety in him. Stuart immediately called his doctor, but was told he would have to wait three days for an appointment. Those three days were filled with severe angst as Stuart had convinced himself that he had cancer. "Would it be too late after three days?" he worried. When his doctor examined the lump manually and immediately diagnosed it as a lipoma, Stuart wondered how she could know for sure and insisted on a radiological exam. Although an ultrasound suggested that his doctor had correctly diagnosed the growth, Stuart remained concerned that he had a cancerous tumor. He became increasingly preoccupied with his health and engaged in frequent checks of his neck (sometimes every few minutes) to see whether the mass had grown. He also became highly irritable and developed concentration problems at work and at home with his family.

to scratch; Gupta, 2006). Uticaria, or "hives," is an eruption of red marks on the skin usually accompanied by itching. It is associated with the release of histamine and other chemicals into the bloodstream, which occurs when the immune system detects a foreign substance such as an allergen. Uticaria can also be caused by stress, infection, heat, or cold. Angioedema, or "welts," are similar to hives yet develop *under* the skin (rather than on the surface). Hyperhidrosis is a medically unexplained condition in which the person perspires excessively from the hands, face, and other parts of the body. In addition to triggering health concerns, these dermatologic conditions can also be a source of social embarrassment (Braddock & Abramowitz, 2007).

Notions: Beliefs and Interpretations that Lead to Health Anxiety

How someone deals with a bodily sensation – ignore it, worry about it, ask a family member about it, take a home remedy, or see a doctor – will depend on what that person believes is the cause or origin of the sensation. Being aware that healthy people can normally experience occasional and transient unexplained and diffuse physical signs or bodily perturbations, most individuals confer little (if any) significance to such events and consequently do nothing "about" them. In fact, non-health-anxious individuals might or might not even be aware of their bodily perturbations and variations. If, however, a generally healthy person appraises benign sensations as highly significant or threatening (i.e., as evidence of a serious medical illness), the harmless sensations take on a negative valence, and health anxiety will result (Abramowitz et al., 2002; Warwick & Salkovskis, 1990).

The idea that health anxiety arises from misinterpreting benign bodily sensations as threatening derives from Beck's (1976) cognitive model of emotion. The cognitive model stipulates that emotions – whether positive or negative – are caused not by situations or stimuli per se, but rather by how the person ascribes meaning to situations or stimuli. Moreover, particular negative emotions (and corresponding behaviors) are linked with specific interpretations. For example, the perception that one has deliberately been treated with disrespect leads to anger and hostility. Interpretations concerned with loss lead to depression and anhedonia. When an individual blames him- or herself for failing to achieve an important goal, the result is guilt. In the case of anxiety, the interpretations are concerned with threat. Once stimuli, such as bodily sensations and other health-relevant information, are misinterpreted as threatening, they become the target of preoccupation (i.e., vigilance) and behavioral responses aimed at avoiding or reducing the perceived threat.

The example of Becky, presented next, illustrates this process:

Case Example

Becky's health anxiety was triggered 2 years ago when she accidentally swallowed a large piece of meat that produced pain and discomfort as it traveled down her esophagus. When she continued to feel soreness in her throat later that evening, she went to the emergency room fearful she still had food stuck in her throat. She became concerned about choking on the food she believed remained lodged in her throat. Although her doctors carefully examined her and assured her it was not the case, Becky was convinced that she had damaged her esophagus and that food continued to remain stuck there. As a result of her concerns, she became preoccupied with her throat and thus constantly aware of how it felt. She also spent time each day searching for information about throat illnesses and injuries on the internet, which maintained her throat-focused attention. She routinely called doctors and nurses to ask for help and reassurance about her suspected problem.

Most likely, the large piece of meat that Becky accidentally swallowed produced a feeling of temporary soreness and discomfort as it went down her esophagus (most readers will be familiar with this sensation). Becky, however, overreacted and interpreted this feeling as indicating that something was *medically wrong*. Searching for an explanation, she decided – erroneously – that the discomfort was caused by food stuck in her throat that could eventually choke her. Thus, it is not the throat sensations per se, but rather how Becky *interpreted* them that led to her health anxiety, preoccupation, and trips to the emergency room. Further concern when her doctors failed to confirm her fear led Becky to become highly vigilant of throat sensations, resulting in "scanning" for any possible discomfort and becoming highly sensitive to normal body noise. This health anxiogenic process is depicted in Figure 3.1.

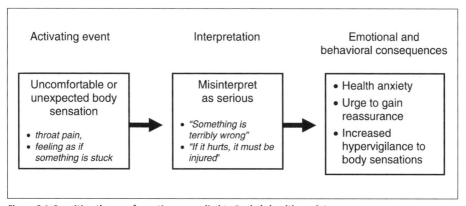

Figure 3.1. Cognitive theory of emotion as applied to Becky's health anxiety.

Salkovskis and Warwick (2001) pointed out that there is an internal consistency to how people with health anxiety misinterpret somatic sensations and variations. In particular, misinterpretations are meaningfully linked in a more or less specific way to particular somatic cues. For example, headaches, uncommon visual experiences, feelings of dizziness, unreality, and faintness are often misinterpreted as indicating a neurological problem. Tingling or loss of sensation in the extremities is often appraised as indicating multiple sclerosis, Lou Gehrig's disease, and some other serious general medical conditions. Tightness in the chest, tachycardia, and sensations on the left side of the body are often misappraised as a heart problem. Skin discoloration and lumps are often misinterpreted as cancerous. Stomach and other lower gastrointestinal sensations are often misinterpreted as signs of cancer or intestinal disease.

Several research studies provide empirical evidence that health anxiety is strongly related to how an individual gives meaning to common somatic sensations. For example, in one study individuals with hypochondriasis considered significantly more types of bodily sensations to be indicative of medical diseases than did nonhypochondriacal individuals (Barsky et al., 1993b). Among college students, health anxiety and hypochondriacal concerns were associated with the misinterpretation of ambiguous bodily sensations as indicating serious illnesses (Marcus, 1999). Moreover, specific illness attributions were more strongly associated with health anxiety symptoms as opposed to other forms of anxiety (e.g., general anxiety; MacLeod, Haynes, & Sensky, 1998; Marcus & Church, 2003).

Table 3.1. Domains of dysfunctional beliefs in health anxiety

Domain	Description
Overestimates of threat	Beliefs that illnesses are more common, more easily transmitted, and more serious than they actually are.
Anxiety sensitivity	Beliefs that the physical sensations associated with anxious arousal are dangerous.
Intolerance of uncertainty	Belief that it is necessary (and possible) to be 100% certain that negative outcomes will not occur.
Rigid health beliefs	Beliefs that being healthy requires being 100% symptom-free, and that all bodily signs and symptoms have a medical explanation.
General health assumptions	Belief that one is sick or especially susceptible to medical ailments.
Distrust of medicine	Beliefs that physicians and medical tests are incompetent.
Beliefs about death	Beliefs involving the assumption that consciousness endures after death.

Why do some people misappraise their benign bodily sensations as threatening whereas most of us do not? Such misinterpretations appear to be linked to the presence of core dysfunctional beliefs and attitudes. Next, we highlight several domains of dysfunctional core beliefs that give rise to threatening misappraisals of benign bodily sensations. These domains are summarized in Table 3.1.

Overestimation of Threat

Health-anxious individuals often exaggerate the probability and seriousness of medical disorders (Barsky et al., 1990a). Whereas most people take their good health for granted and only rarely stop to consider whether they *could* become ill, those suffering from health anxiety assume that serious illnesses are lurking around every corner. This leads to increased vigilance of somatic cues and thus the detection of more benign sensations which are subsequently misinterpreted as threatening.

Overestimates of the *likelihood* of illness interact with overestimates of the perceived *awfulness* of the feared condition. Catastrophic ideas about pain and suffering, functional disability, and disruption to the lives of loved ones predominate. Other beliefs include overly negative assumptions about illness management and the ability to cope; often including the belief that medical help will be ineffective (Salkovskis & Warwick, 2001). Whereas many health-anxious individuals overestimate both the likelihood and awfulness of having an illness, it is possible to be highly health anxious with relatively low perceived probability of illness, given a relatively high perception of the awfulness of being ill. For example, an affected man might acknowledge that his feelings of dizziness are probably not indicative of a neurological disease, yet believe that having such a disease would result in mental decline, being pitied or rejected by loved ones, and being dehumanized.

Overestimates of threat are associated with gross inaccuracies in judgment. For instance, rather than using objective evidence, health-anxious individuals frequently base their health-related predictions on publicized cases. Excellent examples include preoccupations with relatively rare conditions that gain media attention such as West Nile virus, SARS, bird flu, Lou Gherig's disease, and Lyme disease. Further below we will return to a discussion of the origins of such dysfunctional beliefs.

A number of research findings support the idea that health-anxious individuals overestimate the risks and seriousness of medical problems. In one study that examined the perceived risk of illness, primary-care patients with hypochondriasis appraised their personal risk for medical diseases as higher than did patients without hypochondriasis. But this difference did not emerge when rating the perceived risk of criminal victimization (Barsky et al., 2001). This suggests that health-anxious people are prone to overestimating health risks in particular, rather than the risk of harm or danger in general.

Anxiety Sensitivity

Anxiety sensitivity is the tendency toward catastrophically misinterpreting the physiological sensations associated with anxious (sympathetic) arousal based on beliefs that such sensations have harmful physical, cognitive, or social consequences (Reiss, 1991; Taylor, 1999). It is essentially the "fear of fear." To illustrate, a person with high levels of anxiety sensitivity might be afraid of heart palpitations and the feeling of tightness in the chest because he or she – mistakenly – believes they are the symptoms of heart disease. Similarly, someone concerned about having an undiagnosed neurological disorder might fear sensations of dizziness and derealization. In both instances, the sensations are a normal part of the normal sympathetic arousal response. But this poses a problem for the health-anxious person since the fear of these particular sensations directly leads to increased anxiety, increased sympathetic arousal, and therefore more of the feared bodily sensations.

The case of Howard, described below, illustrates how a health-anxious person's physiologic response when apprehensive about medical diseases can actually lead to additional fearful somatic sensations.

Case Example

Howard, a 27-year-old graduate student, was worried that he had a serious neurological condition despite no evidence of such a problem. His main complaint was that he often heard ringing in his ears – a benign condition known as *tinnitus* often successfully treated using behavioral techniques that help the individual reduce daily stress and divert attention away from the ringing. Howard, however, was opposed to any behavioral interventions for his suspected *medical* condition. He was adamant that he required a medical diagnosis and intervention. In support of his argument, Howard described how he had begun to develop feelings of dizziness and unreality when he noticed (and began to worry about) the ringing in his ears. This, he explained, is a sign that his condition is getting worse. Although Howard interpreted his dizziness and unreality as confirmation that he has a neurological disorder, in fact Howard's worrying about the ringing in his hears had led to increased physiologic arousal, which in turn resulted in subtle overbreathing and benign feelings of dizziness stemming from the fight/flight response.

Research on the relationship between anxiety sensitivity and health anxiety indicates that people with hypochondriasis are more anxiety sensitive than are nonclinical individuals (Cox, 1999), and that anxiety sensitivity is positively correlated with symptoms of hypochondriasis and health anxiety in individuals with depression (Otto, Demopulos, McLean, Pollack, & Fava, 1998), anxiety disorders (Abramowitz et al., 2007; Otto et al., 1992), in nonclinical young adults (Abramowitz, Deacon, & Valentiner, 2007; Stewart & Watt, 2000), and in older adults (Bravo & Silverman, 2001). Moreover, anxiety sensitivity contributes to the prediction of disability in chronic pain patients (Asmundson & Norton, 1995) and appears to be a stronger predictor of health anxiety symptoms than either trait anxiety or depression (Bravo & Silverman, 2001). These correlational findings are based largely on self-reported symptoms, yet they are consistent with experimental studies showing that high anxiety sensitivity is associated with more awareness of internal bodily sensations and more catastrophic thoughts and emotional responses to the provocation of somatic sensations in the laboratory (MacDonald, Baker, Stewart, & Skinner, 2000).

Intolerance of Uncertainty

Individuals with health anxiety often hold the erroneous belief that it is possible – and necessary – to be absolutely and 100% certain about one's health. Even the remote possibility of rare or unlikely diseases can become a source of great concern. As a result, individuals who misinterpret ambiguous bodily signs and sensations as indicating an illness typically experience urges to gain reassurance by trying to determine the origins of these sensations, checking and rechecking their own body (e.g., blood pressure, screening for lumps), looking up the meaning of possible symptoms on the internet or in medical texts, and asking others (mostly medical professionals) for assurance. Some individuals indicate they would prefer to be told that they in fact have a serious illness rather than remain uncertain about the meaning of their suspected signs and symptoms. This intolerance for uncertainty is often specific to the feared medical problem and not a problem for the patient in other areas of life.

The relationship between intolerance of uncertainty and health anxiety has not yet been systematically examined. Indirect evidence from research on OCD, however, indicates that the need for certainty plays a key role in compulsive checking behavior (Tolin, Abramowitz, Brigidi, & Foa, 2003), which is also a main feature of health anxiety. Checking – whether locks and appliances in OCD or one's body and the internet in health anxiety – represents the need to gain assurance in order to reduce anxiety and uncertainty about possible negative outcomes.

Rigid Health Beliefs

People with health anxiety may hold overly rigid health-related beliefs, for example, excessively strict definitions of what it means to be "well," such as "a healthy body has absolutely no symptoms"; "any bodily sensation must have a medical explanation"; and "if it's not a serious disease, it must be an *imaginary* symptom" (Warwick & Salkovsis, 1990). Other examples pertain to all-or-nothing ideas about diagnoses and interventions, such as "I cannot go on with life unless I have a clear diagnosis of my problem" and "If I don't get to the doctor as soon as I notice anything unusual, it will be too late." This style of black-and-white thinking fosters a tendency toward catastrophically misinterpreting ambiguous bodily sensations and variations. It also underlies urges to repeatedly contact physicians, repeat medical tests, or seek explanations for suspected symptoms. Such assumptions also lead to feeling disparaged when a physician either cannot find a suitable physiologic explanation or downplays the significance of such bodily stimuli.

Research supports the view that rigid beliefs about health and illness are common among people with health anxiety. Barsky et al. (1993b), for example, found evidence that individuals with hypochondriasis believe they must be symptom-free in order to consider themselves healthy. Similarly, Rief, Hiller, and Margraf (1998) found that individuals with hypochondriasis, and those with somatization disorder, endorsed such rigid beliefs to a greater extent than did a control group of non-health-anxious psychiatric patients.

General Health Assumptions

Another common belief among people with health anxiety is that their bodies are weak and unable to tolerate stress (Taylor & Asmundson, 2004). The perceived weakness might involve a general sense of frailty or fragility ("I know I am only 30, but I have the body of a 90-year-old") or it might be focused on a specific organ or part of the body (e.g., "I have a weak stomach"). It might also result from knowledge of a family history of illness (e.g., "cancer runs in the family"). As a result, such individuals believe they are highly susceptible to medical problems. This may give rise to constant anxiety and hypervigilance, leading to the misinterpretation of benign bodily cues as further signs of the suspected problem. It may also lead the person to restrict his or her activities (e.g., avoidance of vigorous activity) so that the perceived susceptibility is not challenged.

Other sorts of general health assumptions involve unrealistic beliefs about prevention and treatment, such as "I must avoid all vigorous activity in order to preserve my health" and "If I exercise and eat healthy, I can avoid all illnesses." Such beliefs lead to engaging in extreme avoidance strategies and other unnecessary "healthy" behaviors in efforts to reduce the risk or impact of feared (low-risk) diseases.

Studies of clinical and nonclinical samples alike support the notion that the sense of one's body being flawed and highly vulnerable to diseases is linked to health anxiety (e.g., Barsky et al., 2001; Rief et al., 1998). Evidence also suggests health anxiety entails a high degree of perceived susceptibility to medical conditions, but not to physical dangers arising from nonmedical causes such as automobile accidents or crime (Barsky et al., 2001).

Distrust of Medicine

People with health anxiety often hold dysfunctional beliefs about physicians (e.g., "if the doctor can't identify my physical disease, she is not being thorough enough"), the validity of medical tests (e.g., "medical tests can't be trusted"), and the ways in which medical (and psychological) interventions work (e.g., "if this treatment doesn't *immediately* relieve my symptoms, it is no good"). Another example is the belief that "if a physician refers me to a specialist, it is because he or she thinks there is a serious problem." These sorts of assumptions lead medically healthy individuals with health anxiety to view their physician as uncaring, untrustworthy, and dismissive. Such assumptions also increase the level of preoccupation with bodily concerns, thereby increasing attentiveness to somatic cues which may be misinterpreted in threatening ways.

A handful of investigations demonstrate that health-anxious individuals hold dysfunctional beliefs about their physicians. Specifically, people with hypochondriasis report greater distrust of their physicians' judgments, greater dissatisfaction with their medical care, and make more negative comments about their physicians than do psychologically healthy control participants (Barsky, Wyshak, Latham, & Klerman, 1991; Kellner, Abbott, Winslow, & Pathak, 1987; Persing, Stuart, Noyes, & Happel, 2000). In addition, patients with health anxiety perceive their doctors' reassurance as less convincing than do non-health-anxious patients (Lucock, White, Peake, & Morley, 1998).

Beliefs About Death

Many people with health anxiety exhibit unrealistic beliefs and assumptions pertaining to death, the afterlife, and other superstitions. Such beliefs might incorporate the idea of *enduring consciousness*, as exemplified by the following:

- "I'll be cold and all alone in the grave";
- "If I die I'll miss my family and miss out on all the fun"; and
- "If I tell myself I am healthy, I'm just tempting fate" (Taylor & Asmundson, 2004).

Furer, Walker, and Stein (2007) describe other types of dysfunctional death-related beliefs, including the belief that the process of dying will be dreadfully painful, scary, and involve terrible suffering; the belief that dying before one's children are grown will ruin their lives forever; and the idea that finding out one has a life-threatening illness with only a short time to live would be completely unmanageable. Some individuals are so consumed with the fear of death that it takes up an inordinate amount of time and energy. They might feel as if they cannot – or *should* not – enjoy anything unless they can be certain that they will not be dying shortly. Ironically, without realizing it, such individuals spend precious days of their lives preoccupied with an event that, while inevitable, is unlikely to occur for many years.

The clinical literature is full of writings on *thanatophobia* (the fear of death; e.g., Starcevic, 1989), although most of this work is more theoretical and anecdotal than empirical. Scientific research has demonstrated links between the fear of death and health anxiety. For example, Kellner et al. (1987) found that people with hypochondriasis reported greater fears of death relative to nonclinical individuals and a control group of non-health-anxious psychiatric patients. Rief et al. (1998) also found evidence that people with hypochondriasis and somatization disorder endorse dysfunctional beliefs about death.

Nurture: The Origin of Dysfunctional Health Beliefs

Three types of environmental factors can serve as pathways to the development of anxiety and fear, including:
a) Stressful or traumatic experiences,
b) Vicarious or observational learning, and
c) Informational transmission (Rachman, 1977).

In the case of health anxiety, certain events within these domains may be seen as leading to the formation of dysfunctional assumptions about somatic sensations, diseases, death, and the medical profession. We discuss specific factors within each domain that have been identified by researchers as contributing to the development of health anxiety and the types of cognitive distortions described above.

Stressful or Traumatic Experiences

Personally experiencing a very stressful or traumatic event can lead to the development of fear and anxiety because it can stimulate anticipation of future adverse events. Consistent with this notion, studies have found that many people with somatization disorder and hypochondriasis have a history of serious medical diseases or have lived through a family member's bout with a serious illness (e.g., Craig, Boardman, Mills, Daly-Jones, & Drake, 1993). Even healthy adults who were successfully treated for a childhood medical problem (e.g., congenital heart defects) are at increased risk for the development of health anxiety. Such individuals may be prone to seeing themselves as weak and highly vulnerable (general health assumption) or become concerned that their problem was not completely treated (distrust of medicine) and will necessarily return in adulthood (overestimation of threat). Such assumptions foster the misinterpretation of ambiguous bodily sensations as possible signs of the suspected ailment.

The death of a loved one from a serious illness can lead to the types of beliefs described earlier in this chapter. For example, one patient recalled her mother's death from lung cancer in her late 50s. As the patient approached this same age, and despite medical evidence to the contrary, she believed she was destined for a similar fate (i.e., general health assumption) and became preoccupied with somatic cues that might suggest cancer. Other potentially stressful health-related personal experiences can precipitate dysfunctional beliefs. One 46-year-old man, for example, worked as a plumber and complained of the fear of lung cancer from exposure to asbestos. The man recollected that asbestos had been found in some of the buildings where he had installed plumbing. Although it was determined that the levels of any asbestos were very low and not dangerous, this man continued to perceive himself as highly vulnerable to cancer. Finally, there is evidence that childhood physical, sexual, and emotional abuse is associated with hypochondriasis and other manifestations of health anxiety (Barsky et al., 1994). Such stressful events may lead a child to view him- or herself as vulnerable and defenceless, providing a foundation for the misinterpretation of bodily sensations.

Although it is an intuitively appealing idea, the occurrence of stressful and traumatic experiences alone cannot adequately account for the development of health-anxious beliefs. Indeed, not everyone with health anxiety recalls such an experience. Moreover, many individuals who encounter these kinds of experiences fail to develop severe health anxiety (or any emotional disturbance, for that matter). For example, relative to the number of people who are abuse victims, or whose parents (or close relatives) die of serious illnesses, the number of individuals with clinical health anxiety is quite small. Thus, there must be additional environmental factors that contribute to health anxiety.

Observational Learning

Much of our behavior is learned vicariously by watching other people, particularly those who are important to us, such as our caregivers. This explains why many behavioral and personality traits tend to run in families. Thus, a second way dysfunctional, health-relevant beliefs might be shaped is through the observation of close relatives. Consistent with this idea, studies have found that parental ill health and parental health anxiety are associated with medically unexplained somatic complaints among offspring (e.g., Craig et al., 1993). Perhaps offspring internalize parental attitudes toward health and illness, such as the tendency to treat even minor injuries as cataclysmic (e.g., overreactions to cuts and scrapes, frequent emergency room visits, etc.). Liberal use of the healthcare system and frequent physical complaints among parents could convey information to children that forms for the basis for dysfunctional beliefs about illness and health; for example, the idea that *any type of pain or injury is a serious problem and must not be ignored*. Finally, overprotective parenting may lead the child to develop rigid views of medical illness as highly dangerous and beliefs of him- or herself as overly vulnerable and unable to manage such maladies.

As with traumatic conditioning, not all people who develop health anxiety observe health-anxious attitudes and behaviors among their closest caretakers. Similarly, there are many people with health anxiety who do not report growing up in families where dysfunctional attitudes and behavioral responses toward illnesses prevailed. Thus, observational learning does not alone account for the development of health anxiety. For these reasons, it would be inappropriate to place blame for this problem on parents or other particular individuals.

Case Example

Katie was born 2 months prematurely, and her parents were extremely worried that she might not survive infancy or develop normally. Indeed, pediatricians had told the family that Katie was vulnerable to a host of medical problems, and that she would likely need constant medical attention. Concerns were also raised regarding Katie's cognitive development and ability to learn. As it turned out, Katie experienced very few medical or cognitive problems as she grew. Nevertheless, her parents remained extremely vigilant and respondent to even minor health issues. Katie, at 29, told us that her parents spared no opportunity to call doctors or rush her to the hospital even for minor problems such as a simple cold or loose bowel movement. She recalled being told over and over about her premature birth and how her survival was nothing short of a miracle. Katie, however, had developed health anxiety: internalizing the beliefs that her body was weak and extremely susceptible to illness. She had a good deal of insight into the erroneous nature of these beliefs, yet she continued to monitor her vital signs and use various other safety-seeking behaviors and avoidance strategies just to "be on the safe side."

Informational Transmission

Observational learning might be considered a more or less passive process by which knowledge is implicitly communicated from one source (i.e., person) to another. In informational transmission, however, the knowledge is actively and explicitly conveyed. The media, for example, are a highly compelling source of (often erroneous) health-relevant information (Taylor & Asmundson, 2004). Hearing about diseases on the news, seeing afflicted individuals on television (e.g., Peter Jennings, the newscaster who died of lung cancer), and reading about the prevalence, symptoms, treatments, and prognosis of diseases on the internet can lead to overestimates of the probability and severity of such conditions. Moreover, this can make vulnerable people become more attuned to their own bodies in search of evidence to confirm their illness fears.

Informational transmission explains how health anxiety can develop even when a person has never experienced a severe illness, had a close relative suffer or die from a medical disease, or been exposed to abuse or health-anxious parents. A classic example of the effects of informational transmission is so-called *medical students' disease* (Woods, Natteson, & Silverman, 1966), which is common among students in medical school as well as in students of abnormal psychology: As these students become immersed in learning about the signs and symptoms of various serious medical and psychological problems, they scrutinize their own somatic sensations, behaviors, and cognitions, and ponder whether their observations of normal variations in fact represent severe medical or psychiatric problems.

Case Example

In November 2001, shortly after hearing of the anthrax attacks in Washington DC, Susan developed the fear that she had been infected with anthrax and had only a short time to get treated before she would die a terrible death. She spent many hours searching the internet for information about anthrax and watched several cable television specials on the subject. Although she pursued medical attention, diagnostic tests for anthrax infection (as well as other illnesses) repeatedly came up negative. This, however, did not quell Susan's fears. She remained concerned that the recent blister she had developed, her chronic diarrhea, lethargy and fatigue, as well as loss of appetite were all signs of her infection. She was continually referred from doctor to doctor who dismissed the idea of anthrax, yet who couldn't offer any alternative medical diagnosis. This was a further source of worry for Susan, and she was able to convince one physician to prescribe prophylactic doses of antibiotic medication. When the alleged "anthrax symptoms" persisted, Susan became convinced that she had been exposed to an antibiotic-resistant strain.

Informational transmission also explains why many people with health anxiety are preoccupied with having the same highly popularized diseases (e.g., SARS, AIDS), and why these focal diseases changes over time. For example, after the highly popularized outbreak of severe acute respiratory syndrome (SARS) in Asia and North America in 2002 and 2003, many people with health anxiety presented with the preoccupation that their unexplained symptoms were indicative of this very serious condition. The case of Susan, presented on the previous page, is another example of how media coverage of a serious illness can contribute to the development of health anxiety.

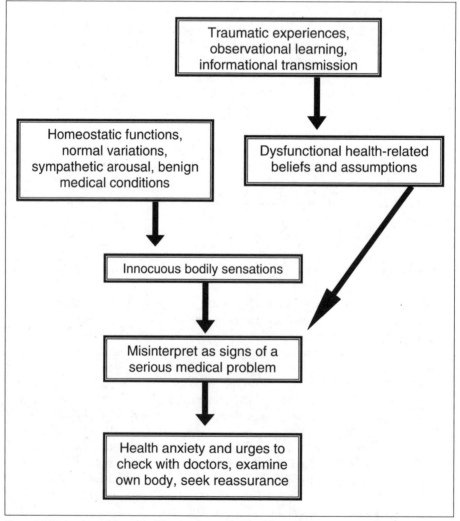

Figure 3.2. Biopsychosocial model of the development of health anxiety.

Implications of the Biopsychosocial Model

We have described a biopsychosocial model of health anxiety in which past experiences with illnesses – or the transmission of illness-related information – foster the development of dysfunctional beliefs and assumptions about health, disease, medicine, and death. The presence of such beliefs leads to the catastrophic misinterpretation of relatively harmless and transient physical and somatic cues. Figure 3.2 graphically depicts this model.

An important implication of the biopsychosocial model is that it assumes people with health anxiety really do experience the "symptoms" they describe. Technically, however, these are not *symptoms* since they do not arise from any medical disease; rather, they are bodily *sensations* that do not portend serious health problems. Accordingly, it is essential to distinguish health anxiety from malingering (in which symptoms are feigned in order to achieve a goal such as an insurance settlement) and from factitious disorder in which symptoms are deliberately induced for no apparent reason (American Psychiatric Association, 2000). In the next chapter we address the question of why health anxiety – and its associated mistaken beliefs and interpretations – persist in the face of what most people would consider to be robust evidence of good health.

4

The Persistence of Health Anxiety

Within a theoretical framework it is important to distinguish between *etiologic* factors (i.e., processes that lead to the *development* of a problem) and *mainte-nance* factors (i.e., processes that lead to the *persistence* of a problem). Indeed, maladaptive thinking and behavior might begin for one reason, yet persist for another (or others). Consider, for example, a teenager who begins using alcohol in response to peer pressure. Factors that might initially contribute to drinking behavior include bullying from same-aged peers and beliefs about the impor-tance of "fitting in." Yet, these factors do not necessarily continue to influence drinking behavior as the individual becomes an adult. Instead, excessive drink-ing might be maintained by the positive feeling of being "buzzed" or by the reduction in emotional distress that alcohol can engender. Thus, alcohol use can develop into a learned habit that is divorced from its initial causal factors.

With respect to health anxiety, knowledge of the causal factors discussed in Chapter 3 might be helpful for the purposes of prevention or relapse prevention following successful treatment. Understanding the factors that *maintain* health anxiety, however, will be most useful in psychological treatment since reversing maintenance factors will weaken *existing* symptoms. Patients, too, benefit from understanding the psychological processes involved in the maintenance of their problem as this provides a rationale for engaging in the types of therapy tech-niques that reduce health anxiety. There is evidence that understanding this rationale plays a role in the successful treatment of other anxiety problems, such as OCD (Abramowitz, Franklin, Zoellner, & DiBernardo, 2002).

The biopsychosocial model presented in Chapter 3 posits that clinical health anxiety develops when ambiguous and generally benign physical sensations and bodily perturbations are misperceived as indicating a threat to one's health. Body checking, reassurance-seeking, avoidance, and other safety-seeking re-sponses are deployed with the aim of reducing health anxiety or the perceived probability of medical illness. But, if the illness concerns of health-anxious per-sons are based on *mistaken beliefs* and *misinterpretations*, why do their thinking and behavioral patterns persist? If the vague and ambiguous bodily sensations and variations are not really as dangerous as health-anxious people anticipate, why don't these individuals recognize this irrationality, listen to their doctors, correct their flawed thinking, and stop their problematic behavior? The first part of this chapter seeks to answer these questions by explaining the factors that maintain health anxiety. Then, we present a biopsychosocial conceptual framework of the development and maintenance of health anxiety that incorporates information from this chapter and from Chapter 3. The present chapter closes with a discussion of treatment implications of this conceptual framework.

Maintenance Factors

Let us begin by considering two observations that highlight the importance of maintenance factors in health anxiety: First, at one point or another, most people experience some sort of unfounded health-related concern. For example, we experience a "new" pain or sensation somewhere in the body and wonder whether something is wrong or if the pain will ever go away; or we become concerned with the latest outbreak of a serious illness dramatized by the media. In the majority of such instances, however, these concerns are self-correcting – the unexplained pain diminishes on its own or seems not to be too serious; the slight and temporary stomach ache we feel appears to be indigestion rather than a serious malady. Among people with clinical health anxiety, however, something appears to prevent such self-correction from occurring.

Second, for many people with hypochondriasis and other forms of health anxiety, the persistence of their health-related concerns seems curiously unreasonable. Consider a patient who believes she has appendicitis based on occasional complaints of abdominal pain. For 10 years before being referred for psychological treatment she has had numerous medical evaluations, tests, and procedures – all indicating that she is medically healthy. Moreover, despite her concerns about dying as a result of sepsis (an occasional consequence of untreated appendicitis in which infecting bacteria enter the bloodstream and travel to the rest of the body), she is still alive. Despite what would appear to a nonsufferer to be dramatic disconfirmation of her fears, her beliefs do not change. In other words, people with health anxiety often fail to spot that the feedback they consistently receive from medical professionals – and their failure to get sick as expected – are inconsistent with their beliefs about the meaning of their feared bodily sensations.

The particular factors that maintain health anxiety can be grouped into three domains: those associated with physiology, with cognition, and with behavior. Below, we elaborate on each domain and provide clinical examples that illustrate the relevant psychopathological processes.

Physiological Factors

As we have discussed in previous chapters, a wide range of somatic stimuli can trigger episodes of health anxiety. The sensations associated with increased physiological arousal (i.e., the fight-or-flight response), for example, if perceived as threatening, can engender health-related apprehension. Indeed, an increase in heart rate, difficulty catching one's breath, tightness in the chest, nausea, and dizziness, may be experienced as anxiety-provoking if one is either unaware of how one' body normally responds to stress; or is unaware of even having experienced stress in the first place. Thus, these sorts of sensations might be misinterpreted as the signs and symptoms of a serious medical disease, leading to episodes of intense health anxiety.

The physiological correlates of anxiety and stress also play a role in the *maintenance* of health anxiety (e.g., Salkovskis & Warwick, 2001). This process occurs as follows: When one becomes anxious, concerned, or otherwise apprehensive about one's health, such an emotional state is accompanied by physiologic arousal as part of the normal fight-or-flight response to perceived threat. Individuals who misconstrue this normally occurring increase in somatic sensations as additional evidence of illness will experience even more health anxiety. Thus, at the very moment one is becoming concerned about one's health, additional threatening "symptoms" appear that seemingly confirm the presence of illness. This invariably produces still more bodily sensations, resulting in a vicious cycle

---

Case Example

Matt was a 36-year-old physician whose health anxiety symptoms interfered so substantially with his functioning that he had to give up his medical practice. His main problem was the belief that he had colon cancer. Matt first became concerned about colon cancer following an episode of minor (benign) rectal bleeding that had occurred about 15 years earlier. He continued to complain of diarrhea since that particular event and frequently engaged in poking and prodding in his rectum. Despite between 10 and 20 consultations with experts in this field – all of whom indicated that he was completely healthy – Matt continued to worry about colon cancer. When his psychologist asked Matt about the evidence upon which the beliefs about his heath were based, Matt said that every time he becomes preoccupied with having colon cancer and touches inside his rectum, symptoms of cancer appear, including tiredness, loss of sleep, stomach distress, sweating, bowel urgency, loose stools, and the subjective feeling of incomplete defecation. When asked, Matt also noted that at other times, he does not experience these symptoms. Matt's therapist helped Matt to understand how his perceived "symptoms" were actually normal physiologic manifestations and correlates of his health-related fear and preoccupation.

of unexpected bodily sensations → threat-related interpretations (e.g., "I am ill") → anxiety/apprehension → more intense bodily sensations, and so on. Changes in bodily processes such as bowel function and sleep pattern that may result from increased arousal can also be misinterpreted. The example below illustrates this phenomenon.

Figure 4.1 graphically depicts this process using examples from Matt's case (on the previous page). There is, however, enormous specificity in the types of physiological reactions that maintain health anxiety. For example, a patient with concerns over losing her vision misinterpreted a floater as a sign of imminent visual impairment. She became anxious and, as a result of her anxiety, experienced lightheadedness and episodes of blurred vision, which served to reinforce her belief that she indeed had a visual disturbance. Another individual who had become preoccupied with fears of neurological diseases worried whether he no-

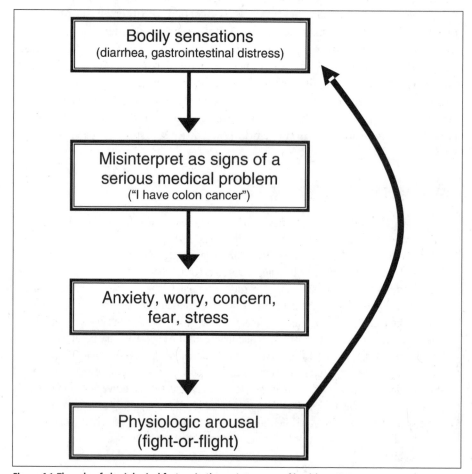

Figure 4.1. The role of physiological factors in the maintenance of health anxiety.

ticed any slight feelings of dizziness. As a result of his worry, he focused on increased sensations of unreality, dizziness, and took these as further evidence of a true neurological condition. A third example is that of a woman with hyperhidrosis (excessive perspiration) who became stressed when she felt herself sweating (i.e., "What could be wrong with me that I sweat so much? I must determine the cause of this problem!"). Her health-focused stress led to focusing on increased sweating, which compounded her concerns.

Readers who are familiar with cognitive-behavioral approaches to panic attacks (e.g., Clark, 1986) will note similarities between the maintenance of panic disorder and the pattern illustrated in Figure 4.1. As others have pointed out, however, this process is somewhat more intense in the case of panic than with health anxiety (Salkovskis & Warwick, 2001). Moreover, whereas health anxiety usually involves the fear of a progressive or long-term illness, panic involves the fear that one is dying, namely, as a result of the panic attack (see Warwick & Salkovskis, 1990). Nevertheless, the overlapping maintenance processes in panic and health anxiety likely account for the high comorbidity rates between these conditions (Salkovskis & Clark, 1993).

Cognitive Factors

Problems with health anxiety can also be maintained by biases in the way people think and reason when they become anxious. We describe below four closely related cognitive factors that contribute to the maintenance of health anxiety.

Selective Attention to Threat Cues

In dangerous circumstances it is adaptive to become vigilant of threat cues. Indeed, *not* paying attention to sources of potential harm in objectively dangerous situations increases the likelihood of serious injury and death. It is therefore not surprising that an immediate and automatic shift in attention (to search one's surroundings for possible danger) is part of the body's normal fight-or-flight response to perceived threat. But what if the perceived threat is irrational, such as the fears of benign bodily sensations in health anxiety? In such instances the deployment of attention toward somatic stimuli results in the person becoming extremely sensitive to feared bodily cues, thereby amplifying vague and normally fluctuating internal events that other people simply do not even recognize (e.g., body noise). In the end this will seem to confirm mistaken and exaggerated health-related beliefs and misinterpretations (e.g., "My doctors have missed a serious illness"; Kellner et al., 1987). The inclination to closely attend

---

Case Example

Dora, a 36-year-old librarian, was concerned that she had a serious neurological condition as evidenced by her seemingly impaired memory. Although she acknowledged no interference with routine daily functioning, and all neurological and neuropsychological tests showed no actual memory deficit, Dora continued to believe her memory was failing her. In fact, Dora had occasionally forgotten the names of people she had recently met (e.g., at her new job, at a party), and also had occasional experiences of being unable to recall which clothes she had worn the day before. Although these are normal cognitive occurrences for someone of Dora's age, she paid a great deal of attention to her memory, which seemed to maintain her health-related fears in two ways. First, it increased her awareness of otherwise "normal" (age-appropriate) failures in memory that most people do not attend to, thus confirming her mistaken beliefs about memory loss. Second, it competed with other cognitive tasks, perhaps resulting in a certain degree of actual memory impairment.

---

to and monitor internal body sensations is called *body vigilance* (Schmidt et al, 1997) and is illustrated in the case example of Dora presented above.

Body vigilance is elevated among individuals with health anxiety (hypochondriasis) relative to most other anxiety disorders except for panic disorder and generalized anxiety disorder (Olatunji, Deacon, Abramowitz, & Valentiner, 2007). Research has also shown that directing attention toward somatic cues intensifies the perception of bodily sensations. And when attention is diverted, the saliency of the sensations declines. Pennebaker (1982) reported a number of elegant experiments demonstrating this phenomenon. In one study, participants, while jogging on a treadmill, were assigned to listen either to the sound of their own panting breath or to other peoples' conversations. Although both groups had similar heart rates, respiratory rates, and blood pressure, participants listening to the sounds of their own breath demonstrated higher levels of fatigue, heart palpitations, and sweating.

Other studies have shown that the more often postoperative patients were asked to rate their pain, the worse the pain seemed. For example, Levine (1982) instructed patients who had just undergone dental extractions to either rate their pain levels every 20 minutes for 2 hours following surgery, or to give only a single pain rating 2 hours after the surgery. Those who reported their pain every 20 minutes complained of significantly more pain at the 2-hour point compared to the second group.

The processes described above occur both for persons with health anxiety (Barsky, Geringer, & Wool, 1988) and among healthy individuals with no physical complaints (Schmidt, Wolfs-Takens, Oosterlaan, & van den Hout, 1994) and have implications for treatment. Specifically, if the treatment aims to reduce the perception and misinterpretation of benign somatic cues, it will be important to instruct people in the patient's life (e.g., friends, relatives) to stop asking the patient about his or her "symptoms." Such behavior serves to maintain, if not increase, body vigilance.

Confirmation Bias

In potentially dangerous situations, individuals are well served by gathering additional evidence relevant to the perceived threat. Thus, in the case of a perceived threat to one's health, it is natural for the individual to actively seek information to validate (or invalidate) his or her concern. Anxious individuals, however, are inclined to err on the side of caution and rely only on *fear-confirming* information since the costs of a false-negative conclusion (assuming good health when an illness is really present) are significantly higher than those of a false-positive conclusion (assuming illness when one is really healthy). Clearly, such a reasoning pattern is functional and adaptive when a true threat exists. If, however, the perceived threat is based on a misinterpretation of a benign bodily sensation, the exclusive reliance on danger-confirming information (i.e., while discounting all danger-disconfirming evidence) serves to maintain the credibility of the faulty perception of threat.

A significant effect of this confirmation bias is that it can prejudice the impact of information provided by doctors during medical consultations as well as information gleaned from other sources such as friends, relatives, and the internet. When even the weakest of evidence in favor of illness is present, individuals with health anxiety have difficulty accurately deducing the logical implications of overwhelming inconsistent evidence. Disconfirmatory evidence,

---

Case Example

Rosemary suffered from growing concerns that she had multiple sclerosis (MS), which is incurable. Her health worries were based on misinterpretations of benign feelings of fatigue, tiredness, and occasional minor (normal and transient) lapses in coordination (e.g., dropping her keys) and speech (e.g., stumbling on a word) for actual symptoms of MS. Although Rosemary had seen more than 10 different physicians and undergone numerous physical examinations, neuroimaging studies, blood tests, and invasive diagnostic procedures (cerebrospinal fluid tests, nerve stimulation), there was no evidence that MS was present. On one occasion, however, a doctor had indicated that one test showed *possible* evidence of minor demyelination (degeneration of the fatty covering of the nerve cells). Rosemary took this – and the presence of minor and transient physical complaints – as confirmation of her fears, despite all the evidence to the contrary. Hence, she continued to believe she was developing MS.

no matter how strong, is explained away as either inadequate or immaterial. This phenomenon accounts for urges to seek second opinions when doctors conclude that there is no sign of illness, as in the example provided on the previous page.

Empirical research on the confirmation bias shows that people with health anxiety (hypochondriasis) as well as healthy individuals show a danger-confirming strategy when it comes to health-related threats (de Jong, Haenen, Schmidt, & Mayer, 1998). This suggests that rather than a cause of health anxiety, such a reasoning strategy serves to prevent individuals with such irrational health fears from giving up their fears even when faced with incompatible data. Put another way, the confirmation bias immunizes health-anxious people against falsification of their anxiogenic beliefs and misinterpretations, thus perpetuating their health anxiety.

Memory Bias

Individuals with health anxiety appear to have a bias in how they recall information relevant to their feared illnesses (Rief, Heitmuller, Reisberg, & Ruddel, 2006). For example, they might remember medical reports incorrectly or inflate estimates of the likelihood of illness as compared to what the doctor actually told them in person. Research indicates that such faulty recall may be specific to medically relevant information, and that individuals without unexplained somatic complaints do not show this biased recall. Thus, this process has clear implications for the maintenance of health anxiety: Even if doctors provide reassurance that the chances of a serious disease are small, such probabilities are likely to be exaggerated in memory. The treatment implications are also clear: Patients need to learn new strategies for reducing health anxiety since seeking reassurance is not a long-term solution, as we discuss in the very next section.

Behavioral Factors

The third domain of maintenance processes in health anxiety includes behaviors that are performed in response to the perception of threat. A person who perceives a situation to be threatening will naturally act to reduce the probability of harm. This might include avoiding the potential threat altogether (refraining from vigorous activity because of the fear of heart failure), or performing certain behaviors that make one feel safer (e.g., breathing a certain way to prevent hypoxia). Such "safety-seeking" behaviors might be adaptive were an actual threat present. However, when there is no objective threat – as in the case of health anxiety – these actions have the unintended negative consequence of

actually maintaining fear and anxiety. Below, we discuss the three most common classes of maladaptive safety-seeking behaviors in health anxiety:
a) Reassurance-seeking and various forms of checking,
b) Situational safety-seeking, and
c) Passive avoidance behavior.

Reassurance-Seeking and Checking

Reassurance-seeking is the most prominent form of safety-seeking behavior in health anxiety. This might take the form of presenting to multiple doctors for "second opinions," repeatedly questioning medical personnel, telephoning medical "hotlines," asking questions of family members or friends, demanding more comprehensive (or the latest) tests, requesting referrals to "experts," and checking the internet or medical texts for information on the feared medical condition. Repeated assurance-seeking behavior can have a variety of functions, although most often it serves as a check of whether or not a feared bodily sensation is dangerous (e.g., "Is this pain in my neck caused by a cancerous tumor?"). Other functions include determining whether a doctor is using the *best* or *most up-to-date* diagnostic tools, and trying to learn new ways of preventing or treating feared diseases (e.g., herbal remedies). Used in moderation, reassurance can be helpful for someone with fleeting health concerns; however, for people with persistent health anxiety about medically unexplained symptoms, reassurance not only fails, but makes the problem worse.

As Salkovskis and Warwick (2001) point out, one way that reassurance-seeking maintains health anxiety is by increasing the likelihood of receiving a false-positive result. If you ask enough questions or undergo enough testing, you are likely at some point to receive fear-confirming information; or at least ambiguous information that could be interpreted as fear-confirming. The case of Rosemary, described in the section on confirmation bias, illustrates this phenomenon and shows how cognition and behavior are interlinked such that each of these processes influences the other (Clark & Fairburn, 1997). In particular, the tendency to confirm one's fear leads to persistent reassurance-seeking that might not desist until fear-confirming information has finally been obtained. This information feeds health anxiety by seemingly (to the patient) substantiating his or her concerns. This leads to further health anxiety and urges to seek additional assurance, thus completing a vicious cycle.

Persistent reassurance-seeking might also result in the individual receiving slightly different (or contradictory) information from different medical sources; or worse, inconsistent information from the same source (e.g., a telephone helpline) on different occasions. Indeed, doctors sometimes provide slightly different impressions (or perhaps state the same impression in slightly different terms; e.g., "almost certainly" vs. "probably") on separate occasions without realizing the effects this has on health-anxious people. Such patients might misinterpret innocent variations in word choice as a sign that something is wrong: "Did I give the doctor *all* the information she needs to figure out what's wrong with me?" – "Have things gotten worse?" In such cases any feeling of reassurance is often fleeting. Additionally, even the slightest inconsistency can undermine the individual's confidence in doctors, further reinforcing the mistrust of medicine that serves as a basis for health anxiety as described in Chapter 3.

Other sorts of reassurance-seeking further maintains health anxiety via the alarming information one is likely to encounter when searching sources such as textbooks and the internet. Taylor and Asmundson (2004) note that the internet provides a treasure trove of health-related information – and *misinformation*. It is easy to obtain data on dreaded diseases using online reference sites (e.g., MayoClinic.com), academic search engines (e.g., Google Scholar), and online forums and discussion groups maintained by laypeople for disease survivors (e.g., the Online Cancer Survivor's Network). By scouring such sources, however, health-anxious people expose themselves to alarming information that is not relevant to their (generally good) health. For example, MayoClinic.com has a "symptom checker" in which a person can input a set of symptoms and generate a possible diagnosis. For example, if one enters "dizziness accompanied by anxiety" into this search, MayoClinic.com tells you that the most likely explanation is a heart attack! The second most likely explanation is a transient ischemic attack (TIA, or "ministroke"). Although dehydration, heart arrhythmia, hypotension (low blood pressure), panic attacks, and stroke follow in the order listed above, the health-anxious individual is likely to focus on the most catastrophic of these possible explanations.

To make matters worse, once a person with health anxiety begins reassurance-seeking, it may be difficult to stop this behavior. This is because reassurance-seeking sometimes seems to "work" – at least in the short term: It produces a temporary reduction in anxiety or uncertainty. From a learning perspective, this behavior is negatively reinforced by the reduction in distress it engenders. As a result, it can quickly become a habitual response to anxiety.

In an empirical study on the effects of reassurance-seeking (Rief et al., 2006), three groups of participants – people with medically unexplained bodily complaints, patients with depression, and healthy individuals – listened to audiotaped medical reports in which a doctor reassured a patient that his or her abdominal pain was *probably not* due to a serious medical disorder. For example:

> "The medical investigation has shown that the reason for your complaints is certainly not a stomach flu, although this was our first idea. We also didn't find any blood in your stool. Blood in the stool can indicate a possible bowel cancer. However, with

this finding, we don't believe that you have bowel cancer; this is very unlikely. Moreover, I palpated your abdomen yesterday and we made ultrasound investigations. Again, this didn't reveal any significant findings. Therefore it is unlikely that you have any serious medical condition." (Rief et al., 2006, p. 1269)

Later, participants were asked to recall the doctor's impressions and answer questions such as, "What does your doctor think the likelihood is that you have a serious medical condition (0%–100%)?" Results of this study indicated that relative to depressed and healthy individuals, those with medically unexplained complaints recalled a higher likelihood of significant medical problems as identified by the doctors. When asked to imagine that the reports were applicable to themselves, participants with unexplained medical complaints also reported higher levels of health concern than the other groups. These findings suggest that when health-anxious individuals seek reassurance, the very act of discussing the possibility of serious illnesses with doctors, even if it is to disconfirm the presence of such illnesses, paradoxically leads to overestimating the probabilities of serious illness, thus maintaining health anxiety.

Medical professionals sometimes recommend that at-risk individuals occasionally check their own bodies for signs of illness. For example, monthly breast self-exams are suggested for all women over the age of 20. Used in this way, such body-checking is adaptive as it serves to ensure early detection of serious conditions such as breast cancer. Individuals with health anxiety, however, often use checking excessively and in ways that maintains irrational health worry. They worry that if they do not check, they are likely to become irreversibly sick. Checking is therefore used incorrectly as a method of trying to determine the exact risk of having a feared illness (e.g., "my body temperature is still normal"; "the mole on my back hasn't gotten bigger"). As described in Chapter 2, the complexity of body-checking can range from simple checks of the skin, to the use of bright lights and tongue depressors to examine the throat, to the use of special equipment for home testing of bodily processes and excreta.

There are at least five ways in which this type of body-checking maintains health anxiety (Taylor & Asmundson, 2004):

- First, it makes the individual exquisitely sensitive to slight, albeit innocuous (normal) internal variations (i.e., "bodily noise") that most people simply do not notice. For example, constantly checking one's pulse makes one aware of its natural variability. This can lead to becoming aware of all sorts of "symptoms" that evoke urges to seek medical reassurance. Further, when a health-anxious person asks friends or relatives (who are not as tuned to their bodies and so do not attend to these normal occurrences) if they ever have such "symptoms" (e.g., "Does your eye ever start twitching for no reason?") the perfunctory denial can lead to feelings of vulnerability ("I'm the only one who has this").

- Second, the apparent discovery of novel "symptoms" strengthens the mistaken idea that the body is unpredictable and so one needs to stay on the alert for rapidly emerging crises.
- Third, excessive body-checking can actually *induce* what might be perceived as the "symptoms" of a feared medical condition. For example, continually poking and prodding at an ordinary mole on the skin can lead to soreness and the appearance that something more serious is festering. Repeated forced swallowing to check for throat problems can make swallowing seem more difficult, etc.
- Fourth, because health-anxious persons are most likely to check their body when anxious, their heart rate and blood pressure, for example, are indeed likely to be elevated – and this is likely to be misinterpreted as a sign of illness. One medically healthy woman we evaluated carried her blood pressure cuff with her wherever she went, but used it only when she was worried her blood pressure might be too high. Not surprisingly, whenever she used the cuff, she obtained very high blood-pressure readings. Instead of attributing this to her worry and anxiety, she continued to believe she had problems with high blood pressure.
- Finally, because body-checking sometimes quells health worries, this behavior is intermittently negatively reinforced. Thus, a self-maintaining vicious cycle develops wherein body-checking produces short-term relief, but in the long run perpetuates health-anxious beliefs.

Wells and Matthews (1994; Wells, 1997) have proposed that one's level of confidence in his or her own thought and memory capabilities is instrumental in the persistence of anxiety problems and emotional disturbances in general. In particular, when someone has poor confidence in their cognitive abilities, it increases the focus of attention on internal processes such as doubts. The focus on doubts, however, further reduces confidence that one has correctly performed an action (such as checking), necessitating further action until the desired goal is eventually met. This model is intuitively appealing for explaining compulsive-like checking and perseveration on doubts about health issues in health-anxious patients. Rachman (2002) also described the "loss of memory confidence" as a significant "contributor to the self-perpetuating mechanism in compulsive checking" (p. 630). He proposed that anxious arousal interferes with memories for a specific event, which is interpreted as evidence of memory (and personal) incompetence. Repeated checking, therefore, might produce a further decline in memory confidence and thereby strengthen maladaptive interpretations of the apparent memory problem, resulting in a vicious cycle. Research indicates that repeated checking leads to reduced memory *confidence*, but not to impaired memory per se (Radomsky, Gilchrist, & Dussault, 2006).

Situational Safety Behaviors

Someone who believes he or she is in danger of becoming very ill can be expected to act in ways that increase safety and reduce the perceived probability of illness. Such behavior is a highly adaptive response to perceived threat, and it results in an immediate reduction in anxiety. Yet, if the perception of danger is based on a misinterpretation, as in the case of health anxiety, the safety-seeking behaviors not only reduce anxiety, but also prevent the person from discovering that the fear of illness is in fact unfounded. Put another way, after events that should verify that a feared illness is unlikely, health-anxious individuals who engage in safety behaviors come to believe erroneously that the feared illness would have otherwise occurred *had it not been for their own actions*. Thus, the faulty illness belief is left intact. Jean's case, described next, illustrates this concept.

Case Example

For years, Jean has held the mistaken belief that she has an aneurysm which will cause her to die if she moves her head too quickly in her sleep. To prevent her death, she believes she must take aspirin before going to bed in order to thin her blood. She is also convinced she must sleep with her head cushioned and braced firmly between two pillows so that it does not move suddenly during sleep. Although doctors have assured her there is no evidence of an aneurysm nor any danger in sleeping normally, Jean is convinced she owes her life to these nighttime habits that she herself concocted.

As described in Chapter 2 (Table 2.5), people with health anxiety deploy a variety of ad hoc safety-seeking behaviors and rely on various types of "safety signals." Whereas *safety behaviors* are things the person does to avert danger (such as avoidance and reassurance-seeking), *safety signals* are situations or stimuli the person associates with the absence of the feared disease. For example, using a blood pressure cuff to check one's blood pressure repeatedly is a safety behavior; the cuff itself would be considered a safety signal if it is carried on one's person *just in case it is needed*.

Research by Salkovskis, Clark, and Gelder (1996) demonstrated that safety behaviors and safety signals are linked to specific catastrophic beliefs. For example, individuals fearful of fainting hold onto sturdy objects, those afraid of not getting enough oxygen consciously attempt to regulate their breathing, and those afraid they are vulnerable to losing their hearing or sight place cotton in their ears or wear heavy-duty sunglasses. The excessive "precautions" and maneuvers health-anxious people engage in paradoxically keep them from realizing that beliefs such as "I am weak" or "I need medical assistance to remain healthy" are completely unfounded. At best, the patient's irrational fears and beliefs are unmodified by such safety behaviors; at worst, the nonoccurrence of the feared disaster is viewed as confirmation that the patient is living on the verge of serious illness or death – and that the safety maneuvers are instrumental.

An experimental study of safety-seeking behaviors in hypochondriasis (Abramowitz & Moore, 2007) revealed that the performance of such behaviors is technically effective in that it leads to a reduction in anxiety more quickly than would have occurred without performance of the behavior. This negatively reinforces safety-seeking, which explains its habitual nature. Moreover, these behaviors prevent the natural extinction of anxiety that would otherwise occur if the behavior were not performed. Finally, safety-seeking maintains health anxiety by promoting preoccupation with the heath-related fear (Salkovskis & Warwick, 2001).

Avoidance

Avoidance of certain illness-related cues also plays a contributing role in the maintenance of health anxiety. In the short-term, avoiding situations or stimuli results in a decrease or termination of one's exposure to the threat, thus reducing fear. This fear reduction, however, negatively reinforces the avoidance response, so that, over time, avoidance sustains itself as it becomes stronger and more widespread. As with safety-seeking, consistent avoidance over the long-term prevents the person from having corrective experiences that might otherwise modify dysfunctional beliefs and mistaken interpretations of health-related stimuli.

By avoiding exposure to health-anxiety cues, patients make themselves more and more preoccupied with their health. Derek (see the case example below), for example, spent hours each day wondering whether or not he actually had an abnormally low white blood cell count, or whether the test was indeed mistaken. If

---

Case Example

Derek had been to the doctor for a routine check-up when the results of his blood test indicated a low white blood cell count. Derek's doctor suggested that such tests are sometimes inaccurate, and that – given Derek's good health, active lifestyle, and healthy diet – the result was probably an anomaly. The doctor further suggested Derek return a week later for a subsequent retest. Derek, however, became worried that something was seriously wrong with his immune system and chose to avoid the second blood test, afraid that it would confirm his fear.

he had taken the second blood test, he would have received the answer to this question and could have either felt reassured or been given help for any medical condition he might have.

Another problem with using safety-seeking behavior to cope with health anxiety is how patients misinterpret the effects of their avoidance. For example, a woman who avoided sick people continued to believe that she remained healthy *only because she had managed to stay clear of those with serious illnesses*. Thus, her dysfunctional beliefs and overestimates of threat that fuel health anxiety remained intact.

Summary of Maintenance Factors

A summary of the factors just described that serve to maintain health anxiety appears in Table 4.1. Health anxiety can be considered a problem in which generally harmless bodily signs, sensations, and perturbations (i.e., body noise)

Table 4.1. Factors that contribute to the persistence of health anxiety

Domain and factor	Description
Physiological	
Normal arousal response to stress	The fight-or-flight response is an innate response to perceived threat which produces harmless bodily sensations that can appear to be true medical conditions. This reaffirms mistaken beliefs about illnesses.
Cognitive	
Selective attention toward threat cues	Hypervigilance (sensitivity) to internal sensations might appear to confirm the presence of fared illnesses.
Confirmation bias	Tendency to actively seek evidence that would validate one's fear – and to discount information that would invalidate the fear.
Memory bias	Tendency to inflate remembered estimates of the likelihood of illness.
Behavioral	
Checking and reassurance-seeking	Excessive attempts to gain absolute certainty of health status that often lead to obtaining alarming information which triggers additional health anxiety. Some types of checking can even produce apparent symptoms of the feared disease.
Safety-seeking behaviors and safety signals	Behaviors, stimuli, and situations associated with safety, which reduce distress in the short-term, but which prevent the disconfirmation of mistaken beliefs about health and illness. They can also lead to increased preoccupation with the feared illness.
Avoidance	Prevents disconfirmation of dysfunctional health beliefs and leads to preoccupation with the feared illness.

have become the focus of fear. Threat-related appraisals and interpretations of innocuous somatic events (and related stimuli) evoke an array of responses that, inadvertently, increase the frequency and intensity of bodily sensations and reinforce maladaptive beliefs about their potential for harm. This leads to a self-sustaining vicious cycle of noticing bodily sensations, misinterpretations, anxiety, excessive responses, increased sensitivity to body noise, and so on – that becomes more and more insidious with every repetition. In a very real sense, the means by which individuals with health anxiety appraise and attempt to manage their "symptoms" eventually become more perilous than the symptoms themselves. A depiction of this biopsychosocial model of health anxiety is presented in Figure 4.2.

We should note here that our account of the development and maintenance of health-anxiety problems provides an empirically verifiable explanation for the symptoms of health anxiety derived from normal human physiologic, cognitive, and behavioral (conditioning) processes. We do not consider chemical imbalances, personality disorders, brain diseases, or neuropsychological and biological deficits to explain the origin or maintenance of this problem. Even the

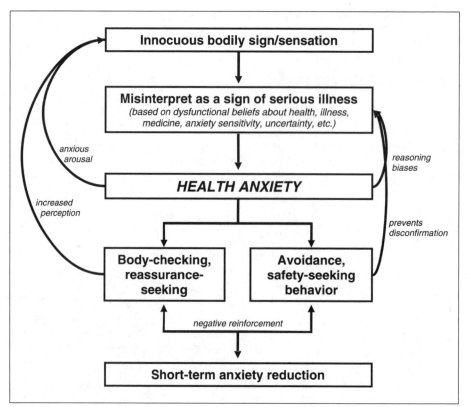

Figure 4.2. Biopsychosocial factors in the maintenance of health anxiety.

kinds of biased and dysfunctional thinking processes are not themselves "disturbed" since everyone is prone to incorrect judgments from time to time. Regrettably, people with health anxiety have fallen into the trap of misinterpreting bodily sensations as dangerous, which in turn has the unfortunate consequence of producing further uncomfortable bodily sensations. And when faced with a perceived threat to one's health, it is highly adaptive to take action to protect oneself. Thus, the reassurance-seeking, doctor-shopping, and checking observed among health-anxious individuals is neither mysterious nor uniquely pathological. It is, however, self-preserving: It prevents the person from correcting his or her faulty beliefs and interpretations.

Treatment Implications of the Biopsychosocial Model

It follows from the biopsychosocial model that effective treatment of health anxiety must help patients
a) Modify their erroneous interpretations of innocuous bodily signs and sensations, and
b) Eliminate excessive behavioral responses such as avoidance, safety-seeking behavior, body-checking, and other forms of reassurance-seeking that serve as barriers to the self-correction of the erroneous interpretations.

Patients must understand their problem not in terms of the risks to their health or well-being, but in terms of how they are thinking and behaving in response to bodily sensations that do not require a catastrophic medical explanation. Specifically, individuals with fears that they will become ill must see their problem not as the need to prevent illness, but as the need to reevaluate what they incorrectly fear are indications of imminent disease. Similarly, those who believe they are already ill may be led to view their problem not as the need for a definitive medical explanation for their complaints, but as one in which they are lending too much significance to ostensibly benign (or minor) bodily sensations.

This conceptualization implies the need for a thorough assessment of the external and internal fear cues, along with appraisals of these stimuli. In addition, particulars about the use of safety behaviors and other tactics for responding to health-relevant stimuli must be precisely understood. Assessment culminates in the careful and collaborative (between patient and therapist) development of an individualized model of the physiologic, cognitive, and behavioral mechanisms underlying the patient's specific health-anxiety symptoms as well as a plan for reversing these mechanisms using empirically validated treatment procedures.

Five such procedures are used in the psychological treatment of health anxiety:
- First, *motivational-enhancement techniques* are used to move the patient toward accepting and commencing psychological treatment.
- Second, patients are *educated* about the biological factors in health anxiety, the ways in which misinterpreting such stimuli leads to anxiety, and the ways in which health anxiety is maintained by excessive patterns of behavior.
- Third, *cognitive-therapy procedures* are implemented to help patients identify and challenge mistaken beliefs that fuel health anxiety, such as beliefs about health, illness, and the medical profession.
- *Exposure therapy* (usually involving response prevention), the fourth technique, is used to further weaken connections between internal and external stimuli and fearfulness.
- Fifth and finally, *response prevention* is used to block the performance of safety-seeking, checking, and reassurance-seeking in order to weaken reliance upon these behaviors and allow dysfunctional cognitions to be modified.

The next chapter provides an overview of these treatment procedures and reviews the evidence for their effectiveness. In the second part of this book we further detail the implementation of these assessment and treatment techniques.

5

Treating Health Anxiety: Overview and Evidence

Historically, the conditions we collectively call health anxiety (e.g., hypochondriasis, somatization disorder) were considered to be treatment-resistant problems. The development of effective psychological and pharmacologic treatments over the past 20 years, however, has changed this perspective (Taylor, Asmundson, & Coons, 2005). Empirical studies of the aforementioned treatments indicate that the frequency, intensity, and duration of symptoms can be significantly reduced, leading to less distress and interference in the individual's life. This chapter delineates the historical course of health-anxiety treatments, beginning with early nonempirically based psychodynamic approaches. The majority of the chapter reviews the recent treatment outcome literature focusing on cognitive-behavioral and pharmacologic interventions. General descriptions of the various techniques used in the cognitive-behavioral treatment of health anxiety are provided here, with details regarding how to apply these techniques to follow in Part 2 of this book.

Psychological Treatments

Psychodynamic Approaches

Given the Freudian influence over much of psychiatry and psychology, it is not surprising that psychoanalytic and psychodynamic therapies were the first modern methods to be utilized in the treatment of health anxiety disorders. These approaches, however, proved ineffective as evidenced by the condition's reputation for being treatment-resistant (Kenyon, 1964; Ladee, 1966). No controlled studies have been conducted on the efficacy of psychodynamic therapy for health anxiety, the few published reports indicating dismal outcomes. For example, Knight (1941) reported a case series in which seven out of eight health-anxious patients evidenced no change following psychodynamic therapy. Within a group of 23 patients deemed to be "well-suited" for psychodynamic therapy, only four noted any improvement (Ladee, 1966).

Later, dynamic therapies were used in conjunction with other methods, including hypnotherapy. A paucity of research on the topic exists; one published case study, however, described a treatment involving three sessions of hypnosis along with seven follow-up sessions of dynamic therapy (Deiker & Counts, 1980). The hypnosis techniques apparently encouraged the patient to focus on her daily problems rather than on her health concerns. The rationale for using these instructions was based on the notion that ruminating about health concerns and seeking confirmation of illness prevented the individual from addressing more important life issues. The authors reported a reduction in the patient's physical complaints and an increased activity level. Treatment response with respect to specific health-anxiety symptoms, however, was not reported.

Given the biopsychosocial conceptual approach to health anxiety as outlined in the previous chapters, it is not surprising that dynamic therapies have generally been associated with poor outcomes. Indeed, such treatments are not consistent with what is known about the nature of health anxiety. These treatments do not correct misinterpretations of benign bodily sensations, nor do they reduce the use of behaviors that interfere with the natural correction of such misinterpretations. In fact, some of the methods employed in dynamic therapy – such as focusing on childhood events and reviewing the origins of health concerns – seem as if they might contribute to the *maintenance* of health-anxiety symptoms, perhaps having iatrogenic effects. This explanation for the ineffectiveness of psychodynamic techniques is not a new observation:

> If patients of this type of neurosis [hypochondriac] are asked by the therapist to give a complete report of their life history and to go back to childhood as far as possible, it often induces them to devote still more attention to their body and state of health than hitherto. As a result their state of health gets worse because their neurosis developed exactly from this excessive attention to themselves (Leonhard, 1961, p. 123).

Despite the poor treatment outcomes with psychodynamic psychotherapy, individuals with health anxiety continued to receive this form of treatment until the development of more current treatments based on more empirically supported theoretical models.

Explanatory Therapy

Kellner (1979) posited that essentially *persuading* patients with health anxiety that they are, in fact, healthy would resolve their symptoms. The main techniques in what he referred to as *explanatory therapy* included unlimited physical examinations based upon the patients' requests, constant reassurance that the patient was physically healthy, and the provision of anxiolytic medication to manage persistent anxiety. Psychoeducation, in the form of medical information provided to clear up misunderstandings about illnesses, was also given liberally. The majority of the treatment, however, was devoted to reassurance delivered verbally and via results from frequent medical exams.

Practically speaking, explanatory therapy requires an extensive time commitment on the part of the medical provider who must conduct numerous (re-)assessments and provide constant (re-)assurance in the hopes of convincing the health-anxious patient that he or she is actually in good health. For example, Romanik and Kellner (1985) described a case in which a 3-hour consultation between patient and physician was necessary in order to quell the patient's unfounded health fears. Whereas decades ago such lengthy doctor-patient interactions might have been more commonplace, the practice of medicine has changed drastically and the contingencies that guide the practice of medicine in most settings today do not allow for such time-consuming interactions on a regular basis.

There is only limited research examining the efficacy and effectiveness of explanatory therapy, although the evidence is encouraging. To date, one case study (Fava, Grandi, Rafanelli, Fabbri, & Cazzaro, 2000), one uncontrolled study (Kellner, 1982), and one controlled study (Romanik & Kellner, 1985) indicate that the techniques discussed above can be effective in reducing health anxiety, specifically hypochondriasis. Moreover, the rate of discontinuation appears to be low. That few patients drop out from explanatory therapy is not surprising given the reduction in distress and uncertainty that medical reassurance engenders (Abramowitz & Moore, 2007). In the only controlled trial, a reduction in health-anxiety symptoms in comparison to the waitlist control group was observed (Romanik & Kellner, 1985).

While intuitively appealing, the rationale for explanatory therapy – that providing repeated guarantees of good health will convince the patient to overcome illness worries – does not have much empirical or theoretical support (e.g., Abramowitz & Braddock, 2006; Abramowitz & Moore, 2007; Rief et al., 2006). As we discuss throughout this volume, medical reassurance may sometimes temporarily reduce illness worries, but this strategy tends not to work over the long-term. Rather, it is often seen as a factor in the maintenance of the problem: It strengthens the patient's mistaken belief that he or she should pay attention to every body perturbation and seek medical examinations in order to ensure good health. It also leads to dysfunctional levels of dependency between the patient and therapist (or medical provider) since the patient fails to learn how to cope independently with health concerns and instead receives the message that good health is maintained by seeking reassurance from external sources. Thus, it is likely that some other nonspecific processes inherent in explanatory therapy, such as attention, expectations of improvement, and psychoeducation account for the majority of the treatment gains found in studies of this intervention (Taylor, Asmundson, & Coons, 2005).

Psychoeducation

Treatment programs based on psychoeducation emphasize the role that faulty psychological and medical information play in health anxiety. This approach differs from simply providing reassurance in that novel, corrective information is provided in psychoeducation. Reassurance, on the other hand, entails providing previously known information. Barsky and colleagues (1988) first suggested that psychoeducation could prove useful in treating health anxiety and developed a course comprising of six weekly sessions primarily focusing on information about factors that can serve to exacerbate or maintain somatic symptoms (e.g., faulty symptom attribution, dysphoric mood). Initial empirical findings were promising: Two separate research teams found that the treatment resulted in reductions in health-anxiety symptoms, medical consultations, and time spent worrying about health (Stern & Fernandez, 1991; Avia et al., 1996). Another psychoeducation group program based on the notion that stress exacerbates the presence of and attendance to bodily sensations revealed that information and relaxation led to greater reductions in health anxiety and physical complaints within a preventative medicine unit compared to the waitlist control group (Lidbeck, 1997). More recently, Bouman (2002) modified the program originally developed by Barsky and colleagues and conducted two studies:
a) An uncontrolled study in a community-based setting ($n = 27$) and
b) A waitlist-controlled trial ($n = 53$; Bouman & Polman, 2007).

In both studies, treatment led to significant reductions in health anxiety, depressive symptoms, trait anxiety, and medical consultations.

The first controlled comparison between psychoeducation in group format and another form of group therapy was reported by Buwalda, Bouman, and van Duijn (2007). They compared the efficacy of psychoeducation based on cognitive-behavioral models of health anxiety to a problem-solving-focused therapy. Both treatments were delivered in a 6-week group format, and both included didactic lectures, demonstrations, videos, focused group discussions, and in-session assignments. Participants were encouraged to be active during the group sessions, providing personal examples whenever possible. Optional homework was also assigned, and booster sessions were held 4 weeks after the last session. The cognitive-behavioral program specifically incorporated psychoeducation about health anxiety, cognitions, and maintaining behaviors. The problem-solving course was meant to provide insight into the larger context within which health anxiety exists, and to facilitate ways in which participants can identify and solve problems. Typical problems included finances, conflicts with partner or family members, and work difficulties. Table 5.1 provides specific treatment outlines for the two programs.

Table 5.1. Cognitive-behavioral and problem-solving treatment programs for health anxiety

Session	Cognitive-behavioral program	Problem-solving program
1	*What is hypochondriasis?:* Provides an introduction to the cognitive-behavioral model of health anxiety with a focus on maintaining factors rather than etiological.	*What is hypochondriasis?:* Purports that general problems and stressors can serve as maintaining factors of health anxiety.
2	*The role of your thoughts:* Introduces the relationship between thoughts and feelings, highlighting catastrophical misinterpretations of body sensations.	*Problem description and goal-setting:* Introduces how to identify a problem and set basic goals, not necessarily specific to health anxiety.
3	*Attention and illness anxiety:* Suggests the role of selective attention as a maintaining factor.	*Which resources do you have?:* Facilitates the awareness and generation of resources related to generic problem-solving.
4	*Safety behaviors and illness anxiety:* Addresses the role of behavioral symptoms such as safety behaviors, avoidance, asking for reassurance, and checking.	*Generating solutions:* Highlights the technique of brainstorming and how to generate alternatives to problems.
5	*Stress and bodily symptoms:* Examines the role of bodily stress symptoms in misinterpreting body sensations.	*Choosing and applying a solution:* Addresses how to select and implement solutions.
6	*Your own vicious circle:* Participants create and present their own cycle of health anxiety.	*Your own problem-solving model:* Encourages the application of problem-solving strategies to the participants' own problems.

Summarized from Buwalda, Bouman, and van Duijn (2006).

Results from the Buwalda et al. (2007) study revealed that immediately after treatment and at 6-month follow-up, the two treatments were equally effective in reducing health anxiety, depressive symptoms, trait anxiety, and the frequency of daily stressors. Additionally, study patients found both treatments to be highly acceptable and feasible. These findings, along with the aforementioned studies, suggest that psychoeducation is a viable treatment option for health anxiety. We present the details of psychoeducation for health anxiety in Chapter 10 of this book.

Exposure and Response Prevention

Exposure and response prevention (ERP) are behavior therapy techniques that include confrontation with anxiety-provoking stimuli objectively posing a low risk of harm. Results from research conducted around the world with thousands of anxious and phobic individuals consistently indicate that this form of therapy is among the most effective treatments for anxiety disorders such as OCD, specific phobias, social phobia, panic, and posttraumatic stress disorder (e.g., Barlow, 2002). Exposure can occur in three forms:
- Repeated actual encounters with the feared situations (situational or *in vivo* exposure; e.g., snakes, water, the dark),
- Imaginal confrontation with anxiety-provoking thoughts and images (e.g., images of being chased by a large dog),
- And confrontation with feared bodily stimuli (interoceptive exposure, e.g., evoking feared sensations of lightheadedness, breathlessness, or tingling).

In planning for such exposure, the patient and therapist together generate a list of the patient's feared situations and stimuli and then incorporate these into a series of exercises or tasks for the patient to practice with. Guided by the therapist, the patient practices confrontation with each feared stimulus and remains exposed instead of engaging in escape or avoidance behaviors.

As expected, when an exposure task begins, the patient's subjective level of anxiety increases. In fact, patients are encouraged to engage in the exposure task fully and not to fight the anxiety. Over time, the distress (and the associated physiological responses) subside naturally – a process known as *habituation*. With repeated exposure, habituation occurs more rapidly as the patient's expectation of the feared stimulus becomes modified. The response prevention component of ERP entails refraining from any behavior (e.g., rituals and other safety-seeking behaviors) that serve as an escape from anxiety before habituation normally occurs. Response prevention therefore is a necessary accessory to exposure since both are required to bring about the natural extinction of phobic anxiety. As described in previous chapters, health anxiety involves phobic avoidance of objectively safe illness-specific stimuli and performance of compulsive safety-seeking behaviors or rituals to reduce fear and prevent the natural extinction of anxiety. Accordingly, ERP has also been employed as a treatment for health-anxious patients.

ERP in health anxiety begins with the patient and therapist constructing a fear hierarchy – a list of the patient's feared stimuli rated from least to most anxiety-inducing. Gradually – and with the help of the therapist – the patient uses the three forms of exposure to confront the feared situations, images, and body sensations. In addition to observing the natural decrease in phobic anxiety, patient and therapist use exposure tasks to test out (and disconfirm) the basis for the patient's fear. For example, a patient with excessive fears of contracting blood-borne illnesses through coincidental skin contact might walk through an emergency room or medical inpatient floor, touching objects feared to be "contaminated" such as walls and door knobs. An explicit hypothesis regarding these fears is thus tested (e.g., "By merely being in the hospital, I'm going to get HIV; the only way I can prevent HIV and to reduce my anxiety is to avoid hospitals and always wash my hands"). Immediately after the exposure, response prevention strategies are used where the patient is discouraged from engaging in any safety behaviors (e.g., body-checking for possible open sores, washing, reassurance-seeking). Instead, the patient is resigned to experiencing the anxiety induced by the exposure until habituation occurs naturally. With repeated and prolonged exposures, the basis for the irrational fear is disconfirmed, and the patient learns that phobic anxiety subsides even without safety-seeking behaviors.

The aim of imaginal exposure for health anxiety is to foster habituation to fear-evoking thoughts or images (e.g., of one's own funeral) and to help patients correct how they misinterpret the presence and significance of such thoughts. The technique may be used in three different ways depending on the patient's symptom presentation (Abramowitz, 2006). *Primary* imaginal exposure is essentially situational exposure to unwanted thoughts. This involves directly confronting feared thoughts and images via methods such as loop tapes or written scripts containing anxiety-evoking material. If situational triggers do not evoke these thoughts or images, primary imaginal exposure might be the only available means of direct exposure to these mental stimuli. For example, a patient may have irrational worries about having cancer, despite reports of good health from multiple medical exams. In order to expose the patient to the feared outcome (i.e., having cancer), a detailed script about suffering from cancer is generated; reading and rereading the script serves as the exposure.

Secondary imaginal exposure is used to augment situational (*in vivo*) exposures when confrontation with actual situations evokes fears of overwhelming consequences. In such instances, imaginal exposure is begun during or after situational exposure, and should involve visualizing the feared outcomes or focusing on uncertainty associated with risk of feared outcomes. For example, a man with concerns about his prostate gland conducted situational exposure to sitting on a cold surface, which he thought would lead to prostate damage and impotence. For a secondary imaginal exposure, he practiced imagining his prostate becoming enlarged and needing surgery, which would ruin his sex life (which he feared as a result of conducting the aforementioned exposure).

Preliminary imaginal exposure involves imagining confronting a feared stimulus as a preliminary step in preparing for situational exposures. For example, a patient may imagine visiting a hospital and touching objects prior to actually completing an *in vivo* exposure. This is often implemented early in a patient's fear hierarchy and is used as a stepping stone to completing the scarier, truly *in vivo* exposures.

The third method of exposure involves confrontation with *interoceptive* (bodily) cues. Individuals with health anxiety carry associations between certain innocuous bodily perturbations (e.g., increased heart rate, foot "falling asleep") and an anxiety or fear, often based on misinterpretation of the body cues as signs of a serious illness (e.g., heart disease, serious neurologic condition). The aim of interoceptive exposure is to help the patient repeatedly confront such sensations in the absence of safety behaviors in order to weaken these associations and cognitions. These methods are similar to those used in the treatment of panic disorder (see Craske & Barlow, 2007). Exercises are individualized to mimic the patient's feared body sensations. Table 5.2 outlines various interceptive exercises and the physical symptoms they elicit.

Table 5.2. Interoceptive exposures for health anxiety

Body sensations	Misinterpretation	Interceptive exposure
Shortness of breath	Suffocating Heart attack/disease	Hyperventilation Stair running Straw breathing Holding breath
Dizziness/loss of balance	Faint Stroke	Spinning
Tingling (lips, fingertips, toes)	Stroke	Hyperventilation Straw breathing
Increased heart rate	Heart attack/disease	Hyperventilation Stair running Caffeine intake
Sweating	Heart/metabolic condition	Hyperventilation Stair running
Headache	Stroke Brain tumor Aneurysm	Hyperventilation Straw breathing Spinning
Numbness	Neurologic condition	Sitting on foot/leg
Flushed/blood rush	Faint Heart attack/disease	Head between legs
Fidgety/restlessness	Heart attack/disease	Caffeine intake

Although extensive research documents the efficacy and effectiveness of ERP for anxiety disorders (for a review, see Deacon & Abramowitz, 2004), far less work has been done to evaluate this treatment for health anxiety. Leonhard (1961) anecdotally reported that ERP was successful in treating several health-anxiety cases. Yet, he was far ahead of his time: Almost 30 years would pass before the first empirical studies confirmed the efficacy of ERP for this condition (Logsdail, Lovell, Warwick, & Marks, 1991; Visser & Bouman, 1992; Warwick & Marks, 1988). A more recent controlled trial demonstrated that ERP was significantly more effective than a waitlist control condition, with gains maintained at 7 months' follow-up (Visser & Bouman, 2001). Presently, ERP occupies a central role in the treatment of health anxiety, and we discuss implementation of these techniques in Chapter 12.

Cognitive-Behavioral Therapy

As we illustrate in detail throughout the chapters of Part 2 of this book, cognitive-behavioral therapy (CBT) for health anxiety is a skills-based approach derived from the conceptual framework presented in earlier chapters. Treatment incorporates a blend of techniques including psychoeducation, cognitive restructuring, and ERP. The main aims of CBT are

a) To help patients recognize and modify faulty health-related beliefs and perceptions, and

b) To eliminate safety-seeking behaviors and other barriers to correcting these faulty beliefs.

Following a careful assessment of the triggers, cognitive aspects, and behavioral aspects of the patient's particular health-anxiety symptoms (i.e., a functional assessment), the therapist creates an individualized case conceptualization diagramming the erroneous illness-related beliefs and the relationship between physiological, cognitive, and behavioral factors that maintain these beliefs. Typically, patients feel discounted by their medical doctors; therefore, the initial thorough and open consideration of their feelings, thoughts, and behaviors fosters acceptance of the conceptual model and treatment plan (Walker, Vincent, Furer, Cox, & Kjernisted, 1999).

Patients are also provided with psychoeducation about health anxiety and its treatment. They are specifically taught that anxiety is a normal and adaptive reaction to a perceived threat to one's health; and that the perception of threat evokes behavioral, mental, and physiological responses aimed at preparing the body for fight or flight. Feared bodily sensations are identified, noncatastrophic explanations for benign body sensations are offered, and the detrimental effects of safety behaviors and signals are explained.

Cognitive restructuring is a technique in which the patient learns to recognize objective evidence for and against faulty beliefs about health and illness (Beck, 1976; Beck, Emery, & Greenberg, 1985). The therapist helps the patient, first, to identify the basis for these beliefs; second, to recognize contradictory events and experiences; and third, to understand the significance of contradictory evidence. The goal is to foster the adoption of rational beliefs about health and illness as well as more helpful responses to normal physiological sensations. This is accomplished through in-session discussions, the use of worksheets, and experimentation to test the logic of beliefs.

There is strong evidence that CBT is an effective treatment for health anxiety (for a meta-analytic review, see Taylor et al., 2005). Several controlled studies indicate that clinically significant and long-lasting improvements can occur after less than 20 sessions (e.g., Clark et al., 1998; Visser & Bouman, 2001). In a waitlist-controlled study, Warwick, Clark, Cobb, and Salkovskis (1996) found that CBT produced significant reductions in reassurance-seeking, overall health anxiety, and checking frequency. General anxiety was reduced by approximately 70% and depressive symptoms by 53%. Moreover, CBT was acceptable to patients: Only 6% of those recruited into the study refused to begin therapy, and another 6% dropped out of treatment prematurely.

A subsequent controlled study involving 16 weekly sessions demonstrated short- and long-term (1 year) efficacy in reducing fears of illness as well as unnecessary medical visits (Clark et al., 1998). Additionally, CBT was more effective than stress-management techniques, which also had beneficial effects. These findings suggest the specific procedures of CBT for health anxiety (i.e., psychoeducation, cognitive restructuring, or ERP) as opposed to nonspecific factors (i.e., attention from the therapist, relaxation techniques) are active ingredients for improvement in health anxiety. Refusal and dropout rates were also low in this study (4%), suggesting good overall acceptability and tolerability of the treatment.

In a large study by Barsky and Ahern (2004), a six-session CBT program that focused on psychoeducation and correcting dysfunctional health-related beliefs was more effective than routine medical care in reducing health anxiety. Modest but beneficial effects on a wide range of behavioral, cognitive, affective, and functional domains were also observed. Impressively, treatment gains were maintained at both 6-month and 1-year follow-up. A limitation of this study, however, was that many otherwise eligible patients declined to participate. Thus, it cannot be ruled out that the effects of CBT have something to do with the patient's general willingness to engage in this treatment. We believe that motivation for change is a critical component of treatment for health anxiety and therefore discuss techniques for motivating patients toward engaging in treatment in Chapter 7 of this volume.

In addition to these controlled trials, numerous uncontrolled studies and case studies support the application of CBT to treating health anxiety (e.g., Furer, Walker, & Freeston, 2001; House, 1989). The primary mode of delivery in these studies is individual therapy, although group treatments have also been found to be effective (e.g., Stern & Fernandez, 1991). The majority of these outcome studies have been conducted in academic research settings, although recent applications indicate the effectiveness of CBT within community clinics (e.g., Bouton, 2002; Wattar et al., 2005). In a study conducted within a specialized inpatient setting for behavioral medicine patients, Bleichhardt, Timmer, and Rief (2005) examined the effectiveness of CBT for two groups of health-anxious individuals: those with somatization disorder alone and those with somatization disorder and co-occurring hypochondriasis. The mean duration of treatment was 51.1 days; patients received individual CBT (as described above) along with group problem-focused therapy, assertiveness training, and, in some cases, treatment for other problems such as depression. Results were encouraging, with patients showing substantial long-term (1-year) reductions in intolerance of bodily complaints, general psychopathology, and the frequency of medical consultation, with life satisfaction increasing. Such an "effectiveness" study – conducted with consecutively referred patients outside of traditional academic research clinics – suggests that the beneficial effects of CBT for health anxiety also extend to general service settings.

CBT vs. ERP

What is the relative efficacy of CBT and ERP? To address this question, Visser and Bouman (2001) randomly assigned 78 patients with hypochondriasis to receive either 12 weeks of ERP, CBT, or a 12-week waitlist-control condition. Patients who received either of the active treatments evidenced significant improvement on all measures of health anxiety, general psychopathology, mood, and dysfunctional cognitions, whereas no improvement was observed in the waitlist condition. Immediately following treatment, there were no differences between the efficacy of ERP and CBT, and improvements proved to be durable: At the 7-month follow-up assessment, patients remained improved without significant differences between the active treatments. Thus, the available evidence does not suggest substantial differences in the efficacy of ERP and CBT approaches. The most likely explanation for this is that each of these treatments incorporates elements of each other: The effective implementation of ERP requires the implicit modification of dysfunctional beliefs that underlie health anxiety, whereas CBT typically involves exposure-like techniques in the form of behavioral experiments in which patients confront feared situations to disconfirm dysfunctional beliefs and attitudes (Deacon & Abramowitz, 2004).

Pharmacologic Treatments

The traditional view that health anxiety exists primarily in the context of depression led to the application of antidepressant medication to treat the disorder (Lesse, 1967). Subsequent research, however, has indicated that it is not necessary for patients to suffer from depression in order to have severe health anxiety (or even benefit from antidepressants). Antidepressant medication, including tricyclics and selective serotonin reuptake inhibitors (SSRIs), show effects for a variety of psychological disorders, including mood and anxiety disorders. In accord, some researchers have posited that these agents might also be useful in reducing health anxiety symptoms. Several case studies and a small number of outcome trials indeed suggest medications can be effective for health anxiety. Table 5.3 displays a listing of such medications, recommended doses as used in research studies.

Table 5.3. Medications with initial empirical support for health anxiety

Medication	Recommended dose	Studies
Clomipramine	25–225 mg/d	Kamlana & Gray (1988); Stone (1993)
Imipramine	125–150 mg/d	Lippert (1986); Wesner & Noyes, (1991)
Fluoxetine	20–80 mg/d	Fallon, (1999); Fallon et al. (1991), (1993, 1996)
Fluvoxamine	300 mg/d	Fallon (2001); Fallon et al. (1996, 2003)
Paroxetine	Up to 60 mg/d	Oosterbaan et al. (2001)
Nefazodone	200–500 mg/d	Kjernisted et al. (2002)

Empirical evidence suggests that these medications are associated with the reduction of illness fears, dysfunctional beliefs, anxiety, somatic complaints, phobic avoidance, and reassurance-seeking behaviors (Fallon, 2001). Little is known, however, about the long-term effects of these agents – or even about the precise mechanisms through which they work. Furthermore, no medication seems to be universally effective. One limitation of using medication for health anxiety is the substantial probability of symptom relapse upon discontinuation (Viswnathan & Paradis, 1991). A second shortcoming is that, because of the side effects of these medications and patients' general tendency to be vigilant of bodily sensations, the medicines can actually appear to make health anxiety *worse* (Fallon, 2001). The medications are not likely to increase the intensity of symptoms per se; rather, they can produce subtle bodily changes – and, perhaps, expectations of bodily changes – that may be misinterpreted as serious medical symptoms.

One study by Fallon and colleagues (1996) also raises the possibility of placebo effects contributing to reports of symptom reduction. These authors randomly assigned 20 hypochondriasis patients to receive either fluoxetine or placebo. After the 12-week medication period, 80% of the fluoxetine group and 60% of the placebo group were classified as responders, with no significant difference between the two groups. This finding suggests that improvement with medication was largely attributable to placebo effects. Fallon and colleagues (2003) continued to research medications for health anxiety, more recently demonstrating a response rate of over 70% to a 12-week open-label trial of fluvoxamine among 18 patients. As they note, however, with this study one cannot rule out placebo effects (because of its open label design).

Despite the paucity of research supporting the effectiveness of medications for health anxiety, they are still frequently prescribed. Some individuals with health anxiety perceive that prescribing antidepressant medications is merely the doctor's way of "getting rid" of a difficult patient, and as a result they may not follow-up with pharmacologic recommendations. To reduce rates of dropout and poor adherence to pharmacotherapy, the therapist should give patients a clear and logical explanation for the use of any antidepressant. Specifically, this rationale should convey that health anxiety involves real body sensations to which the patient is responding in unhelpful ways, and that this approach can increase the uncomfortable sensations as well as the concern about these sensations. The purpose of the medication, therefore, is to reduce the patient's sensitivity to these sensations. Potential side effects should be carefully discussed in advance so as to avoid erroneous interpretations surrounding their etiology.

CBT versus Medication

To date only one study has directly compared pharmacotherapy and CBT in the treatment of health anxiety: Greeven et al. (2007) randomly assigned 112 individuals with hypochondriasis to receive up to 16 sessions of CBT ($n = 40$), 16 weeks of paroxetine therapy ($n = 37$), or 16 weeks on a pill placebo ($n = 35$). About 27% of these patients discontinued the study prematurely, with no differences in dropout rate between the treatment conditions. Results indicated that both CBT and paroxetine produced at least a moderate degree of improvement in health anxiety and related symptoms, but placebo did not (although some placebo response was observed). On many variables, no differences were observed between the efficacy of CBT and paroxetine; on the other hand, the proportion of patients classified as treatment responders (i.e., who evidenced clinically significant and reliable change based on the criteria of Jacobson & Truax, 1991) was significantly greater among patients who received

CBT (54%) than among those who received paroxetine (28%) and placebo (12%). Unfortunately, long-term follow-up results were not presented, so the relative durability of these treatments is unknown.

Meta-Analytic Treatment Comparison

In a comprehensive meta-analysis of the available health-anxiety treatment re-search (focused primarily on hypochondriasis), Taylor and colleagues (2005) examined 25 treatment trials based on data from 15 studies. Participants met criteria either for full or abridged hypochondriasis (i.e., clinically significant health anxiety without fully meeting DSM-IV criteria). Most participants were female, and the mean age was between 30 and 40 years old. On average, patients in these studies reported having experienced symptoms of hypochondriasis for several years. Typical psychological treatment lengths were between 6–12 sessions with 12 hours of therapy contact. The results and conclusions of this meta-analytic review can be summarized as follows:
- Psychological and medication treatments for health anxiety were more effective than waitlist controls.
- CBT appears to be the treatment of choice when patient acceptability and durability of treatment gains are considered.
- Of all the medications examined, fluoxetine is the most effective, although its ability to maintain treatment gains upon discontinuation is unknown.
- Psychoeducation may be most helpful for patients with mild health anxiety and no depression (i.e., abridged hypochondriasis), whereas CBT may be best for more severe cases of health anxiety with concomitant depression (i.e., full hypochondriasis).

Despite these encouraging findings, Taylor et al. (2005) caution that the results should be interpreted with some hesitation because of the small samples sizes of many individual studies. They also note the lack of information about patients' posttreatment psychiatric care: Whether or not they sought poststudy treatment was not reported. Given the nature of the data, they note that no assessment could be made regarding the efficacy or effectiveness of combined psychopharmacologic and psychosocial treatments, psychodynamic therapies, treatment delivery methods (individual vs. group) or treatment settings (community clinic vs. medical). Table 5.4 summarizes the main meta-analytic findings reported by Taylor et al. (2005).

As noted, significant advancements have occurred in the treatment of health anxiety over the last 50 years. A condition previously considered treatment resistant and universally intractable is now viewed to be at least fairly responsive

Table 5.4. Summary of meta-analytic treatment comparison findings by Taylor et al. (2005)

Treatment	Mean % dropout	Mean posttest effect size	Mean f/u effect size
Studies of hypochondriasis			
Control condition			
Waitlist	0	.29	–
Pill placebo	25	–	–
Psychosocial treatments			
Psychoeducation	22	1.05	1.27
Explanatory	16	.91	.88
Cognitive therapy	11	.83	.96
ERP	14	1.00	1.19
CBT	10	2.05	1.74
BSM	4	1.59	1.25
Drug treatments			
Paroxetine	18	1.34	–
Fluoxetine	18	1.92	–
Fluvoxamine	21	–	–
Nefazadone	18	1.07	–
Studies of mixed samples			
Full and abridged			
Waitlist	0	.19	.18
"Optimized" medical care	0	.20	.30
Psychoeducation	2	.74	.87
CBT	13	.51	.61

ERP = exposure and response prevention; CBT = cognitive-behavioral therapy; BSM = behavioral stress management. Adapted from Taylor, Asmundson, and Coons (2005).

to psychoeducation, cognitive techniques, ERP, and/or pharmacotherapy. Questions remain, however, about the relative efficacy of these treatment approaches, and about the mechanisms by which medications reduce symptoms of health anxiety. It is clear that contemporary models of hypochondriasis and somatization, which view these problems not as personality disorders or depression, but as anxiety-based, have opened the doors to more effective treatments.

The Treatment Program in Part 2 of this Book

In Part 2 of this book, we provide the reader with a hands-on manual for using the most effective psychological treatment techniques described above. These techniques are illustrated in depth with plentiful case examples and recommendations for clinicians. While we do not necessarily advocate rigid adherence to any specific session-by-session plan, Table 5.5 provides an idea of how we implement the protocol in our clinics. Rather than being concerned with making sure material "x" is covered within session "y," we emphasize a careful and systematic approach to ensuring the patient has become comfortable with each step before moving on. Though there is no set duration of treatment, we do recommend setting aside no more than 16 to 20 sessions, which are usually sufficient to gauge the patient's response. It is also typical for patients to have appointments once a week, with daily homework assignments between sessions.

Regarding the structure of each session, motivational, psychoeducational, cognitive, and behavioral techniques are often used parallel to one another, even within the same visit. This is consistent with allowing the conceptual model and treatment plan guide what needs to be accomplished in order to change beliefs and behavior. Thus, readers should expect to find themselves moving back and forth across chapters (and techniques) in the book (and treatment program) as therapy proceeds. Finally, although there are occasions where other significant events in the patient's life require an entire session (e.g., a divorce, traumatic death in the family, etc.), we work very hard to keep the agenda and focus of each session on health anxiety.

Table 5.5. Suggested content of CBT sessions for health anxiety

Session	Suggested content	Chapter(s)
1–2	– Initial assessment and diagnosis	6
3–5	– Functional assessment – Case formulation – Treatment planning – Motivational enhancement	7, 8, 9
6	– Psychoeducation	10
7–9	– Cognitive therapy (introduction) – Psychoeducation	10, 11
10–20	– Cognitive therapy – Psychoeducation – Exposure therapy	10, 11, 12

PART 2

Effective Assessment and Treatment of Health Anxiety

6

Initial Assessment and Diagnosis

Psychological consultation entails obtaining a thorough assessment of a patient's problem and then providing education, information, and the necessary recommendations to that individual and the patient's family or support network (Brown, Pryzwansky, & Schulte, 2001). Effective consultation depends on the consultant's own education, training, and experience as well as on one's knowledge of the relevant scientific literature. This chapter provides a detailed description of how to conduct a diagnostic interview, how to assess the nature and severity of health-anxiety symptoms, how to and present treatment recommendations. Collection and discussion of this information constitutes the initial consultation that should precede any therapy. Chapter 7 provides the reader with additional strategies for communicating impressions and recommendations to health-anxious patients who often reject mental-health services.

Assessment is an ongoing and conceptually driven pursuit whereby theories of the causes, maintenance, and treatment of health anxiety determine what is important to evaluate. Initial assessment begins with a clinical interview to determine a diagnosis, rule out organic illnesses, identify possible comorbid conditions, and exclude any problems that may be mistaken for health anxiety. Next, the nature and intensity of the individual's health concerns and safety-seeking behaviors are determined. The presentation of such symptoms, the range of comorbid psychopathology, and the impact of the disorder on the individual's functioning vary widely from patient to patient, so that assessment should also encompass the individual's level of functioning and support network. Understanding the problem within this broad context helps the clinician to identify factors that might exacerbate or ameliorate health-anxious symptoms or impact adherence to treatment recommendations. It also helps one to recognize additional forms of psychopathology that warrant clinical attention, or that might influence treatment planning.

Developing a Therapeutic Relationship

Careful assessment provides an excellent opportunity to begin developing an alliance with the patient and engaging the patient in the process of goal-setting.

Many health-anxious individuals come to their initial psychological consultation feeling distraught and cast off by physicians. They might feel the need to prove to the consultant that theirs is a *medical* and not a psychological problem, and thus present as angry, irritable, and defensive. It can help if the therapist points out that the aim of the evaluation is not to determine whether the problem is medical or psychological, but rather simply to assess the patient's experience. The patient will have the opportunity to describe his or her complaints to someone who will listen and validate them, rather than tell them there is "nothing wrong." Thus, assessment begins the process of encouraging collaboration and cooperation.

Importance of Ongoing Assessment

Continually assessing the nature and severity of health anxiety and related symptoms throughout the course of treatment assists the therapist in evaluating whether, and in what ways, the patient is responding. This is consistent with the emphasis on objective measurement of treatment effectiveness within evidence-based practice. It is not sufficient for the clinician simply to think, "He seems to be less worried about his tonsils"; or "It sounds like she has cut down on her reassurance-seeking;" or even for the patient (or a relative) to report that he or she "is doing better." These might be useful observations, yet progress must also be assessed systematically by comparing current functioning against the baseline obtained at the outset of treatment. Thus, assessment using the psychometrically validated instruments described later in this chapter should be conducted periodically to clarify how treatment has been helpful and what work remains to be done.

Aims of Assessment

The aims of the initial assessment for severe health anxiety are as follows:
- To arrive at an accurate diagnosis of severe health anxiety, ruling out the presence of a medical etiology or a more primary (severe) psychological disorder
- To reveal the patient's idiosyncratic symptom presentation, outlining the associated distress, interference, and impairment
- To obtain a quantifiable measure of health anxiety severity
- To develop a cognitive-behavioral conceptualization of the symptoms
- To determine the appropriateness of cognitive-behavioral therapy for the patient

– To formulate a cognitive-behavioral treatment plan
– To receive releases to exchange information with key medical providers and other relevant sources
– To educate the patient about the diagnosis, conceptualization, and cognitive-behavioral treatment plan and establish a therapeutic alliance.

Prior to the Clinical Interview

Access to Medical Records

Patients with health anxiety are often referred to mental-health professionals by primary-care and specialty physicians who have determined that they can no longer help the patient medically. Sometimes, these patients are referred from one mental-health provider to another, such as from a psychiatrist to a psychologist. Less commonly, patients are referred by friends, family members, or even self-referred. Accordingly, circumstances surrounding the request for an initial assessment can vary. Most patients have a prior history of visiting physicians and therefore a (sometimes long) medical record of consultations, physical exams, laboratory reports, and any treatments or other procedures. Whenever possible, it is best to request access to this information either directly from the patient or by contacting other providers. This information serves as a basis for determining the extent of any actual medical complications, for ruling out serious medical problems, and (later on) for discussing erroneous beliefs and assumptions with the patient. We recommend trying to obtain this documentation by the time of the initial consultation because patients tend to exaggerate their medical concerns.

Self-Report Measures of Symptom Severity

We have patients complete a battery of four self-report questionnaires while in the waiting room immediately prior to the appointment. These measures (described in detail below) include the *Short Health Anxiety Inventory,* the *Anxiety Sensitivity Index – 3rd Version*, the *Body Vigilance Scale*, and the *Beck Depression Inventory 2nd Edition*. We use these instruments to assist in the diagnostic process and to provide a basis for beginning the discussion of the biopsychosocial conceptualization of health anxiety with the patient. Yet, such self-report measures supply supplementary clinical information and do not replace a clinical interview. Although helpful, self-report questionnaire data should be interpreted with caution, especially in the case of severe health anxiety, given the varying levels of insight demonstrated by patients. Moreover, some patients may strongly deny psychological symptoms on such measures – again, to give the impression that theirs is a medical and not a psychological problem. As Taylor and Asmundson (2004) suggest, self-report questionnaires are most effective as clinical tools when used

a) To confirm information gathered from the clinical interview
b) As a screening tool prior to the interview
c) To monitor treatment response.

Below we describe these four recommended self-report instruments as well as a number of additional measures that can be used (either before or after the initial assessment) to further gauge the severity of health anxiety and related symptoms. Chapter 8 describes several additional measures that are used in the context of functional (cognitive-behavioral) assessment. We think it is important not to overwhelm patients with the assessment battery during the initial visit. Thus, we suggest using an initial assessment battery requiring no more than 10–20 minutes to complete. We describe the assessment as necessary to help us better understand how the patient experiences his or her symptoms. Following the initial assessment, and once rapport has been built, additional measures can be administered, if necessary.

Short Health Anxiety Inventory (SHAI; Salkovskis, Rimes, Warwick, & Clark, 2002)

The SHAI is a brief measure containing 18 items that assess health anxiety independent of physical health status. For each of the 18 items, the respondent chooses one from a series of four statements (ranging in severity from 0 [least severe] to 3 [most severe]) that best reflects his or her feelings over the past several months. Items address the following aspects of health anxiety: worry about health, awareness of bodily sensations and changes, and feared consequences of having an illness. Factor analyses have revealed that the SHAI contains two factors:

a) The feared likelihood of becoming ill
b) The feared negative consequences of becoming ill (e.g., Salkovskis et al., 2002).

The measure has good reliability and validity in clinical and nonclinical samples, and can also be used to assess health anxiety across different anxiety disorders (Abramowitz, Olatunji, & Deacon, 2007; Salkovskis et al., 2002). Abramowitz et al. (2007) reported a mean total score of 49.90 ($SD = 9.26$) in a group of individuals diagnosed with hypochondriasis. In the same study, patients given a diagnosis of panic disorder had a mean of 39.67 ($SD = 12.28$). In contrast,

Abramowitz, Deacon, and Valentiner (2007) reported a mean of 10.79 (*SD* = 6.38) in a nonselected group of university students. The full SHAI is reprinted in the article by Salkovskis et al. (2002), which also describes how the scale was developed.

The SHAI is a desirable tool because it is fairly brief and, as mentioned above, assesses health concerns independent of whether or not the individual is truly medically ill. Items also do not have a psychological bias, that is, for the most part, they do not assume either that a medical illness is present or not. Thus, most of our patients seem to complete the measure honestly. In addition to examining the total score, we tend to use individual item responses to give us an idea about what kinds of symptoms to probe. For example, we might say, "You indicated on this questionnaire that you believe having a serious illness would ruin every aspect of your life. Can you tell me what you mean about that?" This helps develop rapport while also demonstrating the importance of the measure.

Anxiety Sensitivity Index-3 (ASI-3; Taylor et al., 2007)

The ASI-3 is an 18-item revision of the 36-item Anxiety Sensitivity Index – Revised (Taylor & Cox; 1998). As with its predecessor, the ASI-3 measures fear of arousal-related sensations based on beliefs about their harmful consequences (i.e., anxiety sensitivity). The respondent rates the degree to which he or she agrees with each item (e.g., "It scares me when my heart beats rapidly") on a five-point scale ranging from "very little" (0) to "very much" (4). The scale contains three factors:
a) Physical concerns (e.g., fears of physical catastrophes such as heart attacks)
b) Cognitive concerns (fears of losing one's mind)
c) Social concerns (fears of the social consequences of being anxious, such as that people will notice the signs of anxiety).

The ASI-3 has demonstrated adequate reliability and validity. The 18 items and scoring procedures for this measure are reprinted in Taylor et al. (2007).

Anxiety sensitivity is a contributor to individual differences in general fearfulness and is thus a risk factor for various anxiety disorders, including health anxiety, panic disorder, phobias, and posttraumatic stress disorder, among others (Taylor, 1999). The physical concerns factor of the ASI-3 contains six items and is most pertinent to health anxiety. Sample items are "When I feel pain in my chest, I worry that I'm going to have a heart attack" and "It scares me when my heart beats rapidly." The only limitation of using the ASI-3 with health-anxious samples is that it is face valid and contains questions that directly assess anxiety and fear. Thus, patients who are resistant to the idea of having anxiety problems can easily deny these cognitions. We discuss the use of the ASI-3 as part of the functional assessment of health anxiety in Chapter 8.

Body Vigilance Scale (BVS; Schmidt et al., 1997)

The BVS measures the tendency to attend to anxiety-related body sensations. The measure is brief, consisting of only four items. Three items assess the degree of
a) Attentional focus
b) Perceived sensitivity to changes in bodily sensations
c) The average amount of time spent attending to bodily sensations

The fourth item involves separate ratings for attention to 15 bodily sensations (e.g., heart palpitations) commonly (but not exclusively) associated with anxiety and stress. Ratings for the 15 sensations are averaged to yield one overall score for Item 4.

The BVS total score is the sum of items 1–4. Olatunji, Deacon, Abramowitz, and Valentiner (2007) reported a mean total score of 21.90 (SD = 12.54) in a sample of patients with hypochondriasis. Panic patients in that study had a mean score of 25.65 (7.85), and nonclinicals had a mean score of 15.52 (SD = 8.74). The measure has good internal consistency and adequate test-retest reliability (Schmidt et al., 1997). We include this measure in the initial assessment to help us ascertain patients' degree of attentiveness to their internal sensations, which plays a role in maintaining their health concerns. The BVS can be found in Schmidt et al. (1997).

Beck Depression Inventory – 2nd Edition (BDI-II; Beck, Steer, & Brown, 1996)

The BDI-II is one of the most widely used measures of depressive symptoms in research and clinical settings. It contains 21 items that measure the cognitive, affective, and somatic features of global distress. The BDI-II has good psychometric properties, is sensitive to treatment, and is easy to administer and score. Patients typically need about 5 minutes to complete the scale, and scores of 20 or greater usually indicate the presence of moderate depression. The BDI-II is available from the Psychological Corporation.

Additional Self-Report Instruments

Numerous other self-report measures may be useful in the assessment of health anxiety. A few we recommend are described below. Some of these instruments are also mentioned again in later chapters as they can be used in the functional assessment of health anxiety – and to help illustrate various points during the psychoeducational modules of treatment.

– The *Whiteley Index* (WI; Pilowsky, 1967) was the first self-report measure developed to assess health anxiety. It is a 14-item instrument by which respondents confirm or disconfirm having experienced symptoms of health anxiety according to three scales: disease fear, disease conviction, and bodily preoccupation. The WI has good reliability and validity as well as predicting treatment outcome and frequency of health care utilization (Speckens, van Hemert, Spinhoven, & Bolk, 1996).

– The *Illness Behavior Questionnaire* (IBQ; Pilowsky & Spence, 1994) was developed to measure maladaptive and inappropriate responses to illness. The questionnaire has two versions, clinical and nonclinical: The former uses language suggesting the presence of a medical illness, whereas the latter does not assume one. Accordingly, it is recommended to use the nonclinical version with patients experiencing severe health anxiety who might be defensive about psychological symptoms. The 62-item questionnaire has seven subscales: (a) phobic concern about having an illness, (b) disease conviction, (c) perception of illness, (d) affective inhibition, (e) affective disturbance, (f) denial of stress, and (g) irritability. More recently, research has indicated that these subscales can be streamlined into two factors: affective state and disease affirmation (Pilowsky & Spence, 1994). The IBQ has demonstrated good reliability and validity (Pilowsky, Chapman, & Bonica, 1977) but is often not used because of its length.

– The *Illness Attitudes Scale* (IAS; Kellner, 1986, 1987) is a 29-item measure of health anxiety consisting of subscales measuring
   1) worry about illness
   2) concerns about pain
   3) health habits
   4) hypochondriacal beliefs
   5) thanatophobia (fear of death)
   6) disease phobia
   7) bodily preoccupation
   8) treatment experience
   9) effects of symptoms.

Respondents are asked how often these thoughts or behaviors occur, with responses ranging from "never" to "most of the time." Overall, the measure has good reliability and validity (Speckens, 2001; Stewart & Watt, 2001); a recent factor analysis, however, reveals that the subscales can be further reduced to just four factors:

1) fear of illness/disease/pain/death
2) symptoms interference with lifestyle
3) treatment experience
4) disease conviction (Hadjistavropoulos et al., 1999).

- The *Somatosensory Amplification Scale* (SSAS; Barsky, Wyshak, & Klerman, 1990) is a 10-item inventory measuring body sensations not typically associated with a serious medical disease. Barsky, Goodson, Lane, and Cleary (1988) coined the phrase *somatosensory amplification* to refer to the perception of normal bodily perturbations as negative and distressing experiences. Respondents are asked to rate whether statements are "not at all true" to "extremely true" on a 5-point scale. The psychometric properties of the SSAS are adequate overall, but evidence is lacking for discriminant validity, that is, it might not measure anything distinct from health anxiety itself.

- The *Cognitions about Body and Health Questionnaire* (CBHQ; Rief et al., 1998) is a 31-item measure developed to help differentiate individuals with severe health anxiety from those with somatization disorder. It contains five factors, each consisting of a different number of items. The factors are (a) catastrophic interpretations of bodily complaints, (b) autonomic sensations, (c) bodily weakness, (d) bodily complaints, and (e) health habits. Items assess agreement catastrophic interpretations of bodily complaints (autonomic sensations, bodily weakness, and intolerance of bodily complaints) and are rated on a 4-point scale ranging from "completely wrong" to "completely right." Overall, the psychometric properties of the CBHQ are adequate, particularly for distinguishing the cognitions associated with severe health anxiety versus somatization. The CBHQ is reprinted in Rief et al. (1998) and discussed further in Chapter 8.

- The *Sheehan Disability Scale* (SDS; Sheehan, 1983). The SDS is a three-item measure of functional impairment associated with psychological symptoms and conditions. The scale consists of only three items on which the respondent rates the extent to which symptoms interfere with work, social, and family life using a scale ranging from 0 (not at all) to 10 (extremely).

The Clinical Interview

The clinical interview provides an opportunity to obtain a firsthand account of patients' symptoms. Together with the self-report data and medical evaluations, the interview should provide the clinician with sufficient information for an accurate diagnosis of the patient. We recommend beginning the interview with an unstructured inquiry into the present symptoms, history, and feelings about treatment. Also, at this juncture, we tend to refer to the problem as "unexplained physical (or medical) symptoms" as opposed to "health anxiety," "somatization," or (least of all) "hypochondriasis." This is a more accurate description of the problem from the patient's perspective, and it reduces the perceived negative connotations associated with these other labels.

Assessing the Chief Complaint and History

It is best to begin the initial assessment by allowing the patient to articulate his or her reasons for attending the session. As discussed, patients with health anxiety present with varying degrees of insight and understanding about their symptoms: Some state that they only came to appease their medical doctor – to rule out any psychological symptoms; others may be there at the insistence of a frustrated partner or loved one; still others, however, believe their symptoms have at least some psychological basis and are quite open to exploring this with the help of a mental-health provider.

Regardless of the reason for attending the evaluation, we think it is important to allow patients to articulate their story and discuss feelings about a psychological approach. Before coming to a mental-health appointment, patients will likely have explored a myriad of medical avenues – and will have heard numerous times (eloquently and sometimes not so eloquently) that all medical test results are negative, and that they are in good health. Although most of us would be delighted by this news, the health anxious individual in fact might feel perplexed (e.g., "How can I have these physical symptoms and not have a real disease?") or ignored (e.g., "No one will listen to me! I'm really sick!"). The mental health professional's task is to validate this frustration, acknowledge the physical signs and sensations as real (as opposed to "in their head"), and align the patient toward wanting to improve their overall well-being *in addition to* finding relief from physical concerns.

The assessor's job is also to determine whether the patient's symptoms fit into the category of health anxiety, and whether comorbid conditions are present. It is useful to begin by asking the patient to describe the chief complaint and purpose for coming to the session (e.g., "Who referred you to see me?"). The patient might also be asked to describe a typical day, highlighting the frequency, intensity, and duration of bodily symptoms, thoughts and concerns about illness, and behaviors performed in response to these concerns (e.g., "What do you do when you notice the pain in your abdomen?"). The interviewer can probe for information about how the problem is managed and how symptoms interfere with functioning. Table 6.1 contains a list of questions for eliciting information about health-anxiety symptoms and safety-seeking strategies. In-

Table 6.1. Open-ended interview questions for assessing unexplained medical symptoms and health anxiety

- What body sensations concern you? What do you think they mean?
- What happens when you have a body sensation of an unknown origin and/or you have a health-related worry pop in your mind? What do you think? What do you do? Then, what do you avoid?
- How often do the health-related worries come to mind? How long do they last?
- What triggers these health-related worries?
- What do you avoid in order to reduce the health-related thoughts?
- What do you do to prevent yourself from thinking these thoughts?
- How many times a day do you have these thoughts?
- How much time is spent a day doing activities related to these thoughts and symptoms (e.g., checking your body, surfing the internet, contacting doctors, going to doctors, asking for reassurance, etc.)?
- After you have done these activities (see above), how do you feel? How anxious are you?
- How many times have you been to the doctor in the last month? How many times have you wanted to go to the doctor in the last month?
- When you are worrying about your health, how do you assure yourself that you're ok?
- What precautions do you take to ensure you're in good health?
- If you were unable to _____ (e.g., body-checking, surf the web, call the doctor, etc), how would you feel? What would you be afraid might happen?
- How much do you think these thoughts and behaviors are senseless or excessive?
- How often do you resist or delay acting after you have a health-related worry?
- How do these health-related worries and behaviors interfere with your life? What are you avoiding because of your fears?
- How does your family and friends react to your symptoms? What do the think?
- Are other people involved in your rituals? Do they constantly reassure you and help you avoid situations?
- What is your experience with illness in the past? Have you ever been seriously ill? Has a loved one? What happened? What did you learn from this experience?

formation about the onset, historical course of the problem, comorbid conditions, social and developmental history, and personal/family history of psychiatric treatment should also be obtained.

Mood

Since many individuals with unexplained medical complaints also suffer from frustration, irritability, or even depressive symptoms, it is important to assess mood state. Because of the tendency to underreport psychological distress, the experience of mood symptoms should be normalized, such as the following: "With all that you've been through because of your unexplained symptoms, I'm wondering what your mood is like. I could imagine someone feeling pretty upset about all of this. Tell me what this has been like for you."

For patients who endorse severe mood disturbance, clinicians should also inquire about the presence of a major depressive episode (e.g., 2 weeks or more of constant low mood, disinterest in activities, etc.). The chronological history of mood complaints should also be determined in order to establish whether such symptoms should be considered as a primary diagnosis or as secondary to health concerns. Primary depression develops parallel to health anxiety and might precede the onset of severe health concerns. In contrast, when depressive symptoms develop subsequent to the unexplained medical concerns – and when the patient describes being depressed *about having health concerns* – the depression is considered secondary to health anxiety.

Social Functioning

Clinicians should assess the degree of impairment in leisure/social, family, and occupational or academic functioning. Where appropriate, this information should be incorporated into the treatment plan so that difficulties can be addressed in the appropriate context. Many patients with unexplained medical symptoms have difficulties working and with social relationships because of the extent of their health preoccupation and engagement in safety-seeking behaviors.

History

When did the patient first notice the unexplained body symptoms? Were the sensations initially disconcerting, or did they become more and more severe over time? When did reassurance-seeking and checking begin? Circumstances surrounding the onset of the problem and the course of symptoms should be assessed. Some patients' symptoms wax and wane over time, whereas other patients describe a general worsening in their physical (and therefore anxiety) complaints. Although some individuals are able to report an exact date when their complaints begin (although the validity of such retrospective reports may be questionable), many cannot, either because onset was not discrete or because the symptoms began so long ago that the memory has since faded. Fortunately, it is not essential to know the exact causes or predisposing factors of health anxiety in order for treatment to be successful. Nevertheless, if the patient has a hypothesis about this, it can be validating (and informative) to collect this information.

Previous Treatment

Discussing psychological treatment is a touchy issue with many health-anxious patients; still, it is important to collect information about what has previously been done to treat or manage the problem from a mental-health perspective to determine or not whether the patient has received an adequate treatment trial (most likely, not). Perhaps the patient has been prescribed medications that are not known to be helpful for this condition, or rather low dosages of potentially helpful medicines. Many patients resist taking medications altogether because of concerns about side effects and the potential to exacerbate unexplained symptoms. Another issue is whether psychodynamic or analytic psychotherapy has been tried. If so, former therapists (or physicians) might have told the patient that their health concerns were caused by intrapsychic conflicts or traumatic events from childhood, and that insight into the nature of such phenomena is required for improvement. In this case, the clinician should explain that there is no evidence that problems with unexplained medical symptoms are necessarily caused by trauma or internal conflicts, nor is there evidence that working on resolving or understanding conflicts reduces symptoms.

Family Issues

The therapist should ask the patient about his or her family of origin. What was growing up like? Did relatives suffer from medical problems or psychological disorders? How did parents react when someone at home became ill? Perhaps catastrophic messages about illness or the importance of getting to the doctor were learned from early experiences growing up. Although there is no way to verify whether such experiences set the stage for the development of health anxiety, they may have led to core beliefs that influence how health-relevant situations and stimuli are interpreted and handled. For example, many patients with concerns about cancer report having family members who died of cancer, and that their parents reinforced the importance of their having a "family history of cancer." One health-anxious patient we evaluated described her parents as being overprotective and constantly reminding her that she had had serious health problems as an infant and was therefore highly vulnerable to being sick.

Assessment should also address relatives' behavioral and emotional responses to the patient's bodily complaints. In some families, relatives are highly critical and express hostility toward a loved one with unsubstantiated health complaints. This may be manifested as meddling or intrusiveness into the person's daily activities. Asking patients to discuss how critical relatives are using a scale from 1 (not at all critical) to 10 (extremely critical) can help determine whether family issues require further assessment or intervention (Chambless & Steketee, 1999).

In other families, relatives may in turn enable or accommodate patients' health-anxiety symptoms by helping with checking behavior, providing frequent reassurance to ease preoccupation and anxiety, and by helping the patient to avoid situations that evoke distress (e.g., certain restaurants that allow smoking). In one extreme example, the parents of a 30-year-old patient purchased numerous expensive medical devices to allow for frequent checks of blood, stool, urine, and other vital signs. This sort of accommodation often occurs either to avoid confrontations over health anxiety, or because family members do not want to see loved ones suffer from extreme distress. Although such behavior reduces distress in the short term, in the long term it serves to reinforce health preoccupation and anxiety. If not addressed, such accommodation practices will adversely impact treatment outcome.

Including family members in the assessment process and gaining their perspectives on the problem can shed light on family reactions and the degree to which symptoms are accommodated. This also affords an opportunity to view how the relative responds to the patient. Are they supportive, constructively critical, or hostile? In an open-ended fashion, relatives can be asked about the extent to which they reassure the patient or enable checking or avoidance. How do they respond when repeatedly asked questions for reassurance? What consequences do they fear if symptoms are not accommodated (e.g., will the patient leave home, commit suicide, or "go crazy"?)? To what extent are the family's activities modified because of the patient's complaints? The clinician should explain that the purpose of involving family members in the interview is to collect information from a variety of viewpoints. We typically invite relatives

---

Table 6.2. Questions for assessing partner or relative involvement in health-anxiety symptoms

- What effects do _____ 's unexplained medical symptoms have on your relationship (or the family) in terms of daily life?
- If there are any patterns that seem to have developed because of _____ 's symptoms, what are they?
- How do you think your relationship/family life might be different if _____ did not have difficulties with these symptoms?
- Is there anyone else (e.g., children) who is affected in any way by _____ 's problems with unexplained medical symptoms? (If so, explore who and how.)
- What have the two of you (or what has your family) tended to do to cope with _____ 's problems with unexplained medical symptoms? (After getting their response, ask the following as well:)
- When _____ either is experiencing symptoms or asking for help or reassurance, does it ever lead to anger or arguments; what is that like?
- Do family members ever have a tendency to help _____ assist or become involved in the reassurance-seeking or checking behaviors? If so, how well has this worked?

into the session after all information has been collected from the patient, but before reviewing this information or presenting recommendations for treatment. Table 6.2 includes questions that can be used to assess the extent of partner or family involvement in symptoms

Individual Strengths and Areas of Difficulty

To help attain a global impression of the patient, one can ask about their personal strengths and shortcomings. How does the patient view him-/herself in light of the fact that they struggle with unexplained medical symptoms and difficulty relating with physicians? How do they perceive their ability to manage their health concerns?

Motivation for Treatment

Because compliance with CBT procedures requires a great deal of effort on the patient's part, it is critical to assess the patient's motivation for therapy. Was it their own or someone else's idea to seek treatment? If the patient is presenting on their own volition, what was it that drove them to ask for help when they did? If others have "forced" or "dragged" them into seeking therapy, what is the patient's understanding of why this is the case? Determination of how much an individual is willing to consider a psychological approach to reducing unexplained physical symptoms may present clinicians with a challenge; and straightforward questioning is not always the best strategy since individuals may be tempted to give the socially most desirable response. On the other hand, some patients are completely adamant about rejecting this approach. Miller and Rollnick (2002) describe some excellent ways of conceptualizing and assessing motivation for change. These motivational interviewing techniques are directly applicable to the treatment of health anxiety, and they are discussed in the Chapter 7.

Structured Diagnostic Interviews

Open-ended, unstructured clinical interviews are preferable to structured interviews in order to develop a strong therapeutic alliance with patients. The less-structured approach allows patients to describe symptoms in their own words, which helps the patient to feel listened to. Merit also exists, however, in using structured clinical interviews that comprehensively assess symptoms in an empirically valid and reliable manner. Two anxiety-focused structured interviews are recommended: the Anxiety Disorders Interview Schedule for DSM-IV (ADIS-IV; Brown, DiNardo, & Barlow, 1994) and the Structured Diagnostic Interview for Hypochondriasis (SDIH; Barsky et al., 1992). Some consider the latter to be the gold standard for the assessment of hypochondriasis (Speckens, 2001), whereas others note no significant differences between these two instruments (Stewart & Watt, 2001). Additional structured interviews include the Structured Clinical Interview for DSM-IV-TR (SCID-IV; First, Spitzer, Gibbon, & Williams, 2002) and the Mini International Neuropsychiatric Interview (MINI; Sheehan et al., 1998). The latter may be preferable to the other methods because of its brevity and excellent reliability and validity. A limitation of some of these interviews, however, is that they do not contain a sufficient number of items assessing somatoform disorders, making them perhaps best used for ruling out anxiety and mood disorders.

Collateral and Release of Information

As noted previously, it is essential to receive information directly from medical providers indicating no medical etiology for the patient's symptoms before determining the presence of health anxiety. Thus, it is helpful from the beginning for patients to sign releases of information allowing for open communication between the mental health and medical providers. Most patients understand the merit of this. If they resist, it is best to explain that you are working as a member of his or her treatment team, and that communication is necessary in order to provide the best care possible.

Also, with the consent of the patient one can include a spouse, partner, or other loved one in at least part of the initial session to gain additional perspectives on the patient's symptoms. Sometimes patients are accompanied by such individuals and might even *prefer* having them present, whereas other patients may be highly resistant to the idea of including a family member in treatment. For the sake of confidentiality, such wishes must be respected.

Measuring Symptom Severity

Measuring the severity of current symptoms provides a way of quantifying the patient's experience. It also helps the clinician to offer a rationale for considering treatment and for discussing what might be expected as treatment response. A multitrait, multimethod approach to assessing symptom severity is suggested. This involves the use of both self-report measures (described earlier in this chapter) and clinician-administered instruments. Below, we describe clinician-administered measures that can be used to assess various facets of health anxiety.

Health Anxiety Symptom Severity

Although developed to measure the symptoms of OCD, the Yale-Brown Obsessive Compulsive Scale (Y-BOCS; Goodman et al., 1989a, 1989b) also serves as a useful measure of the severity of health anxiety. The Y-BOCS contains 10 items – 5 that assess obsessions and 5 that assess compulsions – each of which is rated on a 5-point scale from 0 (no symptoms) to 4 (extremely severe). Items address
a) The time occupied by current symptoms
b) Interference with functioning
c) Associated distress
d) Attempts to resist obsessions and compulsions
e) The degree of control over symptoms.

When used to assess health anxiety, the obsessions subscale is used to score preoccupation with illness, whereas the compulsions subscale scores safety-seeking behaviors. Scores on each of the 10 items are summed to produce a total score ranging from 0 to 40. In most instances, scores of 0 to 7 represent sub-clinical symptoms, those from 8 to 15 represent mild symptoms, scores of 16 to 23 indicate moderate symptoms, scores from 24 to 31 suggest severe symptoms, and scores of 32 to 40 imply extreme symptoms. Our adapted version of this measure appears in the Appendix.

One strength of the Y-BOCS is that it is sensitive to multiple aspects of symptom severity independent of the *number* or *types* of health concerns and safety-seeking behaviors. However, the clinician must be careful to ensure that only bona fide health-anxiety symptoms are rated. The discussion spawned by administration of this instrument may also provide pertinent information. Unfortunately, we have not examined the reliability or validity of the Y-BOCS when used in this way, although as a measure of OCD it is reliable and valid as well as sensitive to the effects of treatment (Goodman et al., 1989a, 1989b).

Insight

The Brown Assessment of Beliefs Scale (BABS; Eisen et al., 1998) is a brief (7 items) continuous measure of insight into the senselessness of psychological symptoms with good reliability, validity, and sensitivity to change. Administration begins with the interviewer and patient identifying one or two of the patient's specific illness beliefs that have been of significant concern over the past week. Examples include "I have a rare stomach disorder that no physician can identify," "My heart is weak and is likely to fail, causing me to die in my sleep," and "The floaters in my eye indicate that I have a serious medical condition." Next, individual items assess the patient's

a) Conviction in this belief
b) Perceptions of how others view this belief
c) Explanation for why others hold a different view
d) Willingness to challenge the belief
e) Attempts to disprove the belief
f) Insight into the senselessness of the belief
g) Ideas/delusions of reference.

Only the first six items are summed to produce a total score. The BABS is also included in the Appendix of this volume.

Depressive Symptoms

Because many health-anxious individuals report mood symptoms, assessment of such complaints should be routine. The Hamilton Rating Scale for Depression (HRSD; Hamilton, 1960) is a well-studied, semistructured interview measuring cognitive (e.g., feelings of guilt), affective (e.g., current mood state), and somatic (e.g., appetite, sleep) aspects of depression. The scale has adequate psychometric properties and is sensitive to the effects of treatment (Hedlund & Vieweg, 1979). It is used widely for assessing depressive symptoms in patients with anxiety disorders.

Providing Feedback to the Patient

Patients are typically eager to find out the assessor's impressions of their problem. Thus, feedback should begin with a review of the interview results. First, the clinician should summarize the information that has been collected and place this in the context of the biopsychosocial model, which then provides the basis for explaining psychological treatment approaches. In Chapter 7 we provide an in-depth discussion of strategies for presenting this psychologically oriented approach to patients who tend to reject psychological accounts, looking rather for a medical explanation. Thus, we suggest the reader closely examine the next chapter before beginning the initial assessment and providing clinical impressions.

Referrals

Educating patients about treatment options is an important part of a clinician's job. While it may be evident that cognitive-behavioral therapy would be helpful to treat a patient's health anxiety, appropriate referrals should be made to address other issues if they are the primary concern. For example, it may be best first to treat the patient's depression and then to address health anxiety. If the clinician does not feel competent to provide both treatments, he or she should make a referral for specialized treatment. If the patient is abusing substances (e.g., alcohol, narcotics, benzodiazepines), treatment for health anxiety should only begin after having addressed these issues. Similarly, should the patient be experiencing disabling anxiety, a referral for a medication evaluation may be indicated.

Cultural Issues in Assessment

While the symptoms of health anxiety are experienced by people of varied backgrounds, culture clearly influences the expression and presentation of these symptoms. Cross-cultural research has demonstrated that the phenomenology of disorders varies greatly across cultures (Good & Kleinman, 1985). The clinician must take this into account, making the clinical interview culturally relevant and sensitive. Standardized assessment measures, particularly self-report questionnaires, should be interpreted with caution and through a culture-specific lens. A culturally sensitive approach involves assessing the patient's religious and spiritual identity, values and social reference group, and "idioms of distress" (Friedman, 2001). That is, the clinician should determine how people of the patient's cultural group view medicine, anxiety, and psychopathology; and how they view others who express such symptoms. Their expectations for treatment and the role of friends and family members in therapy should be identified as well (Friedman, 2001). Cultural groups vary widely in their expression of symptoms, with great variability within the respective group. The clinician's is obliged to educate him- or herself about relevant cultural groups, while expecting individual differences within the cultural group itself.

Obstacles in Assessment

By the time patients with health anxiety reach a mental-health provider, they have typically seen a plethora of physicians. While these professionals have attempted to send the message that the patient is not suffering from a feared illness, this message has not always been received as intended. Health-anxious patients often feel ignored or believe the doctors consider them nuisances or even malingerers. Not surprisingly, they expect similar treatment from mental-health providers. They might seem suspicious of the mental-health provider's competence and ability to help, and consequently may offer guarded responses. They might demonstrate a pessimistic attitude suggesting that there is no hope for treatment, and that no one can help them short of figuring out the etiology of their suspected medical problem. Therefore, it is imperative that the clinician align with the patient, empathizing with his/her frustration and acknowledge that the physical signs and sensations they experience are indeed *real*. As we discuss in Chapter 7, most patients will have never heard this from a healthcare provider before. In our experience, this renders them more open to hearing what else the clinician has to say.

7

Enhancing Motivation and Communication

Case Example

Shereece was 29 years old and had suffered from health anxiety for about 10 years. She believed her body was literally "falling apart" and been to more than 10 different doctors in her hometown. Yet, numerous head CT scans, cardiac workups, and GI studies had revealed no serious medical conditions. On more than one occasion, psychotherapy had been suggested, and Shereece had accumulated a file of referral information and other handouts on psychological approaches to unexplained medical symptoms. Occasionally, when worrying about her physical symptoms, Shereece would open the folder and start to read this material. However, instead of feeling hopeful that she might get relief from psychological treatment, reading about this form of treatment evoked feelings of agitation and the sense that she had been misunderstood by her doctors. She created mental pictures of a therapist trying to convince her that her problems were all in her head. A part of her understood that psychotherapy would probably not be harmful and could perhaps be beneficial in light of the results of her medical tests. But there was another part of her that believed her symptoms were "real" and could be managed only from a medical standpoint. After all, she was not making this up.

Shereece's story is typical of people with health anxiety. Many, though certainly not all, individuals with such problems believe strongly that they are physically ill, and that psychological processes are not involved in their medical difficulties. They often reject psychological and psychiatric treatments, viewing them as obstacles to pursuing much needed medical attention. Our observations suggest an inverse correlation between the strength of disease conviction (i.e., how strongly the person believes he or she has a medical disease) and willingness to consider psychological treatment. Individuals with moderate or low conviction might view therapy in a more favorable light than those with very strong disease conviction. Those with strong conviction are often quite adamant in their focus on seeking further medical assessment to confirm the origin and authenticity of their physical complaints.

It is important for the clinician to consider, therefore, that simply *showing up* to the consultation or therapy session is not necessarily an indication that the health-anxious person has embraced psychological treatment (Wells, 1997). Our patients have told us a variety of reasons they attended consultations and early treatment sessions, including:

– "Just to see what the psychologist would say about the physical problem"
– "To get help for my problem of too much worrying about health"
– "To convince the psychologist that his/her approach doesn't work for *real* medical problems"
– "To finally get reassurance that I am not sick"
– "Because my family keeps pressuring me to go."

These statements suggest that it is common for the clinician and patient to have vastly different agendas during the initial session (Warwick, 1995).

As Shereece's story illustrates, health-anxious patients typically have some degree of *ambivalence* about psychological treatment. They might at once recognize its potential benefits and yet also see it as somehow admitting that their problems are mental and not medical. Ambivalence among health-anxious patients may be about (a) the *general idea* of seeing a psychologist for a "medical" problem or (b) the *specific approach* used in psychological treatment.

The first type of ambivalence is often based on a misconception of the therapist's agenda: Patients often believe the therapist will simply try to convince them that their problems are "all in their head." The second type of ambivalence involves the concern that, by focusing on psychological issues, the more salient medical concerns will be overlooked.

In this chapter, we discuss and illustrate general strategies for communicating with health-anxious patients in ways that serve to strengthen, rather than weaken, the patient-therapist rapport. We also discuss and give examples of ways to help the patient recognize his or her ambivalence and resolve it in a way that increases acceptance of the biopsychosocial conceptual model of health anxiety and increases motivation for psychological treatment. Clinicians may find these methods useful during the initial interview and consultation as well as throughout the treatment-delivery process. An important consideration is that, as with many therapeutic tactics, successful communication with health-anxious patients requires much patience and practice. Many clinicians (the authors included) have had unfulfilling experiences (i.e., failures) before achieving success on a routine basis.

General Communication Strategies

It would be nice if we could present the clinician with a clear-cut list of things to say that would dependably generate good rapport between patient and therapist. Yet, each individual presenting with health anxiety is different, and what works for one patient might not work for another. There are, however, some general principles that are at least *often* useful. Being able to call on one or more of these with any particular patient may be of great help. Many of these principles are derived from Miller and Rollnick's (2002) work on motivational interviewing (MI).

Initially developed in the context of substance abuse treatment, MI incorporates principles and strategies that are quite applicable to health-anxiety treatment (Taylor & Asmundson, 2004). MI is best conceptualized not as a specific treatment or technique, but as a basic way of understanding patients' ambivalence and overcoming their resistance to change. Thus, a "flavor" of MI is typically present throughout treatment.

A key assumption here is that the responsibility for a positive patient-therapist relationship lies with the *therapist*, not with the patient. This departs from traditional thinking where it is common for a therapist to say, "This patient is just not motivated." Based on the principles of MI, we advocate it being the therapist's job to help the ambivalent (and sometimes fractious) health-anxious patient keep an open mind and indeed reach the conclusion that psychological treatment is worth pursuing. Thus, we suggest the clinician approach a seemingly unmotivated health-anxious patient from the following perspective: "What must I do to help this person decide to engage in therapy?" Next, we present some broad principles to keep in mind when communicating with health-anxious individuals – especially during initial sessions when motivation for therapy might wavers the most.

Demonstrate Empathy with Reflective Listening

Expressing an interest in understanding the patient's dilemma – without criticism or judgment – is an important rapport-building strategy. An empathic attitude accepts ambivalence about change as normal (Engle & Arkowitz, 2006). One of the most straightforward ways of doing this is to use reflective listening as described by Carl Rogers (1951). Through reflective listening the therapist can gain a deeper understanding of the problem while also deepening the patient's experience of ambivalence. This might lead the patient to question the status quo and move closer to engagement in treatment. It also communicates to the patient that the therapist respects his or her point of view, particularly

Table 7.1. Reflective listening strategies

Strategy	Examples
– Asking genuine open-ended questions about the problem	– "What do you like and dislike about going for all of these medical tests?"
– Making statements that represent just a small step beyond the patient's account, and that make a reasonable guess as to how he or she is thinking or feeling	– "It must be frustrating when your family harps on you to see a psychologist."
– Eliciting self-motivational statements by selectively reinforcing certain utterances	– "You said you know that looking up information about your symptoms on the internet only makes things worse. Explain what you mean."
– Giving affirmation in the form of compliments, showing appreciation, and understanding	– "I know it's not easy for you to talk about this with a psychologist, and I wanted you to know that I appreciate your willingness to share this information with me."
– Providing summary statements to link together material that has been discussed, particularly self-motivational statements	– "So as you seem to be pointing out, going to another neurology specialist would have some advantages and disadvantages for you. On the one hand, you feel you cannot go on without getting to the bottom of what is causing the dizziness problems. But on the other hand, you mentioned that you already think you know what the specialist is going to say, and that this is only going to further frustrate you."

crucial to health-anxious individuals, who often feel they (and their complaints) are not being taken seriously enough by doctors. Some specific strategies and examples of reflective listening appear in Table 7.1.

Avoid Lecturing

Miller and Rollnick (2002) suggest that ambivalent patients are most likely to engage in treatment when they hear *themselves* making the argument for change. Thus, it is unwise to try to lecture or persuade health-anxious individuals to begin psychological treatment (e.g., "Let me tell you all the reasons why you should do therapy . . ."). Instead, the clinician should work to elicit and reinforce self-motivational statements (i.e., "change talk") *from the pa-*

tient. Miller and Rollnick (2002) list four categories of self-motivational statements:

– Problem recognition (e.g., a statement that one has a problem)
– Expression of concern (e.g., a statement that the problem is serious, or that help is needed)
– Intention to change (e.g., a statement that one has decided to do something about the problem)
– Optimism (e.g., a statement that it is possible to change the problem).

Again, we emphasize that these statements are most helpful if they come from the patient, not from the therapist. Often the techniques described in the previous section on reflective listening can be used to solicit these sorts of statements.

Medicalize – Don't Psychologize

In order to develop rapport, we recommend that therapists – at least initially – refer to patients' complaints using medical terms, preferably the same terms used by the patient. This helps the patient feel listened to and taken seriously. It also maintains consistency with the patient's view of his or her own complaints. Reassuring the patient that you understand his or her complaints are genuine is very important. In contrast, saying there is "nothing wrong" or that the symptoms are caused by "stress," "anxiety," "depression," or some sort of abuse is likely to alienate the patient from the psychological approach (unless, of course, the patient has already acknowledged that these factors play a role in the problem). In trying to be helpful, physicians sometimes send these incorrect and disparaging messages when medical tests turn up negative or when a referral for psychotherapy seems like a good idea. Thus, not only are patients likely to disagree strongly with such explanations, they are likely to perceive the clinician as being unconcerned and dismissive. For patients who react negatively to psychological explanations for their problems, we use the term "unexplained medical symptoms" to refer to their complaints.

As we illustrate later in this chapter, our approach to applying the concept of anxiety to patients with medically unexplained symptoms includes referring to the three specific response systems (i.e., physiologic, cognitive, and behavioral), so that we do not even need to use the term "anxiety." For example, we talk about the *fight-or-flight response* (the physiological [biomedical] correlate of anxiety), gut feelings or *perceptions* of body sensations (the cognitive correlate), and *avoidance* or *taking precautions* (behavioral correlates). Not only do patients respond more agreeably to this language as opposed to being told they are "anxious," this conceptual approach is highly consistent with the biopsychosocial model and treatment. Anxiety, after all, is the heuristic we use when referring to these types of responses.

Avoid Arguments

Health-anxious patients sometimes become argumentative and contest the therapist's accuracy, expertise, or integrity. This tendency can be activated if the therapist becomes overly dynamic or tries too vigorously to push the patient in a certain direction, for example, by minimizing the importance of a medical complaint or persuading the patient that the problem is one of health *anxiety* rather than a legitimate medical problem. If patients perceive the therapist as trying too forcefully to present or argue one side of an issue, they are likely to dig in their heels and generate arguments to the contrary, often indicated by "yes, but . . ." statements, as in this dialog:

Therapist: I've looked over your medical records; there is no sign of any serious disease.

Patient: Yes, but my doctors haven't conducted the right tests. They just disregard me because they think I'm a hypochondriac.

Engaging in arguments is likely to increase resistance to treatment and perhaps damage the therapist-patient rapport. Some additional conversational styles to avoid when working with health-anxious patients include those listed in Table 7.2. Instead of directly presenting patients with arguments for changing their

Table 7.2. Conversational styles to avoid when working with health-anxiety patients to accept psychological treatment

- Ordering, directing, or commanding
- Warning or threatening
- Giving unsolicited advice, making suggestions, and providing solutions
- Persuading with logic, arguing, or lecturing
- Moralizing, preaching, or telling patients what they "should" do
- Criticizing, blaming, or labeling
- Interpreting or analyzing
- Asking rapid-fire questions that elicit defensiveness
- Reminding the patient how serious his/her problem is
- Insisting on talking about the problem behavior when the patient has other concerns he/she wants to discuss

position or attitude, clinicians will have greater success by helping patients to generate their own arguments for change (Emmons & Rollnick, 2001). This can be done using the other strategies presented in this chapter (e.g., demonstrating empathy, rolling with resistance).

Roll with Resistance

Health-anxious patients sometimes demonstrate resistance to treatment in one or more of the following ways (Miller & Rollnick, 2002):
- Interrupting – cutting off the therapist and breaking in with a defensive statement
- Denying – being unwilling to recognize problems, cooperate, or accept responsibility
- Ignoring – disregarding or discounting the therapist.

Regardless of the language and tact with which resistance is vocalized (some patients may be quite unpleasant and aggressive whereas others resist in a more agreeable way) these behaviors are all signs that the therapist and patient are not aligned with one another with respect to readiness for treatment. We recommend the therapist responding to resistance with reflective listening and making more explicit the patient's concerns and desires both for and against change (i.e., ambivalence). One way of accomplishing this is to slightly overstate the patient's resistance in a genuine way. This strategy of *amplified reflection* can get the patient to back off and even make arguments in favor of change, as is illustrated next:

Therapist: One of the goals of treatment is to help you learn that you do not need to keep going to doctors to get more opinions about your rectal pain. You're going to learn a new approach to –

Patient: (interrupting) No, no, that doesn't make any sense. I need to get to the bottom of this *medically*, not *psychologically*.

Therapist: (genuinely) Oh, ok. You're saying you think you should continue going to the doctor every time your rectum hurts since this strategy has been helpful for you in the past as far as finding a good explanation and treatment for your symptoms.

Patient: Well, actually, no. The doctors *haven't* been helpful. They don't know what they're doing. All they do is tell me I'm healthy – that they can't find anything wrong. They must think I'm making it up or that I'm crazy.

Therapist: I see. So you must feel that the *next* doctor you go to will have all the answers, then. It sounds like you are pretty confident he or she will finally be able to help you put all of this to rest.

Patient: Well, they'll probably just tell me the same thing all the others have told me . . .

Another strategy, referred to as *agreement with a twist* (Miller & Rollnick, 2002), involves letting patients know you see eye to eye with them, but also incorporate a slight change of direction. This is illustrated in the following example:

Therapist: One of the goals of treatment is to help you learn that you do not need to keep going to doctors to get more opinions about your rectal pain. You're going to learn a new approach to –
Patient: (interrupting) No, no, that doesn't make any sense. I need to get to the bottom of this *medically*, not *psychologically*.
Therapist: You're absolutely right that you've got real medical symptoms. And I am not a physician so I can't give you an explanation for them. You also told me how frustrated you've become with your physicians. If you reduce this frustration think of how it could help you develop better relationships with your doctors. Perhaps they will be able to help you more effectively that way.

A third technique is to reflect the resistance and pair it with a self-motivational statement. This forces the patient to examine the discrepancy in his or her beliefs:

Therapist: One of the goals of treatment is to help you learn that you do not need to keep going to doctors to get more opinions about your rectal pain. You're going to learn a new approach to –
Patient: (interrupting) No, no, that doesn't make any sense. I need to get to the bottom of this *medically*, not *psychologically*.
Therapist: Right, so you have been trying very hard to get a medical explanation for your symptoms. After all, they're real. And, as you said before, this approach hasn't been helpful. In fact, it's made you feel very frustrated.
Patient: Yeah, that's exactly my problem.
Therapist: What are some things you might do about this problem?

A final recommendation for managing resistance is to emphasize the patient's control and personal choice. This usually leads to reduced defensiveness:

Therapist: One of the goals of treatment is to help you learn that you do not need to keep going to doctors to get more opinions about your rectal pain. You're going to learn a new approach to –
Patient: (interrupting) No, no, that doesn't make any sense. I need to get to the bottom of this *medically*, not *psychologically*.
Therapist: Well, ultimately, the decision about how to deal with your symptoms is completely yours. I cannot tell you what you should or should not do. What

I will point out is that you seem to be saying that your way of handling this has not been very helpful. Perhaps it's time to try something new.

Patient: Well, I guess it can't hurt to hear a little about your therapy, even though I may decide not to come back.

A common denominator of the strategies just described for rolling with resistance is conveying acceptance and empathy. This helps expand the patient's understanding of the pros and cons of treatment, and helps him or her to clarify both the hesitancy and appeal of beginning therapy. It is often a profound experience for patients to air grievances about their experiences with medical specialists, voice their reservations about psychotherapy, and still find the therapist listening and responding thoughtfully and compassionately without dismissing these concerns or trying harder to "sell" psychological treatment. The patient feels understood and may be more likely to opt to engage in therapy. The alternative is for the therapist to respond with further attempts to persuade the patient to change; yet, as we mentioned earlier, this typically evokes even stronger resistance on the part of the patient.

Discussing the Biopsychosocial Model

Socialization is the process of helping patients view their problems from a particular conceptual angle. For health-anxious patients, the goals of socialization are (a) for the patient to consider (at least to some degree) that his or her problem is one of anxiety and worry about health, rather than the presence of a serious medical disease; and (b) to increase the patient's willingness to engage in psychological treatment.

Whereas some health-anxious patients readily acknowledge the role anxiety plays in their difficulties, many do not have good insight into the senselessness of their medical complaints. Especially in the latter instance does an introduction of the psychological model require no small amount of skill and tact. There is a risk that the patient will feel labeled as a "hypochondriac," which will almost certainly evoke strong resistance. On the other hand, the patient needs to understand the biopsychosocial model in order to benefit maximally from therapy. In this section, we present some strategies for helping patients build acceptance of the conceptual framework that guides psychological treatment. Clearly, our strategy is infused with the MI approach described above.

Getting a Foot in the Door

We begin the process of socializing the patient at the first assessment or consultation session. The goal is to raise ambivalence about the status quo and help the patient make an argument for addressing the problem from a new and different perspective. This is typically initiated by asking the patient about why he or she has been referred to a mental health professional. Whether or not the clinician has prior knowledge of this, it is often best to begin by inquiring in a genuine way about the nature of the referral.

Therapist: So, what can you tell me about how you were referred to see me?

Patient: I was referred by my family doctor. She has been telling me I need to see a psychologist for a while now, and I finally broke down and did it.

Therapist: OK. I give you credit for trying it out. But why has she been telling you that you need a psychologist?

Patient: I think I have all sorts of medical problems, but she can't find anything wrong with me. She thinks I'm healthy.

Therapist: Well, gee, that sounds like *good* news to me. Why do you need a psychologist, then?

Patient: It's not good news for me. I *know* there is something wrong with me. I keep trying to get doctors to figure out what it is, but they keep telling me that it's all in my head. That's why I was referred.

Therapist: I see. So, what *have* your doctors said or done about your medical complaints?

Patient: Well, I've had lots of tests, but they don't show anything wrong physically. Like, right now, my main problem is that I feel cold all the time. I think there is something wrong with my circulatory system, but Dr. Hatton tells me I'm wrong. She even sent me to a specialist who also couldn't find anything. But I keep having cold and tingly feelings in my feet, hands, arms, and legs – like I have MS.

Therapist: I see. What's that like for you – not getting a diagnosis when you feel there is something seriously wrong?

Patient: It makes me upset. Very frustrated and worried.

Therapist: Sure. I can understand feeling that way. Do you have any guess as to why the doctors haven't been able to give you a medical diagnosis?

Patient: Well, they *say* that my complaints are not real, that there is nothing medically wrong with my body, and that I need psychological help. They keep telling me that I am stressed, and that this is psychological.

Therapist: OK, and what do you think of that?

Patient: I'm angry. It doesn't make sense. I don't see how stress or psychological problems can make me have physical symptoms.

Therapist: Sure, and I want you to know that I do not think you are just making this all up. I believe you when you say you really have the coldness, tingling, and other symptoms.

Patient: I'm glad you understand. But I need to find out what's really wrong. This is not just a psychological problem. It's not just stress.

Note that in this exchange the therapist generally asks open-ended questions and expresses interest in the patient's responses. The therapist also demonstrates acceptance of the patient's physical complaints as authentic and attempts to solicit the patient's own explanations for the doctor's conclusion of good health despite the presence of symptoms. If, at this point, the therapist were simply to suggest that the patient pursue a psychological angle, the patient would likely resist; instead, the maneuver illustrated gently shifts the direction of the discussion and – without pressuring the patient to change his or her attitude – gives the therapist permission to talk about a psychological perspective. Note that this places the *patient* in the role of describing the role of psychological factors. Also note that the therapist uses the term "psychological" only after the patient has begun to use it.

Therapist: Well, in light of all you have been through with your doctors, I'd like to know your guess as to what percent of your health issues – out of 100% – might be due to medical causes versus what percent might be due to some sort of psychological factors? So, give me a ratio, like 50–50 or 60–40.

Patient: Umm . . . I'd say my problems are much more due to medical causes. So, it's probably 80% medical and 20% psychological. Yeah . . . 80–20.

Therapist: OK, so psychological factors only account for 20%. And, why even give them 20%? I mean, why not even less than that? Why not 10% or 5%?

Patient: Well, I've been through so many tests and check-ups, and the doctors never find anything. It sometimes makes me wonder about whether there is a psychological cause.

Therapist: I see. And tell me about *how* you think psychological factors might play a role in your problems with your health, even if it's only 20%?

Patient: I don't know for sure. Maybe I don't realize how much stress I have and maybe that causes me to have symptoms.

Therapist: Well, as you know, I am not a physician so I cannot answer your medical questions or determine what is wrong with you physically. But since I am a psychologist, we could spend some time trying to understand better the other 20% of the equation. Would it be OK if we talk some about the 20% that you're saying *could* be psychological?

Patient: I guess so. I've never thought about it like that before.

Therapist: Sure. So you thought that it was one *or* the other, huh? Either it's a medical disorder *or* a psychological problem.

Patient: Yeah.

Therapist: I understand. Can you think of any advantages to considering that perhaps there are psychological *and* physical factors working together?

Patient: Well, maybe the mind and body are related. And if you can help even with 20% of the problem, I'll be better off than where I am right now.

Therapist: Right, I agree. And are there disadvantages to seeing the problem as either completely medical or completely psychological?

Patient: Well, I might ignore some little piece of the puzzle if I focus exclusively on medical issues . . .

Body Vigilance and Body Noise

We find it helpful to introduce the biopsychosocial model by focusing on the patent's tendency to closely monitor his or her body (i.e., body vigilance). This issue is raised by reviewing the patient's responses on the Body Vigilance Scale, which typically indicate high levels of attention to internal processes. Once the idea of body vigilance is presented, its "side effects" – such as heightened sensitivity to innocuous "body noise" – can be discussed. Key points to be conveyed include that

a) Even healthy bodies produce noticeable sensations and perturbations (body noise)

b) Although such body noise is noticeable and perhaps uncomfortable, it is not necessarily an indication of a serious medical illness

c) Body vigilance leads to increased perception of body noise, leading to the belief that a serious medical condition is present.

Therapist (referring to the Body Vigilance Scale): Let's take a look at your responses to this questionnaire. You seem to be saying that you tend to pay close attention to internal body sensations, that you notice these changes a lot, and that you spend quite a bit of time scanning your body for changes. Tell me more about that.

Patient: Well, yeah. I've got all of these symptoms, so of course I pay attention to them. Wouldn't you? I mean, what if they got out of control or something? Plus, I feel like I have to keep track so I can let doctors know what's wrong.

Therapist: Sure. And that must be a lot of work for you – constantly monitoring what's going on with your body.

Patient: Yes. It seems to take up a lot of time, and I start thinking about it even when I don't want to. Even when I'm trying to go to sleep, I can feel things going on inside of me.

Therapist: So, you've got some good reasons for paying such close attention to your body. But can you think of any *disadvantages* of paying such close attention?

Patient: What do you mean?

Therapist: Well, if you measured your heart rate (pulse rate) or blood pressure every five minutes throughout the day, would it be the same all the time?

Patient: No, probably not.

Therapist: Right – definitely not in fact: It fluctuates. What if you measured your body temperature every few minutes?

Patient: It probably changes, too.

Therapist: Yes it does – more than we realize. What about your visual acuity, level of concentration, muscle tone, breathing rate, and level of alertness throughout the day? If you measured these all the time would they be stable all day long?

Patient: No, I guess not.

Therapist: Do you know why all of these things change all the time?

Patient: Well, aren't there always changes going on inside our bodies?

Therapist: That's right. In fact, I like to say that we have rather *noisy bodies*. What do you think that means?

Patient: I guess that our bodies are always changing.

Therapist: Exactly. Your visual acuity actually changes slightly through the day. The same with your blood pressure, vestibular functioning (balance), breathing rate, digestion, muscle tension, skin, and many other bodily processes, too. As you said, our bodies are normally in a state of flux. Now, if you are constantly monitoring your body for symptoms, what are you inevitably going to pick up on?

Patient: I see what you mean. I'm probably sensing these changes in my body because of how much I pay attention to my insides.

Therapist: Right. It's like you've got your dial tuned to the "body-noise channel," and the volume is turned *way up*! This seems to fit with your experience of having *real* symptoms that the doctors cannot attribute to any serious medical disease.

Patient: Wait a minute. Are you just saying that my problems are because of normal changes in my body? That can't be true. This is more than just body noise.

Therapist: I understand where you're coming from. On the one hand, you experience real bodily symptoms that feel like something is wrong. But on the other hand, you've had numerous doctors examine you carefully, and all of them have told you that they can't find any evidence of a medical disorder. (Pause) But remember, we are only talking about 20% of the symptoms. We're not looking to explain all of your health problems. Also, remember that we agreed you have nothing to lose by trying this new approach along with consulting with physicians.

Patients sometimes report that other professionals have suggested that problems with unexplained medical symptoms result from too much "stress" or "anxiety," or that they are caused by some traumatic event or a history of abuse. Patients, however, often argue they are not stressed, do not experience anxiety, and many deny significant histories of abuse or trauma. Although the therapist's first inclination might be to try to convince the patient that he or she is overlooking how much stress or anxiety is present, this could be perceived as too strongly advocating a psychological explanation. Instead, the vigilance to body noise explanation provides an explanation for the patient's physical complaints independent of stress and anxiety levels, and regardless of whether or not previous trauma or abuse has occurred. Thus, in the interest of building rapport and promoting commitment to treatment, the clinician can agree with patients who deny too much stress. This sidesteps having to "psychologize" the patient's perceived medical problem: The therapist can point to a physiological basis for the unexplained symptoms (e.g., "I want to reassure you that I do not think your physical symptoms are *caused* by a psychological problem such as anxiety, trauma, or abuse; rather, I think there are good physical explanations for your physical symptoms"). Chapter 10, which focuses on psychoeducation, provides more suggestions for conveying this information.

The Dichotomous Nature of Medical Results and Diagnoses

Health-anxious patients commonly hold an "all-or-nothing" view of health status: "Any physical sign indicates the presence of a medical diagnosis." Accordingly, when test results are negative and no diagnosis is given, such individuals become perplexed since they seem still to be experiencing physical signs and symptoms. Patients, however, fail to consider that whereas most medical diagnoses are dichotomous (e.g., one either has cystic fibrosis or does not), most bodily signs and sensations (including the symptoms of many illnesses) occur on a continuum of frequency, intensity, and duration, and might have different origins altogether. This is to say, a negative test result and the absence of a medical diagnosis do not preclude one from experiencing *subclinical* signs and "symptoms" that, although innocuous or minor, could seem like any number of medical conditions. Witness such a "middle ground" scenario in the following dialog:

Therapist: What do you think it means when a doctor doesn't give you a diagnosis?

Patient: It means the doctor thinks I'm making up the symptoms.

Therapist: Lots of people think that, too. But, actually, it's not a perfect relationship between feeling symptoms and having a disease. For example, do you know of any diseases that *don't* produce any noticeable symptoms?

Patient: Well, I've heard of people having cancer and not realizing it until it's too late.

Therapist: That's right. So, some diseases can be present without any noticeable symptoms. And the reverse is also true. Sometimes we experience noticeable physical symptoms even in the absence of a disease.

Patient: Hmm. Really? I never thought about it that way before.

Therapist: That's right. So, even someone without a medical diagnosis can have symptoms. Most medical tests are designed so that they come out negative unless the symptoms rise to a certain critical level of severity determined by research on the disease. So, a person might have actual *symptoms* that occur in a particular disease, but the symptoms might not be severe enough to either show up as a positive test result or meet criteria for a clinical diagnosis. Do you see what I mean? I'm saying that just because tests don't come out positive – and just because a doctor doesn't give you a medical diagnosis – doesn't mean you don't have any symptoms whatsoever.

The Mind-Body Connection

The next step is to help the patient consider how his or her thinking and behavior effect the experience of physical signs and symptoms; that is, how one's responses to unfamiliar, vague, or otherwise disconcerting bodily sensations actually serve to *exacerbate* these sensations. Because this is a sensitive issue, especially for many patients who minimize the role of psychological factors in their difficulties, we cloak references to psychological processes such as anxiety within the concept of the "mind-body connection." Initially, we focus on the relationship between the perception of threat and physiologic arousal. Patient responses to the Anxiety Sensitivity Index (which we label as the "Body Symptoms Questionnaire") usually indicate the presence of catastrophic thoughts regarding one or more physiologic processes; thus, these results can be used to initiate the discussion. Even when high levels of anxiety sensitivity are not present, other threatening or catastrophic misinterpretations of bodily sensations the patient has described can be used to illustrate the points below:

Therapist: This questionnaire lets us know how you experience and think about certain body symptoms such as dizziness, nauseousness, and tightness in your throat. I see that you agreed strongly with the statements "When my stomach is upset I worry that I might be seriously ill" and "When my throat feels tight I worry that I could choke to death." Can you tell me what that's like for you?

Patient: It's awful. I feel like something terrible is happening to me, and that no one will do anything about it! No one believes me that there is something wrong.

Therapist: You're saying the symptoms are threatening, and you feel like you could be in danger.

Patient: Yeah.

Therapist: I'd like to focus for a minute on the strong connection between mind and body. You know about the mind-body connection, right?

Patient: Sure.

Therapist: In particular, let's talk about what happens physically when a person feels as if they are in danger – like when you say to yourself "Something terrible is happening to me." What does the body usually do when the mind perceives some sort of serious threat or danger?

Patient: I don't know … It gets tense and I feel my heart beating faster sometimes.

Therapist: Right. That's a medical term called the "fight-or-flight" response. Have you ever heard of that before?

Patient: Yes.

Therapist: Do you know what the purpose of the fight-or-flight response is?

Patient: Yeah, it's to keep ourselves safe, right?

Therapist: That's right. When we perceive something that could be threatening, such as a serious medical problem, the body automatically shifts into this fight/flight alarm mode, and we experience certain physical symptoms: We get tense, the heart beats faster, our breathing becomes deeper and faster, we sometimes feel like we have to go to the bathroom or throw-up; some people break out in a sweat, others have other medical signs such as dizziness or blurred vision. Can you recognize how that alarm goes off when *you* notice certain symptoms and start thinking about what's wrong with your health? I bet you didn't realize how much the mind can influence medical symptoms.

Patient: Sure. That makes sense.

Therapist: Good. Although the aim of the fight-or-flight response is to alert you to potential danger, it also produces some uncomfortable "side effects" such as feeling tired, dizzy, out of breath, or nauseous – and sometimes even things like ringing in the ears, blurred vision, and the sensation of choking. So, it turns out that if you tell yourself something as disconcerting as "Something terrible is happening" or that "No one will believe me," it actually causes *more* symptoms in your body and makes you feel *worse*. Can you see that? Again, the body and mind work very closely together.

Patient: Yes, I see that this sometimes happens to me.

Therapist: OK. So, something we might explore together is a more helpful way to respond to those uncomfortable physical symptoms so that you can stop the fight-or-flight cycle that makes them worse.

Patients sometimes then raise the point that it seems as if symptoms are occurring *before* they are interpreted as being threatening; and that if this is the case, doesn't the presence of symptoms in the first place indicate that something is medically wrong? The therapist can handle this issue be referring back to the previous points about body vigilance and noisy bodies, as in the following dialog:

Patient: Yes, but the symptoms come first – even before I think about danger. You see, there must be something wrong that we are ignoring here.

Therapist: So, you're wondering why you have any physical symptoms in the first place.

Patient: Right.

Therapist: Well, remember that we all have noisy bodies, and you said that you tend to pay lots of attention to . . .

Patient: (interrupting) Well, wouldn't *you* if *you* had something wrong!?

Therapist: (calmly) Yes, I would. In fact, anyone would. So, I think I understand how you feel. Health is a vitally important thing to most everyone. That's exactly the point – I am not criticizing you for paying close attention to your body. It's a perfectly natural thing to do, especially if you are concerned about illness. It's just that doing this has some unfortunate side effects: Because you are constantly monitoring your body, you have inadvertently become very sensitive to all sorts of sensations, some of which probably fall into the category of bodily noise. Do you see what I mean?

Patient: I guess so. I can see where it makes some sense.

Effects of Behavioral Responses

The final step in presenting the biopsychosocial model is to help the patient understand that behaviors such as frequently discussing health issues, looking up information on the internet, and doctor shopping are part of the *problem*, rather than a solution. Using the MI techniques described above, we engage patients in a discussion of the advantages and disadvantages of these behaviors as well as the pros and cons of stopping them. The point of this discussion is not to launch into a full educational module (this takes place once therapy commences; see Chapter 10). Instead, the aim here is simply to provide a new perspective on the patient's maladaptive behaviors and amplify his or her ambivalence with regards to the utility of such strategies for managing bodily sensations. Here a sample dialog about the effects of searching the internet:

Therapist: You mentioned that you search the internet for information about the symptoms you experience. How often do you do this?

Patient: Whenever I notice symptoms. Sometimes it's once a day, sometimes more.

Therapist: Lots of people search the internet for medical information. What's it like for you when you search the web?

Patient: Well, I like to read about illnesses and the symptoms I have so I can find out whether or not I have something serious. I also chat with other people who have unexplained medical symptoms.

Therapist: Sure. There is some valuable information out there, but also there are some websites that have inaccurate information. So, some advantages of using the internet are that you can find out some important facts about illnesses and get support from other people going through similar experiences. Have you found any down sides to using the internet for these purposes?

Patient: Well, it's hard to know if the information I'm getting is really accurate. I mean, it seems like every website says something a little different.

Therapist: And how does that make you feel?

Patient: It can get confusing – frustrating, sometimes.

Therapist: So, it sounds like using the internet has some advantages and disadvantages. On the one hand, it connects you with other people and provides information for you. It sounds like sometimes you get some short-term comfort or reassurance from using the internet. But on the other hand, it's hard to tell whether you're getting *accurate* information. Another problem with using the internet this way is that it might keep you more closely attuned to your bodily symptoms, and we know why that can be a problem. I also wonder whether you tend to pay more attention to the more serious explanations for your symptoms and discount or ignore other benign explanations you read about.

Patient: Yes, I guess I do that.

Therapist: What effect do you think that has on how much attention you pay to your body?

Patient: I see what you mean. It probably makes me focus on it more strongly.

Therapist: Yes. And it probably also puts all sorts of unnecessary and scary explanations in your mind. Just for the sake of discussion, what might be some of the pros and cons of stopping your use of the internet in this way?

Patient: Well, it would be hard to stop because I rely on it for understanding my symptoms. But I can see that it has kind of become addicting.

Therapist: How has it become addicting?

Patient: Well, it feels like a crutch. Every time I feel something in my belly, I need to check just to make sure it's not anything serious.

Therapist: And you also said sometimes it makes you unnecessarily scared.

Patient: Yeah. So that might be a good reason to give it up. But what would I do when those symptoms come up? How would I cope?

Therapist: Perhaps we can try to solve that problem and come up with more effective ways to mange these symptoms.

Providing a Rationale for Psychological Treatment

Summary Statement

Once the patient has been introduced to the biopsychosocial (or "mind-body") approach to their problem with unexplained medical symptoms, it is time to summarize the conversation and discuss the possibility of starting psychological treatment. The following is a typical example of how we present the treatment rationale:

Therapist: We have covered a lot of ground today, so let's see if we can pull it all together to see where we are and where we're going. It is clear that you're experiencing real physical symptoms that bother you; but it also seems that, at least to some extent, there are things you could do to manage these symptoms in more helpful and healthy ways than in the past. We talked about certain thoughts that trigger your body to produce more physical symptoms. We also talked about strategies such as looking up information on the internet and so on, which seem to temporarily work, but which backfire in the long run instead of actually making you feel better. It sounds like you find yourself relying more and more on these strategies – that don't work very well to begin with – to the extent that they are beginning to interfere with your life. You've seen lots of doctors and had many, many tests and examinations, but these have left you feeling frustrated and without good clear answers. How do you feel about our working together to see if we can figure out how to address some of these problems from a new perspective?

Eliciting Change Talk

Sometimes patients respond to the summary statement in a positive manner and see psychological treatment as a good option. Others, however, continue to express arguments for the status quo. In such cases, the therapist can work to elicit arguments in favor of treatment (i.e., change talk) without advocating change too strongly. Change talk includes statements by the patient that reflect commitment, desire, perceived ability, need, readiness, or reasons to change (Amrhein, Miller, Yahne, Palmer, & Fulcher, 2003). Miller and Rollnick (2002) suggest eliciting change talk by asking evocative questions that force the patient to consider the relevant topics (shown in Table 7.3).

A second strategy for eliciting change talk is to explore collaboratively with patients the short- and long-term advantages and disadvantages of psychological treatment. The patient may be asked to write down and discuss both the pros and cons of the psychological model and psychological therapy as he or

Table 7.3. Topics and questions for eliciting change talk from patients with health anxiety

Topic	Sample questions
Disadvantages of the status quo	– How have your unexplained symptoms interfered with your life?
	– What bothers you the most when your physicians cannot find a medical explanation for your symptoms?
Advantages of change	– How would life be different if you didn't need an explanation for every symptom your body produces?
	– What are some of the advantages of being medically healthy?
Optimism about change	– What difficult challenges have you overcome in the past?
Intent to change	– How important is it for you to get some help for your unexplained medical symptoms?
Negative extremes	– What would the rest of your life be like if your doctors never gave you an adequate explanation for these symptoms?
	– How much more time and money are you going to spend on doctor appointments that only seem to make you more frustrated?
Positive extremes	– How would life be different if you could control these symptoms better?
	– How will the other people in your life react when you can manage these symptoms in more helpful ways?

she perceives them. Engaging in treatment might have a number of short-term disadvantages (e.g., trying a new and nonmedical approach), whereas the advantages are more long-term and can be difficult to envision (e.g., not needing a medical explanation for bodily signs and sensations). On the other hand, avoiding treatment may have short-term advantages to the patient (e.g., keeping a medical focus), but is disadvantageous in the long-term (e.g., functional impairment). The therapist can use the MI strategies described in this chapter to help the patient examine the short- and long-term pros and cons. The patient has a choice to remain at the status quo or to try a new approach that is very much at odds with his or her previous view of the problem. Advantages of therapy can be increased in scope, and disadvantages can be gently challenged.

A third approach, as suggested by Wells (1997), is to present psychological treatment as a no-lose opportunity. This can be done by discussing the length of time the patient has been pursuing a medical explanation for complaints, and how effective this pursuit has been in solving the problem. The therapist can point out that the patient has little to lose by engaging in an alternative (or augmentative) psychological treatment approach. Moreover, if the psychological approach does not turn out to be helpful, one can return to the previous strategy.

Wells (1997) also points out that, in some instances, individuals with health anxiety and strong disease conviction perceive the status quo as useful in maintaining the upper hand in certain types of interpersonal relationships. For example, patients might find that they are able to control personal relationships, avoid intimacy, or maintain dependency if they continue to suffer. Of course, such individuals will argue strongly against change (and for maintaining the status quo). If the therapist suspects that unexplained medical symptoms serve a protective function, this can be raised sensitively by pointing out that making changes to one's life can be daunting because of the large impact such changes might have on how the patient is treated by others.

The Transition into Treatment

The transition into psychological treatment is a delicate process for the patient, and it is important for the therapist not to underestimate the patient's degree of ambivalence. The decision to begin treatment might occur gradually rather than all at once, and the clinician must not confuse the decision-making *process* with an actual *decision*. Once it is clear the patient has committed to treatment, the therapist works to route this motivation into a practical plan for change. The patient's autonomy should be reaffirmed throughout this process. For example, the therapist might discuss the pros and cons of continuing with a medical approach versus a psychological one and ask the patient what he or she wishes to do. Once an initial plan has been developed, the patient's motivation can be further strengthened by setting short- and long-term goals. Handout 7.1 is a change plan worksheet that can be completed collaboratively by the patient and therapist.

8

Functional Assessment

This is the first of five chapters (i.e., Chapters 8–12) that describe and illustrate specific strategies once the patient has agreed to begin treatment for health anxiety. The present chapter delineates our approach to functional assessment – the gathering of patient-specific information required to generate a case conceptualization and cognitive-behavioral treatment plan. *Functional assessment* is different from *diagnostic assessment* (as described in Chapter 6) in that the former involves a theoretically driven and idiographic approach to understanding the development and maintenance of the symptoms, whereas the latter is based on more or less atheoretical diagnostic criteria and is a nomothetic approach. In Chapter 9, we discuss how to synthesize information gleaned from the functional assessment to derive a case formulation and treatment plan based on the biopsychosocial model.

As a note to the reader, we could just as easily have included the topics of case conceptualization and treatment planning in the present chapter, but chose (somewhat arbitrarily) to present such matters in Chapter 9. Taken together, the materials covered in this and the following chapter set the table for the cognitive and behavioral treatment techniques described in Chapters 11 (cognitive therapy) and 12 (behavioral [exposure therapy] techniques).

Overview of Functional Assessment

The initial assessment and diagnostic procedures described in Chapter 6 are necessary, though not sufficient, for successful treatment of health anxiety. Nevertheless, diagnosis sets the stage for a more comprehensive functional assessment in which idiosyncratic, circumstantial, physiologic, cognitive, and behavioral features of the patient's health-anxiety symptoms are carefully identified, and the links between these features are understood using the biopsychosocial framework discussed in Part 1 of this book. This patient-specific information guides the treatment process. The clinician should expect to spend up to 2 to 4 hours conducting the functional assessment, which typically means setting aside multiple sessions for this process at the beginning of therapy. These sessions also serve to strengthen the therapeutic relationship and further reinforce for the patient the conceptual model of health anxiety and philosophy of treatment.

We inform the patient from the beginning that the first few treatment sessions are used to get to know one another and to develop a plan for treatment. This provides patients with a clear expectation of what will likely occur during the initial sessions and may help to reduce anticipatory anxiety. The process of functional assessment, case conceptualization, and treatment planning can even be viewed as an exchange of information between patients, who are presumably able to describe their own symptoms, and the clinician, who has the expertise to draw on the biopsychosocial conceptual framework in deriving a conceptualization and treatment plan that addresses the respective patient's particular symptoms. To this end, the therapist must ascertain the specific nuances of each patient's health anxiety, while the patient must learn how to understand these symptoms from the biopsychosocial perspective in order to optimize assessment and treatment.

The composition of a functional assessment for health anxiety is summarized in Table 8.1. We have developed approaches to help ensure that therapists ask all the necessary questions and collect all the pertinent information to develop a fairly complete idea of the patient's symptoms. These include the use of a therapist form for recording information obtained in the functional assessment (see Figure 8.1), and the use of self-report inventories to augment the clinical

Table 8.1. Components of functional assessment of health anxiety
Historical events giving rise to idiosyncratic dysfunctional beliefs
Personal and family history of physical health difficulties
Parental reactions to illness
Other events (e.g., media reports, illness outbreaks)
Triggers
Bodily signs, sensations, and perturbations
External situations and stimuli
Intrusive thoughts, ideas, and doubts
Attitudes, beliefs, and misinterpretations
Threat-related misinterpretations of bodily triggers and intrusive thoughts
Feared consequences of exposure to external (situational) triggers
Dysfunctional beliefs and attitudes about own health/illness, medicine/doctors, etc.
Intolerance for uncertainty
Safety-seeking behaviors, their cognitive links to anxiety, and their maladaptive effects
Passive avoidance
Checking
Reassurance-seeking
Safety signals

FUNCTIONAL ASSESSMENT OF HEALTH ANXETY

Patient's name: _____

Age: _____

Duration of symptoms: _____

Educational level: _____

Occupation: _____

Relationship status: _____

Current living arrangement: _____

I. POTENTIALLY RELEVANT HISTORICAL VARIABLES

(Personal or family history of illnesses, significant events, etc. that might give rise to dysfunctional beliefs)

II. TRIGGERS

A. Physical signs, sensations, perturbations (bodily signs and "symptoms" that evoke health concerns; e.g., headaches, bumps on the skin, lightheadedness)

Figure 8.1. Forms for conducting a functional assessment of health anxiety.

B. **External stimuli** (e.g., hospitals, new stories about illnesses)

C. **Intrusive thoughts, images, ideas, doubts** (e.g., images of dying, thoughts of the word "death", doubts about whether the doctor is correct)

III.   **COGNITIVE FEATURES (DYSFUNCTIONAL BELIEFS)**

A. **Misinterpretations of bodily signs and sensations** (e.g., "when I have a headache, it means I have a brain tumor", "When I notice a lump in my throat I think it means my airway is closing in")

B. **Feared consequences of exposure to external cues** (e.g., "If I read about cancer, I will think I have all the symptoms", "If I go to a hospital, I will get sick")

C. **Dysfunctional health-related beliefs** (e.g., concerning, general health/illness, vulnerability to sicknesses, beliefs about doctors and medicine, beliefs about death)

D. **Problems with intolerance of uncertainty concerning health** (e.g., "I can't stand not knowing for sure whether these symptoms are serious or not")

Figure 8.1. (continued)

IV. SAFETY-SEEKING BEHAVIORS

A. **Passive avoidance and its relationship to health anxiety** (e.g., avoids books and movies about illnesses to keep from noticing bodily sensations; avoids doctors because of the fear of being told he/she is really sick)

B. **Body monitoring and checking (describe in detail) and its relationship to health anxiety** (e.g., checking color and odor of stool, excessive monitoring of vital signs, repetitive checking the body for lumps, etc.)

C. **Reassurance-seeking and other forms of checking** (e.g., looking up symptoms in books or on the Internet, excessive doctor visits for tests/exams/consults, discussing symptoms with others or asking questions)

D. **Safety signals** (stimuli and behaviors associated with the absence of illness; e.g., sitting down when notices sensations, keeping bottle of water on hand)

Figure 8.1. (continued)

interview. The steps involved in a functional assessment of health anxiety are detailed next.

The therapist should aim to maximize the amount of information provided by the patient, as long as it is relevant to the patient's health-anxiety symptoms. Therefore, we recommend providing the patient with a clear goal for the first session, which can be introduced as follows:

> "We have a lot of work to do today. In particular, we need to figure out how we can work together to help you reduce the problems you are having with bodily symptoms. During the first few sessions, we are going to spend some time getting to know one another and exchanging important information. The way I like to think about this process is that *you* are the expert on your own symptoms, and *I* know a great deal about how to help people with unexplained medical symptoms and concerns. So, we need to put our heads together to figure out how best to treat your *particular* symptoms.
>
> I need to understand, as completely as I can, what your experience of your physical symptoms is like. The more you can teach me about what you struggle with, and how you try to deal with, the better we'll be able to develop a plan to help you. Ultimately, what I need is a list of the situations, physical symptoms, thoughts and attitudes associated with health concerns as well as a list of the strategies you use to manage these symptoms and cope with your health concerns. Does that make sense?"

Review of Recent Episodes

To gain additional information about the patient's experience and how he or she copes with the perceived health risk, the clinician can ask for a description of a typical day in the patient's life. "Play-by-play" descriptions of a few recent health anxiety episodes are also helpful and can be used to focus the assessment on a particular symptom the clinician is having difficulty understanding. The clinician should listen carefully and begin to consider how the patient's symptoms can be conceptualized within the biopsychosocial framework.

> "What I would like you to do is to walk me through a recent time when you experienced these symptoms, or a 'bad day' when you experienced lots of symptoms. I'll probably stop you here and there to ask you some questions to make sure that I understand what you were thinking, feeling, and doing at various points. It's very important that I understand every aspect of your problems. So, I want you to try to answer my questions in as much detail as you can. Again, I will probably ask you lots of questions to make sure that I understand exactly what you're dealing with. Sometimes you might think that certain details are not really important, perhaps because some of these symptoms have become almost automatic for you; but knowing this information will help me to understand your symptoms better and that's important if treatment is going to be effective. Okay?"

The patient is urged to walk through recent episodes and report any emotional, cognitive, and behavioral responses. What triggered the episode? How long did it last? What were the thoughts and feelings? What did he or she do? Was there any checking of medical records or other kinds of assurance-seeking? What happened next? How did the situation finally resolve itself and how did the patient feel afterward? The clinician should be sure to point out for the patient how physical or environmental triggers *evoke* a sense of threat, and how reassurance-seeking, risk-avoiding, safety-seeking, and checking behaviors are associated with the *reduction* of distress. For example:

> "That's a great example of how your interpretation of the stomach pain made you feel threatened. Then, when you looked up the symptoms of appendicitis on the internet and saw that you didn't have most of them, you said that you felt relieved. Do you see how checking the internet temporarily reduced your fear?"

The information obtained throughout the review of recent episodes provides clues about situations and bodily stimuli that evoke health anxiety, and how various coping strategies (i.e., safety-seeking behavior) are used to manage the associated distress. Importantly, the therapist must be willing to ask detailed and personal questions to obtain a full understanding of the symptoms. For example, detail discussions of genitals, sexual functioning, urine, and defecation are sometimes necessary to assess completely the patient's fears, cognitive distortions, and behavioral responses (e.g., "There is something wrong with my clitoris"). Even aspects of the patient's life that seem relatively benign, such as walking, eating, and sleeping, should be explored in depth to assess possible safety signals (e.g., walking very slowly because of a health concern).

The therapist should also inquire about the nature and purpose of all medical tests and treatments that have been conducted. What is the patient's understanding of any test results? What kinds of feedback have been obtained from doctors? And why has seemingly convincing feedback indicating good health not been accepted as such? If feedback has been ambiguous, the patient's thoughts about this are also critical to understand.

Historical Factors Potentially Giving Rise to Dysfunctional Beliefs

It might be useful to help the patient identify events that might have given rise to health anxiety – or at least to dysfunctional beliefs underlying excessive health worries. As discussed in Chapter 3, these events include personal experiences with illness, having close family members who suffered illnesses or death, and exposure to information about medical problems transmitted via the media. Questions to solicit this information include the following:

– "When did you first became concerned about your health?"
– "What was happening in your life at that time?"
– "Describe your physical health as you were growing up."
– "How did your parents (or caregivers) respond to you when you got sick as a child?"
– "What has occurred in your life that could have influenced the way you think about getting sick? For example, was there a disease outbreak? Did any friends become seriously ill?"

It is not problematic if no particular historical factors can be identified. Although identifying such factors can set a context for the possible development of health anxiety, treatment is aimed at reversing maintaining factors (as assessed below) rather than possible etiologic factors.

Identifying Triggers

The therapist should collect specific information about the full range of triggers that evoke health anxiety episodes. Triggers generally fall into three domains: (a) bodily signs and sensations, (b) external situations and stimuli, and (c) intrusive or worrisome thoughts and images.

There is no specific reason to begin with any particular domain (or to begin with triggers as opposed to cognitions or behavioral responses, for that matter), although health-anxious patients generally wish to focus on the physical domain first. Clinicians can expect to find themselves "going with what the patient gives you," which typically means working back and forth across these domains (as well as across triggers, cognitions, and behaviors) – and that is fine! *That* the information is accurately and thoroughly collected is more important than the *order* in which it is collected.

Assessing Bodily Signs, Sensations, and Perturbations

It is important to obtain a detailed account of the bodily signs, sensations, perturbations, and variations that have triggered episodes of health anxiety. These may be medically explained or unexplained, but are typically catastrophically misinterpreted in threatening ways. Questions to elicit this information include the following:
– "Which bodily symptoms are you concerned with?"
– "What kinds of symptoms set off concerns about your health?"

Signs and sensations might be internal, but can also be associated with the skin, hair, or products that are expelled from the body.

To ensure receiving a comprehensive list of feared bodily stimuli, Warwick (1995) recommends asking the patient to record for one week the incidence of each feared sensation, its severity, and the situation in which it occurred. A monitoring form for this use appears in Handout 8.1. For some individuals, the list of feared sensations will be circumscribed around a particular region of the body (e.g., head), organ system (e.g., digestive tract), or bodily disturbance (e.g., bowel function). For others, feared sensations might be highly diverse, in which case it might be helpful to narrow down the self-monitoring to the most frequent or problematic sensations.

Sometimes patients confuse their *interpretation* of the bodily sensation for its description. For example, the feeling that "my brain is swimming" might be a subjective interpretation of dizziness or vertigo. Similarly, a patient who recorded "my butt is on fire" as a feared symptom was taught to differentiate this rather subjective account from the actual sensation of "anal itching and soreness." The clinician can commence helping patients to think more objectively about their body sensations, which in turn will help to deescalate the strong negative affects associated with catastrophic descriptions. Only objective descriptions of the bodily sensations should be noted on the form in Handout 8.1.

Assessing External Situations and Stimuli

Specific information about the full range of external situations and stimuli that trigger preoccupation with health and illness should be identified. The most straightforward way to identify such triggers is to inquire about situations that are avoided or that evoke distressing health-related thoughts and concerns. As shown in earlier chapters, typical external triggers include hospitals, doctors, seeing or hearing about sick people, books, and news stories about illnesses as well as any stimuli that serve as reminders of health concerns. For some patients, being alone, or being "too far" from a hospital or medical center might be situational triggers. Finally, seeing oneself naked or giving oneself an examination (e.g., breast or testicular) can trigger health anxiety. Most patients are well aware of, and most forthcoming in describing, the stimuli that trigger heath preoccupation.

Assessing Intrusive Thoughts, Ideas, and Doubts

As described in earlier chapters, persistent unwanted negative thoughts, ideas, and doubts are common in health anxiety. For example, recurrent thoughts about diseases such as multiple sclerosis, AIDS, or cancer might be present. The patient might have persistent senseless doubts about having provided adequate detail when describing bodily symptoms to the doctor, or about having correctly heard the doctor's impressions and recommendations. Health-anxiety intrusions can also take different *forms*: Some patients describe complete thoughts or scenarios that are played out in their mind (e.g., going to the doctor, being tested, being told one is terminally ill, and dying); others report intrusions in the form of incomplete unsettling ideas or single distressing words (e.g., "melanoma"). Intrusive stimuli can also occur in the form of vivid images of unpleasant events (e.g., one's own funeral) or damage to internal organs (e.g., the image of a *perforated* colon).

Conceptually, such intrusions are regarded as normal stimuli that evoke inappropriate fear, uncertainty, and excessive behavioral responses because they are appraised as being significant and meaningful (e.g., "If I am thinking about this, then it must be true"). In this case, one aim of treatment would be to modify the maladaptive appraisals and weaken the connection between intrusions and anxiety. For this reason, it is important to gain a clear understanding of the nature and intensity of such stimuli. This can be done using questions such as, "What kinds of upsetting thoughts or images flash through your mind when you start to think about your health or illnesses?" Typically, intrusions are cued by some external or internal stimulus or bodily sensation. However, they might also occur spontaneously (e.g., from "out of the blue"). Therefore, it is a good idea to ask about the relationship of intrusive thoughts to the other kinds of triggers. If the patient cannot describe the specifics of these intrusions, a diary or monitoring form similar to that used to monitor physical sensations (e.g., Handout 8.1) can be developed for this purpose.

Identifying Dysfunctional Attitudes, Beliefs, and Misinterpretations

Clinical Interview Techniques

As described, the biopsychosocial model of health anxiety distinguishes between (a) the *stimuli* (internal and external) that *trigger* health preoccupations and (b) the *meaning* that patients give to these stimuli.

Derived from the cognitive theory of emotion (e.g., Beck, 1976), the model proposes that health anxiety results when health-relevant stimuli – which objectively pose little or no risk of harm – are catastrophically misperceived and misinterpreted as being highly threatening based on more general dysfunctional beliefs and attitudes about health and illness. Because treatment aims to modify such dysfunctional beliefs, attitudes, and misinterpretations, the therapist must be aware of such cognitions (i.e., those described in Chapter 2). Accordingly, Figure 8.1 includes space for recording the patient's particular catastrophic misinterpretations of bodily sensations, feared consequences of exposure to external cues, dysfunctional attitudes about health, illnesses in general and about doctors and medicine, and his or her difficulties with intolerance of uncertainty.

Examples of the types of questions that may be used to assess the presence of dysfunctional cognitions include the following:

– "*What do you think it means* that your doctors keep telling you that you do not have the medical diseases you are concerned about?"
– "*What do you tell yourself* when you notice the strange sensations in your stomach?"
– "*Why is it so bad for you* if you do not have a definitive medical explanation for your symptoms?"
– "*What might happen* if you were to give yourself a breast exam or spend time with a cancer patient?"

Note that these are open-ended questions that allow the clinician to observe mistaken, exaggerated, and otherwise dysfunctional attitudes and thought patterns.

The downward-arrow technique (Burns, 1980) is another useful way of identifying specific beliefs, such as catastrophic overestimates of the severity of bodily sensations, the perceived likelihood of illness or death, or the feared consequences of not having a definitive diagnosis. This method involves asking the patient to describe an episode of health anxiety, followed by the use of particular probe questions to identify the fundamental or "core" beliefs that evoke fear, avoidance, or safety behaviors (e.g., "If that were so, what would be the worst thing that could happen?"). The following transcript illustrates the use of the downward-arrow technique:

Therapist: You said that when you see pictures of your aunt who died of cancer last year it makes you worry about your own health. What in particular goes through your mind?

Patient: I tell myself that if my aunt had cancer, then it runs in our family and so I will probably get it, too.

Therapist: I know this seems like a strange question, but tell me: What would it be like for you if that really happened? What would be the worst part of having cancer?

Patient: Well, she had breast cancer, so I probably wouldn't get that. But I would get something equally as devastating and probably die also.

Therapist: I see. Again, this may seem like a strange question, but what do you think would be the worst part of dying?

Patient: I focus on how terrible it would be for my family. I am the breadwinner, and to think about my wife and kids having to survive on their own without me makes me very, very anxious and depressed.

Therapist: Okay. Can you tell me how you think they would make it? Would they even survive?

Patient: I don't know. I don't think they would survive. And it would all be my fault.

Therapist: It's very helpful to know how you feel about all of that. Thank you for explaining it to me.

Let's consider a few points from this exchange. Clearly, the patient overestimates the probability and severity of becoming ill. Also, whereas many patients fear death because of what it means for him- or herself, this individual expressed fears of what would happen to *significant others* if he died. This highlights the importance of conducting a thorough assessment of cognitions – not just assuming what the patient *probably* fears. Observe also that at this point the therapist does not question or challenge the patient's clearly unrealistic assumptions; instead, the focus is on developing rapport and collecting information about the cognitive basis of the health anxiety.

Not all patients articulate the kinds of explicit fears of disastrous consequences illustrated above. Some report that external or internal cues evoke only a vague sense that "something is wrong." The downward-arrow method often reveals that the underlying catastrophic beliefs of such individuals are that their anxiety or distress will persist indefinitely, spiral toward unmanageable levels, or lead to some harmful medical condition (e.g., "I will have a breakdown"). Research suggests that it is important to help patients with anxiety problems clarify the consequences they fear, even if these consist merely of anxiety (or some bodily symptom or sensation) persisting indefinitely – fears that can be explicitly disconfirmed during treatment (Foa, Abramowitz, Franklin, & Kozak, 1999).

The patient's difficulty with intolerance of uncertainty is also an important cognitive target of functional assessment. What are the ambiguous situations and stimuli (triggers) for which the patient desires certainty and reassurance? What are the patient's concerns relevant to not having a guarantee of good health, or of a particular diagnosis or result?

Self-Report Questionnaires Assessing Cognitions

A number of self-report questionnaires exist to assess the sorts of dysfunctional cognitions observed in health anxiety, some of which are described in Chapter 6. We recommend incorporating data from such instruments into the functional assessment in order to augment (and corroborate) information collected via clinical interview. Because they have been carefully developed and examined empirically, self-report measures of cognitive phenomena have a number of advantages. First, as it were they do the question-asking for the clinician and in an objective and standardized manner. Second, they are known to be comprehensive in their scope, reliable, and valid.

The following measures are useful for assessing beliefs in health-anxious patients:
– The SHAI (Salkovskis et al., 2002, described in Chapter 6) consists of two factors assessing (a) the perceived likelihood of becoming seriously ill ("illness likelihood"), and (b) the perceived negative consequences of being seriously ill ("negative consequences"). The SHAI is reprinted in Salkovskis et al. (2002).
– The Anxiety Sensitivity Index – 3rd revision (ASI-3; Taylor et al., 2007) is an 18-item questionnaire that assesses anxiety sensitivity (AS); the fear of arousal-related body sensations (e.g., racing heart, dizziness) based on beliefs that these sensations have adverse consequences such as death, insanity, or social rejection (Reiss & McNally, 1985). As discussed in Chapter 6, the physical concerns factor of the ASI-3 contains the items most relevant to health anxiety.
– The Cognitions about Body and Health Questionnaire (CBHQ; Rief et al; 1998), also described in Chapter 6, contains five factors, three of which assess cognitions. The first factor pertains to catastrophic interpretations of bodily complaints and includes 14 items, such as "A healthy body doesn't cause complaints." The second factor pertains to autonomic sensations and contains four items, including, "I hate to be too hot or too cold." The third factor pertains to beliefs and attitudes about bodily weakness and contains six items, such as "I am not as healthy as most of my friends and acquaintances."
– The Intolerance of Uncertainty Scale (IUS; Freeston et al., 1994) includes 27 items relating to the idea that uncertainty is unacceptable, reflects badly on the person, and leads to frustration and stress, and the inability to take action. Sample items include "Uncertainty makes life intolerable" and "It frustrates me not having all the information I need." The measure is reprinted in Buhr and Dugas (2002).

– The Multidimensional Fear of Death Scale (Neimeyer & Moore, 1994) is a 42-item instrument containing eight factors, including (a) fear of the dying process (concerns regarding a painful or violent death), (b) fear of the dead, (c) fear of being destroyed, such as concerns about dissection or cremation, (d) fear for significant others (concerns about the impact of one's own death on others and vice versa, (e) fear of the unknown, including fear of nonexistence, (f) fear of conscious death, including concerns about falsely been declared dead, (g) fear for the body after death, and (h) fear of premature death. The scale is published in Neimeyer (1994).

Although the clinician may wish to compute total scores for each of the measures (or their subscales), reviewing particular items that have been endorsed by the patient can provide a better means of discussing specific dysfunctional cognitions. For example, the patient can be asked to give details about specific beliefs they hold as well as to talk further about where these attitudes may have originated ("Where do you think you got the idea that it hurts to be dead?"). Thus, the total score obtained on the measure might be less clinically useful than the individual item responses.

Identifying Maladaptive Behaviors

It is essential that the functional analysis include a comprehensive assessment of overt and covert safety behaviors and safety signals since these responses serve to maintain health anxiety and must be targeted in treatment. *Safety behaviors* are things the person does to avert perceived danger, such as avoidance, checking, and reassurance-seeking. *Safety signals* are stimuli that the person associates with the absence of feared outcomes, such as aspirin or a blood pressure cuff that are kept on hand, even if they are not used. Safety signals and safety behaviors arise from the dysfunctional beliefs, attitudes, and perceptions discussed in the preceding section. For example, avoiding exercise might be motivated by the belief that one's body is weak and not able to tolerate stress. Urges to check with doctors for reassurance about a feared body sensation are often motivated by catastrophic misinterpretations of the sensations and by intolerance of even acceptable levels of uncertainty. Compulsive checking is typically motivated by the belief that a serious medical illness is present and must be identified as otherwise it will be too late. More subtle safety behaviors and signals show a similar link to dysfunctional beliefs, such as sleeping without covers because of the possibility of suffocating, and wearing sunglasses at all times because of an exaggerated fear of exposure to ultraviolet light.

As the examples above illustrate, the patterns of thinking and behavior in health anxiety are meaningful and, to the patient, internally consistent (who *wouldn't* regularly check their body if they truly believed they had a serious disease that could kill them at any time!). Thus, from within the context of the patient's thinking, the therapist can often anticipate what safety-seeking behavior is used in a given situation (a rhetorical move that may increase the patient's confidence and help build rapport).

Avoidance, reassurance-seeking, checking, and other safety-seeking strategies are targeted in treatment not only because they are wasteful and interfere with daily functioning, but because they prevent extinction of health-related anxiety and hinder the correction of catastrophic and otherwise dysfunctional beliefs that maintain health anxiety. Clinicians should inquire about how the patient interprets the outcome of their safety behaviors and safety signals. Often, the lack of a disastrous outcome is perceived as a "near miss," implying that safety-seeking *prevented* the harm (e.g., "If I were to use a pillow when I sleep, my head would be propped up higher than my heart so my brain would not get enough blood and I would die."). Accordingly, to reduce health anxiety, these maladaptive and irrational behaviors must be faded out during therapy (i.e., via response prevention techniques as described in Chapter 12).

It is unusual for patients to spontaneously describe their full array of safety-seeking behaviors and safety signals during the functional assessment. Some avoidance, checking, reassurance-seeking, and other covert strategies might be so subtle or so routine that they are not recognized as problematic. To facilitate reporting of these covert and surreptitious responses, the therapist should introduce the concepts of safety-seeking and reliance on safety signals as "protective responses" to health concerns. Patients can be given examples of these strategies and encouraged throughout assessment and treatment to report any behaviors or mental strategies performed with the intent of alleviating such distress. Self-report instruments can also be of help in this regard and are discussed later in this section. Excellent interview questions include:

– "What (else) do you do when you notice this symptom?"
– "When you become concerned that you are ill, how do you manage this?"
– "What do you do to prevent yourself from becoming sick?"

Passive Avoidance

Passive avoidance, defined as the deliberate failure to engage in a low-risk activity, can often be predicted from knowledge of health anxiety cues (external and internal) and catastrophic beliefs. For example, the fear of rabies or Lyme disease might lead to avoidance of certain animals or outdoor situations; preoccupation with thoughts about dying of cancer might lead to avoidance of media stories about this topic; the fear of having a blood disease can lead to avoidance of blood tests that might confirm the fear (although other health-anxious individuals might engage in excessive blood-testing to rule out the disease); the fear that one has weak lungs might lead to excessive behavior aimed at avoiding cigarette smoke. A few good ways to assess avoidance is to ask: "What kinds of things do you not do because of your concerns about _____?"; and "What situations do you routinely avoid?" It is also necessary to inquire about the cognitive basis of avoidance. A good way to access this information is to inquire about what might happen if the situation or trigger could not be avoided.

Avoidance patterns are highly patient-specific, but often include staying away from hospitals and avoiding people with certain illnesses or diseases, funerals, and cemeteries. Patients might also avoid health- or disease-related movies, TV shows, news articles, and other information in the media. Discussions of diseases, death, and dying might also be avoided, as might physical exertion or any other activity believed to overly "stress the body." Finally, whereas some health-anxious patients engage in excessive checking and doctor-shopping (see the upcoming sections on checking and reassurance-seeking), others avoid these activities altogether for fear that the presence of an illness will be confirmed.

Body-Checking

The clinician should obtain information about the frequency, duration, and method of body-checking as well as the deployment of attention to one's body. Body-checking can be extensive and may include a check of the body's general condition or of the structure and function of a particular body part that causes immediate concern. For example, patients might poke and prod at bumps or blemishes on their skin, probe the inside of bodily orifices digitally or with tools (e.g., a dentist's mirror), use devices to measure bodily signs (temperature, blood pressure, auditory functioning), and try to smell certain areas of the body. We have evaluated patients who use their digital camera to obtain pictures or video of areas that are otherwise difficult to inspect (e.g., the genitals and anus). Bodily fluids and waste might also be checked for "normalcy," as in making sure that urine or feces "smell right." Body-checking sometimes involves assistance from others – and this is important to assess as well: Does the patient question relatives about whether they appear normal (e.g., "Do I look like I have scoliosis?") or ask their partner to examine less accessible areas of the body?

Clinicians should also ask for a complete description of each checking behavior, including a demonstration (when practical), if the description is unclear. Some body-checking might be embarrassing to describe (e.g., probing orifices, checking the genitals). If this appears to be the case, the therapist should inquire in an understanding yet straightforward way; for example:

> "I've worked with people who, like you, were concerned about deformities, pain, or damage to their genitals. Many of them would spend a great deal of time checking themselves by touching the area or probing with their fingers. I know it's difficult to talk about, but is this something you have been doing? Would you feel comfortable describing this for me?"

Clinicians should also assess the functional relationship between body-checking and health anxiety. What purpose does it serve the patient? What might happen were a check not to be performed? Recall that, in general, checking (bodily or otherwise) is a deliberate attempt to *escape* from anxiety or *prevent* a feared consequence. Inquiry might also include questions such as "How do you feel after you have checked yourself?" and "How does this sort of checking keep you safe?" Answers to these questions will help the clinician understand the basis for the behavior, which is typically a distorted belief or assumption that can be challenged later in therapy (e.g., "If I don't check my testicles everyday I might not notice that I have testicular cancer until it is too late . . ."). Of course, as we have described, body-checking is often reinforced by immediate anxiety reduction. Some body-checking, however, leads to increased distress, such as the man in the above example who manipulated his testicles to the point that his scrotum became sore. This, in turn, he took as a possible sign of cancer.

Reassurance Seeking via Other Forms of Compulsive Checking

Other forms of checking that serve a reassurance-seeking function are typically present, such as repeated doctor visits for exams and consultations regarding the same "symptoms"; repeatedly asking health professionals and relatives for their opinions about the same (or similar) health issues; reviewing lab and test results and medical reports; and searching medical texts and internet sites for information about diseases. As with body-checking, the nature, intensity, frequency, and duration of such behaviors should be specified during the functional assessment. The patient should be told it is quite routine for the scope of checking to be extensive, and that this will not necessarily attenuate treatment outcome (Warwick, 1995). As with body-checking, it is important to know whether others are involved in reassurance-seeking so that such individuals can be helped to refrain from providing such "help." During the assessment, the therapist can also point out possible ways in which checking behaviors are maladaptive, i.e., preventing the natural decline of anxiety and leading to greater preoccupation with the bodily sensations of concern.

Questions that help in the assessment of reassurance-seeking include the following:

- How often do you read about your [insert the feared illness, symptoms]?
- How do you go about collecting information about your [insert the feared symptoms/disease]?
- Do you ever look your symptoms up in medical textbooks?
- How is your relationship with doctors? Do you ask them lots of questions over and over?
- Tell me about the tests you've completed to rule out or get a better explanation for [insert the disease/symptoms].
- What kinds of checking behaviors do you have that relate to your symptoms?
- Are there other things you do to get reassurance that you do/do not have [insert specific illness]?
- Why do you feel like you need to check with the doctor or get this reassurance?
- What would it be like for you if you failed to check or get reassurance? What would you be worried about?

Miscellaneous Overt and Covert Safety-Seeking Behaviors and Signals

Some safety-seeking behaviors and signals are brief or unobtrusive, or they are integrated within the person's daily routine: This inaccessibility makes them a challenge to recognize. Moreover, the list of possible safety signals is limitless and highly patient-specific. Examples include the use of a cane, getting at least 8 hours of sleep every night, carrying a cell phone, medication, or Medic Alert bracelet at all times, and always remaining within easy access to a medical facility. Patients themselves sometimes do not recognize such safety signals as part of their problem, especially if these behaviors have become routine or could be justified in other ways.

For example, one woman we evaluated carried in her purse a bright red card with the names and telephone numbers of 10 relatives to contact in case she suffered a stroke. She justified this by saying that it was a "good idea" since she was getting older (she was only 48 years old). Another patient who required himself to have 8 hours of sleep per night rationalized that such behavior is a "normal part of a healthy lifestyle." While true, these rationalizations miss the point entirely: These patients were not as interested in being healthy as they were in using these behaviors to prevent some feared health-related consequence, the likelihood of which was grossly overestimated. Thus, the safety signal prevented the patients from recognizing the senselessness of their fears. Instead, nonoccurrences of the feared event were interpreted as "near misses" averted by the safety behavior or signal ("If I didn't sleep at least 8 hours, my immune system would be weakened and I would get very ill").

Patients might invest a great deal of time and money in safety signals, such as one individual who purchased numerous pieces of transportable medical equipment (e.g., portable oxygen tank, portable defibrillator) and convinced his parents to get training in CPR so that even when he was on vacation with his family, he would feel safe. The individual and his parents traveled several hundred miles to our center for treatment, arriving in a van packed with medical equipment and boxes of medical records – "just in case something terrible happened while on the road away from the doctor."

Because safety cues produce short-term anxiety reduction, yet maintain health anxiety in the long-term (e.g., they reinforce dysfunctional beliefs about helplessness and personal vulnerability to medical conditions; Taylor & Asmundson, 2004), they must be identified and targeted for reduction during therapy. In other words, patients must come to no longer view this "insurance" as vital to maintaining their health. Some questions to help elucidate additional safety behaviors and signals are:

- "Are there things you do to protect yourself from [specify disease or condition]?"
- "Are there things you do to make yourself feel more comfortable or to reduce symptoms?"
- "Do you carry anything with you to help you feel safe about your health?"
- "What precautions do you take so that you are prepared if you should have a medical emergency (such as a cell phone, safe person, certain medications, remaining close to hospitals/medical centers)?"

Self-Report Inventories

Some of the self-report instruments described in earlier sections contain items that assess the maladaptive behavioral responses described in this section.

- The CBHQ (Rief et al., 1998) contains two factors addressing behaviors related to health anxiety. Items on the "Intolerance of Bodily Complaints" factor inquire about possible checking and reassurance-seeking activities (e.g., "I consult a doctor as soon as possible when I have bodily complaints"). The "Health Habits" factor contains three items that pertain to (a) taking excessive care to live healthfully, (b) making sure to eat healthy, and (c) getting fresh air when feeling physically weak. Of course, such habits can contribute to good health. Yet individuals with health anxiety might engage in such behaviors excessively.
- The IAS (Kellner, 1986, 1987) contains two subscales that specifically inquire about maladaptive health-anxious behavior. The "Health Habits" subscale is

similar to the CBHQ's subscale of the same name and includes items such as "Do you avoid foods which may not be healthy?" The "Treatment Experience" subscale contains questions concerning both the frequency and the reasons for doctor visits.

- The Texas Safety Maneuver Scale (TSMS; Kamphuis & Telch, 1998), designed to assess safety behaviors among individuals with panic disorder and agoraphobia, is also recommended for use with health-anxious patients. The TSMS contains 50 items in self-report format. Each item describes a more-or-less subtle within-situation safety behavior or safety signal that patients might employ to manage anxiety or panic. Examples include "avoiding vigorous exercise," "avoiding alcohol," and "using meditation or yoga." The respondent places a check mark in the appropriate column corresponding to how often he or she uses the particular strategy to manage anxiety or panic. Responses include *Never, Rarely, Sometimes, Usually,* and *Always.* Six subscales of safety maneuvers are assessed, including (a) agoraphobic avoidance, (b) relaxation techniques, (c) stress avoidance, (d) somatic avoidance, (e) distraction techniques, and (f) escape. To ensure that the safety behavior is in fact related to anxiety, a sixth column is present for respondents to indicate whether they use the strategy, albeit not to manage anxiety. As described above, many of the TSMS items are applicable to health-anxious patients, so this measure can provide valuable assessment information. There are also four rows for "other" behaviors in which the respondent can enter any safety maneuvers not mentioned in the scale items. The TSMS requires between 5–10 minutes to complete, and it possesses good to excellent reliability and validity (Kamphuis & Telch, 1998). The TSMS is reprinted in Antony, Orsillo, and Roemer (2001).

Self-Monitoring

During the functional assessment, the patient should be introduced to self-monitoring. Asking patients to keep a log of their symptoms is a standard procedure in virtually all forms of cognitive-behavioral therapy. Self-monitoring involves recording instances of bodily sensations, level of distress and anxiety, anxious thinking, and behavioral responses *as they occur in real time.* It is an important tool since it furnishes the patient and clinician with precise information about the situational cues, frequency, intensity, and duration of these symptoms.

When patients attempt to retrospectively recall past episodes of health anxiety, they often inflate estimates of the intensity frequency and duration of their symptoms. This exaggeration contributes to the vicious cycle of illness worry and further misattribution of bodily sensations. To the degree that ongoing self-monitoring yields more accurate reporting and more objective self-awareness, it is a therapeutic tool. Exaggerated and negative affect-laden self-statements such as "I feel horrible – this is the worst it's ever been – I'm getting sicker and sicker!" are replaced with more adaptive self-statements such as "My distress level is 6 out of 10 – I'm experiencing dizziness and feelings of fatigue – I'm telling myself that I have a brain tumor." In other words, increasing objective self-awareness reduces negative affect.

Episodes of feared body sensations and health anxiety are recorded on the Health Concerns Log form shown in Handout 8.2 (a packet of several duplicated forms is given to the patient, and each episode is recorded on a separate form). Records are to be completed as soon as possible during or after an episode of feared symptoms or health anxiety, and are therefore to be carried on one's person. In addition, average daily levels of general anxiety, depression, and body activity are monitored using the Daily Monitoring Form shown in Handout 8.3. This form is completed at the end of each day.

Clinicians can instruct patients on how to use these forms by having them record actual recent examples. Because it is a novel and somewhat arduous task, patients might have difficulty adhering to self-monitoring; sometimes noncompliance stems from misunderstandings or a lack of perceived credibility in self-monitoring. Noncompliance might also be result from anticipation of *more* anxiety as a result of monitoring. It is therefore essential to acknowledge that the exercise requires substantial effort. Nevertheless, it is an important component of treatment: A cogent rationale for self-monitoring should be presented that underscores the need for accurate and timely recording of symptoms:

> "I realize that doing self-monitoring might seem demanding. After all, you probably have never done this kind of exercise before. Let me give you three reasons why self-monitoring is an important part of treatment. First, it will give us accurate information about the problems you are having with bodily sensations. In other words, it will tell us about the various triggers and thoughts that evoke concerns about your health and urges to check, seek assurances, or use other maladaptive coping strategies. Second, it will help us assess your improvement. In other words, toward the end of therapy we can look back and see how much less often and how much less intense your symptoms and illness concerns have become. Finally, self-monitoring can actually help you reduce your illness concerns by helping you to face these symptoms more objectively. So, I encourage you to do an honest job, and I will be looking forward to seeing your completed forms at the beginning of the next session. In fact, the first thing we will do next time will be to review your forms together. They will be an important part of treatment."

When examining the completed Daily Monitoring and Health Concern forms, the clinician should stop to ask the patient to review a few exemplary episodes in greater detail. Critical information for the clinician to acquire includes how health anxiety is triggered (e.g., "What is it about having these symptoms/hearing about someone with rabies that made you concerned?"), what situations are avoided (e.g., "Do you always avoid watching the Discovery Health Channel?"), and why ("What do you think might happen if you watched a show about children with brain tumors?"). Also, how does the patient respond to health anxiety ("What else, besides constantly clearing your throat, do you do to reduce your concerns about your airways becoming restricted?"). Self-monitoring aids in the clarification of internally consistent associations between the patient's triggers, cognitions, and maladaptive behaviors. These associations should be clear to the therapist, and if not, further examples should be reviewed until they are clear. Situations and thoughts that trigger distress and safety behaviors should be considered for inclusion as exposure exercises (see Chapter 12).

Practical Issues

Whereas some patients with health anxiety evince straightforward complaints, most present with a complex symptom pattern. Yet the internal and external triggers, cognitions, and behavioral responses are highly patient-specific, and successful treatment depends upon implementing treatment procedures dictated by the patient's specific symptom presentation. In the next chapter, we take a look at how the information collected during the functional assessment is used to generate a case conceptualization and treatment plan. Synthesizing the case conceptualization also provides opportunities to educate the patient and continue the process of socializing him or her to the biopsychosocial model.

9

Case Formulation and Treatment Planning

As described in the previous chapter, functional assessment is an ongoing process that involves gathering information about symptoms and verifying this information with the patient. Once the clinician has assessed the parameters outlined in Chapter 8, he or she can construct an individualized model of the patient's specific health-anxiety symptoms. Such *case formulation* forms a template or framework for understanding the problem comprising the relevant physiologic, cognitive, and behavioral variables, along with the processes that link these phenomena and serve to maintain health anxiety. The conceptualization also serves as a roadmap for treatment and must therefore be credible to the patient. If the individualized model does not make sense to the patient – or if it does not explain the patient's experience – he or she cannot be expected to completely buy into therapy.

This chapter outlines the case-formulation approach to health anxiety and illustrates the process of developing an individualized formulation and treatment plan. It is advantageous to impart a collaborative ownership of this formulation and plan. Therefore, sketching the conceptual model for the patient to see (e.g., on a whiteboard) and inviting his or her input are recommended in order to convey transparency and openness – as opposed to secretiveness – about this process. This is likely to foster acceptance of the model and the recommended treatment strategies.

Overview of Case Formulation

Case formulation is a conceptually driven roadmap of an individual patient's difficulties including the factors contributing to the development and maintenance of the problem. Although the interplay of directly observable and self-reported cognitive, physiological (e.g., body sensations), emotional, and behavioral factors are important aspects of the formulation, it also incorporates empirically based inferences about underlying psychological processes and constructs that are not immediately observable. Case formulation also provides the basis for deriving a treatment plan that incorporates specific techniques to target particular symptoms as well as reverse key underlying maintenance processes. Thus, it is critical to effective treatment planning and successful therapy outcome: The alternative would be an ill-defined, unplanned, or ad-hoc approach to therapy.

Taking the time to carefully build a case formulation has a number of advantages over less directive approaches to treatment planning (Bieling & Kuyken, 2003): First, case formulation makes use of operationally defined terms to describe psychopathological processes. Second, consistent with a hypothesis-testing approach, the formulation is constantly evaluated and updated as additional information about the patient comes to light (iterative approach). Third, the formulation makes clear how particular treatment techniques can be used to ameliorate various aspects of the problem, and it therefore provides the basis for a coherent treatment rationale. Fourth, case formulation and the respective treatment planning process are consistent with the scientist-practitioner model that draws on empirical knowledge of psychopathology and treatment to inform clinical decision-making. That is, the treatment techniques suggested by the formulation are theoretically consistent and empirically supported.

We should also differentiate the case-formulation approach from *treatment manuals*. Although the case-formulation template is necessarily guided by a particular theoretical model – in this case, the biopsychosocial model outlined in earlier chapters – the derivation of a patient-specific formulation is driven by the patient's idiosyncratic symptoms as opposed to a one-size-fits-all therapy manual. Successful case formulation requires that the therapist use his or her own clinical judgment and knowledge of the relevant psychopathology to synthesize information gathered from sources such as self-report inventories and the functional assessment. Similarly, the clinician draws up a treatment plan as suggested by the case formulation that he or she generates – as opposed to using a prescripted session-by-session intervention typically found in therapy manuals. In short, case formulation achieves a balance in which – from within an empirically consistent theoretical and conceptual framework – the clinician uses his or her own expertise and judgment to understand and adopt a treatment plan expressly for the patient's particular symptom presentation.

Biopsychosocial Case Formulation

The biopsychosocial case-formulation framework for health anxiety presented in this chapter provides a clear structural template for mapping out the relevant physiological, cognitive, affective, and behavioral components of health anxiety,

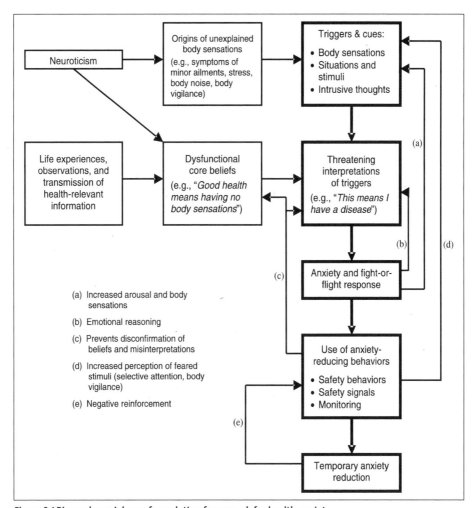

Figure 9.1 Biopsychosocial case-formulation framework for health anxiety.

as well as the psychological processes that link these components and contribute to the development and persistence of the problem. This allows the clinician to systematically choose interventions suggested by the conceptualization. The template shown in Figure 9.1 appears in a "top-to-bottom" flowchart to enhance its utility. By clearly depicting the various steps, this format is intuitive and easy on the eyes. We have in part adopted Boschen and Oei's (in press) exemplary framework for anxiety disorders for our own approach to case formulation in health anxiety.

The top-to-bottom sequence of boxes and arrows (shown in **bold**) by and large describes a chain of events in which a health-anxious person confronted with triggers interprets them as threatening, leading to anxiety, and who then engages in anxiety-reducing behavior. The arrows leading upward represent maintenance factors, such as selective attention, that occur as consequences of anxiety, anxiety-reducing behavior, and successful anxiety reduction. These maintenance processes complete vicious cycles that perpetuate health anxiety. Boxes to the left of the **bolded** column represent more or less distal factors giving rise to medically unexplained body sensations and the increased perception and misinterpretation of these phenomena. Flow-chart depictions of case formulations have long been considered effective aids in behavioral and cognitive-behavioral treatments and in the training of clinicians to use these types of interventions (e.g., Craighead et al., 1979).

Components of Case Formulation

In this section we explain the structure and function of each component of the biopsychosocial case formulation for health anxiety as depicted in Figure 9.1. Since detailed discussions of most of these components appear in earlier chapters, we present only basic descriptions here; rather, we prefer to highlight how each component is linked to other components of the formulation, and the interventions that can be directed at each component.

Triggers and Cues

Specific health-anxiety triggers vary from patient to patient and typically include bodily signs and sensations, external situations and stimuli, and intrusive thoughts and images. These stimuli themselves are not directly targeted by any particular cognitive behavioral intervention. They are ubiquitous, and the aim of treatment is to help the patient respond to them in healthy ways. These stimuli, however, are presented during exposure therapy with the aim of reducing the anxiety they elicit. It is therefore essential to identify the precise triggers and cues that activate the patient's health-anxiety symptoms.

Origins of Unexplained Body Sensations

The bodily sensations that trigger health anxiety are generally innocuous and universal occurrences that are part of normal human experience – most likely harmless "body noise" or perhaps the symptoms of minor medical ailments that do not pose significant threat – and that most people simply overlook (e.g., a lingering cough, cold, or allergic reaction). The biopsychosocial model proposes that such experiences can be intensified by stress, which escalates body noise by increasing the level of physiological arousal. Because the processes in this component of the formulation are generally normal and nonthreatening, they are not directly addressed by any treatment procedures. However, an important effect of treatment techniques that reduce anxiety is that they also result in a reduction of stress and hypervigilance – leading to reductions in body noise and reported "symptoms."

Threatening Automatic Thoughts and Interpretations

The biopsychosocial model draws on the cognitive theory of emotion (e.g., Beck, 1976), which posits that automatic thoughts and misinterpretations of stimuli – not the stimuli themselves – provoke distress. In the case of health anxiety, it is threatening thoughts and interpretations of health-relevant situations and stimuli (e.g., body sensations) that lead to anxiousness. Thus, an important aim of treatment is to help the individual identify misinterpretations and overly catastrophic thoughts, and to replace them with more realistic beliefs and interpretations. Cognitive therapy is a set of techniques designed to reduce emotional distress by modifying automatic thoughts (Beck & Emery, 1985). Exposure therapy also fosters the correction of mistaken cognitions through the provision of corrective information and experiential learning.

Dysfunctional Core Beliefs

Cognitive models (e.g., Beck, 1976) also posit the presence of pan-situational dysfunctional core beliefs that give rise to automatic thoughts and misinterpretations when a particular situation or when certain stimuli are present; for example, the core belief that good health is associated with the absence of body sensations. This belief becomes activated if the person experiences sharp unexplained chest pain, and it leads to a misinterpretation of the body sensation as perhaps indicating a severe heart problem. Both cognitive therapy and exposure techniques have effects on core beliefs by allowing the individual to consider verbal and experiential evidence that disconfirms such convictions. Psychoeducation is also aimed at correcting core beliefs through a more didactic approach.

Neuroticism

Neuroticism (or negative temperament), which is a personality variable characterized by the tendency to experience negative emotions and overreact to stress (Watson & Clark, 1984), is highly correlated with hypochondriasis and health anxiety (e.g., Cox et al., 2000; Ferguson, 2000; Noyes, Happel, & Yagla, 1999; Noyes et al., 2005; Pennebaker & Watson, 1991). Accordingly, in the bio-psychosocial case formulation, neuroticism is viewed as making one vulnerable to an increase in life stress, bodily noise (e.g., associated with physiologic arous-al), and hypervigilance. Moreover, individuals high in neuroticism are prone to holding dysfunctional core beliefs that lead to interpreting innocuous bodily sensations as signs of serious illness (Barsky et al., 2001; Ferguson et al., 2000). No cognitive-behavioral interventions directly target neuroticism; nevertheless, scores on measures of this trait may change with successful treatment. Such changes occur gradually and often as an indirect result of targeting other com-ponents of the formulation.

Life Experiences, Observations, and Transmission of Health-Relevant Information

Dysfunctional core beliefs concerning health and illness can be learned via a number of sources (e.g, Rachman, 1977). Most prominent among these for the purposes of the case formulation are
a) Past personal experiences with illness,
b) Observing loved ones suffer with illnesses, and
c) The transmission of information about health and illness through sources such as the authority figures (e.g., parents, teachers) and the media.

Obviously, treatment cannot change one's past experiences; however, psycho-education includes the presentation of didactic information to correct core be-liefs and misconceptions based on previous experiences and observations. Sim-ilarly, cognitive therapy and exposure techniques use Socratic dialog and "col-laborative discovery" as well as experiential evidence to challenge and undo the effects of such early experiences.

Anxiety and the Fight-or-Flight Response

Anxiety is viewed as an automatic response arising directly from threatening appraisals and misinterpretations of internal and external health-relevant stim-uli. It is comprised of three response systems: physiologic, cognitive, and behav-ioral, each of which plays an important role in the maintenance of health anx-iety (depicted in Figure 9.1):
– First, anxiety is associated with an immediate and perceptible increase in

physiologic arousal (i.e., the fight-or-flight response), which in turn produces an intensification of (uncomfortable) bodily sensations. This is represented by arrow "a" leading back up to triggers and cues.
– Second, the feeling of anxiety often triggers emotional reasoning, a cognitive error in which it is assumed that the experience of feeling anxious implies the presence of danger (i.e., "If I am anxious, there must be danger"), thus maintaining threatening thinking as represented by the arrow leading up to threatening automatic thoughts and interpretations. This is indicated by arrow "b."
– Third, because of its aversive nature, anxiety motivates the individual to behave in specific ways to reduce anxiety – although these behaviors ironically make the problem worse, as we discuss further below.

Anxiety is, of course, an adaptive response to perceived threat serving to motivate us to act to protect ourselves. As aversive as the physiologic effects of anxiety might *seem*, they are in fact harmless. Thus, the goal of eliminating anxiety and its physiologic correlates altogether is unrealistic and indeed undesirable. The reader should note that, for this reason, we advise against the use of techniques such as muscle relaxation, deep breathing, and biofeedback, which are sometimes used for directly reducing in-situation anxious arousal. We view the use of such techniques as implicitly (or explicitly) *perpetuating* the dysfunctional belief that anxious arousal is dangerous and therefore something to be avoided or minimized. Rather, a key element of treatment for health anxiety involves learning to tolerate and accept (as opposed to resist or reduce) anxious arousal. Indeed, exposure therapy – a core element in treatment – involves the purposeful *evocation* of anxiety in order that the patient can learn that the physiologic arousal, associated cognitions, and behavioral urges subside on their own and without the need for anxiety-reducing (safety-seeking) behavior.

Use of Anxiety-Reducing Behavior

When faced with an actual threat, human beings use highly adaptive escape and avoidance behaviors to get the organism to safety. In health anxiety, however, such safety-seeking behaviors are used to excess. Indeed, there is no objective threat present, making such behaviors completely superfluous. Not only can they be costly (e.g., doctor visits), potentially dangerous (e.g., invasive medical tests), and functionally interfering (e.g., spending hours checking the internet), they serve to maintain health anxiety in several ways as we discuss further below.

The choice of anxiety-reducing behavior is influenced by the nature of the anxiety-provoking trigger and the cognitive basis of the anxiety (i.e., core beliefs and automatic thoughts). Where the feared stimulus is an object or situation perceived as either a cause or a reminder of symptoms and illness (e.g., caffeine, administering a self-breast exam, a news program about illnesses), the simplest means of reducing anxiety is to withdraw from or avoid the stimulus. In the case of feared body sensations, the individual might act to minimize their frequency, intensity, or duration if he or she believes that not doing so could have serious consequences. Avoiding exercise, stimulants, and overexcitement are examples of such behaviors. Where the feared stimulus is an intrusive thought or doubt about illnesses (or whether one is present), the mechanism to reduce anxiety is often one of reassurance-seeking, such as by asking others for information, checking sources such as the internet, and checking one's own body for signs. Another response to disturbing health-related doubts and images is cognitive avoidance, in which the person attempts simply to suppress such thoughts.

In contrast to safety behaviors, which function as an escape from anxiety, *safety signals* are stimuli that have become associated with the perception that the feared medical problem is less likely. For example, drinking water may be a safety behavior used to reduce anxiety about choking or smothering. On the other hand, always carrying a bottle of water on one's person is a behavior aimed at *perpetuating* the safety signal of the water's presence – a stimulus that has become associated with anxiety reduction. Other examples of safety signals include the presence of a "safe person," cell phone, Medicaid bracelet, blood pressure cuff, knowledge of the location of the nearest hospital, etc.

In the case formulation, safety behaviors are elicited by the experience of increased anxiety. Elevated anxiety serves as a discriminative stimulus to indicate that certain behaviors are followed by anxiety reduction. Safety signals represent preemptive strikes against anxiety and feared medical problems presumed to be more likely in the absence of the safety signal. Both types of response, however, result in similar effects, as depicted in Figure 9.1.

The links to dysfunctional core beliefs and threatening automatic thoughts (arrow "c") represent the ways in which anxiety-reducing behaviors prevent the correction of these distorted cognitions. Avoidance of exercise, for example, robs the individual of the opportunity to correct faulty beliefs about the danger of physical exertion. Similarly, if a water bottle is omnipresent, the individual can never learn that feared throat sensations would not have led to choking after all. Another way in which consistently relying on excessive and rigid anxiety-reducing behaviors in fact maintains dysfunctional beliefs is by strengthening the belief that individual is unable to cope: Seeking reassurance or checking with medical personnel and other sources such as the internet leads to greater uncertainty and catastrophic thinking when ambiguous or conflicting information is obtained. Finally, selectively attending to information suggesting a medical problem – while giving less weight to normalizing information – only serves to confirm distorted cognitions about one's health.

Anxiety-reducing behaviors are also linked to triggers and cues because some safety behaviors tend to increase the perception of bodily sensations and perturbations (arrow "d"). For example, poking and probing at lymph nodes, a sore, or some other body part can leave the area discolored, sore, or even infected, leading to even more perceived "symptoms." Refraining from exercise can also lead to changes in the body including feelings of tiredness, fatigue, pain, and increased heart rate. Continual body-checking also leads to detecting suspicious symptoms.

Because anxiety-reducing behavior completes a number of vicious cycles, it must be directly targeted in treatment. Response prevention is the technique used to fade out reliance on safety behaviors and signals. When these behaviors have ceased, the individual is able to correct faulty cognitions, which in turn reduces anxiety levels and attention toward feared body sensations. As in the treatment of OCD, response prevention is used in tandem with exposure so that the individual confronts a feared stimulus and simultaneously refrains from anxiety-reducing behavior to demonstrate the nonoccurrence of feared consequences, including the fear that anxiety will persist indefinitely or lead to a physical catastrophe. With repeated exposure and response prevention, the individual learns that anxiety-reducing behaviors are essentially redundant and unnecessary.

Anxiety Reduction

As discussed, technically speaking anxiety-reducing behaviors do work – they result in an immediate, albeit short-term decline in anxiety. These responses, however, are not beneficial long-term solutions since (a) they have so many maladaptive effects as discussed above, and (b) the reduction in anxiety they engender is only fleeting.

Nevertheless, since these responses do result in anxiety reduction (and a reduction in feelings of arousal) more quickly than would occur naturally, they are negatively reinforced and thus become habitual. Commonly observed patterns of avoidance, checking, scouring the internet, and repeating medical examinations can be explained via this mechanism. Arrow "e" in Figure 9.1 shows visually the negative reinforcement contingency operating on anxiety-reducing behavior. During treatment, the individual is helped to refrain from their anxiety-reducing behavior, thus preventing it from being further reinforced. And over time, if the behavior is not reinforced, it is extinguished.

Treatment Planning

The purpose of the case formulation is to inform treatment decision-making. Decisions about treatment include not only which procedures to use, but also the specifics of implementing these techniques. Which stimuli should the patient confront during exposure? What faulty beliefs and interpretations need to be corrected? Which safety behaviors and safety signals need to be dropped? Developing a patient-specific case formulation clarifies these treatment targets and specifies an internally consistent relationship between the symptoms and treatment. Table 9.1 shows cognitive-behavioral treatment techniques and procedures indicated for intervening at various points in the case formulation. To illustrate the process of case formulation and treatment planning, we present an example of an individual case.

Table 9.1. Treatment procedures that address elements of the case formulation

Treatment procedure	Target	Explanation
Psychoeducation	Threatening automatic thoughts Dysfunctional core beliefs	Didactic information aimed at providing information to correct dysfunctional core beliefs leading to accurate and less threatening interpretations of body sensations and other cues and triggers
Cognitive therapy	Threatening automatic thoughts Dysfunctional core beliefs	Collaboratively exploration of the validity of health-relevant beliefs, attitudes, and interpretations leading to the generation of more accurate and less threatening alternative cognitions
Exposure	Threatening automatic thoughts Dysfunctional core beliefs Anxiety and the fight-or-flight response	Confronting situations (situational exposure), body sensations (interoceptive exposure), and intrusive thoughts and doubts (imaginal exposure) that evoke irrational fear demonstrates that feared consequences are unlikely and that anxiety subsides, leading to the reduction (extinction) of pathological anxiety
Response prevention	Safety signals and behaviors	When the patient is helped to resist urges to engage in anxiety-reducing behaviors, he/she learns that such behaviors are unnecessary for managing anxiety, leading to reduced urges

Case Example

Brandon had no history of anxiety problems (although both of his parents had previously been prescribed anxiolytic medication) when he left for a summer field trip to Central America that involved exploring caves and visiting tropical rain forests. During the trip, however, he fell ill, and the leader of his trip suggested he seek immediate medical attention since the group had been exposed to rabid bats and other potentially dangerous animals. Brandon became concerned that perhaps he had contacted rabies; although the physician he saw found no evidence of this and instead diagnosed Brandon with a bacterial sinus infection, prescribing an antibiotic. Still very concerned that he had been misdiagnosed, Brandon ended his trip early and returned to his parents' home in the United States to seek "more trusted" medical examinations. But local physicians also concluded that Brandon did not have rabies, and they prescribed a different antibiotic. Shortly thereafter, his illness cleared, yet Brandon continued to worry that perhaps he had a serious disease that was now in remission.

That fall, Brandon returned to school, yet continued to check the internet to learn more about the symptoms of rabies and other serious illnesses such as ALS. Gradually, he came to the conclusion that he probably did not have such a condition since his only symptoms were feelings of fatigue, occasional tachycardia, occasional stiffness, and cracking of his fingers, shoulders, and elbow joints. Around that time, however, he began to notice floaters in his field of vision. After spending great lengths of time searching the internet for the cause of floaters, Brandon concluded that he was suffering from the side effects of the antibiotics he had taken the previous summer. Although his physicians disagreed with this conclusion and presented Brandon with numerous negative lab findings, Brandon continued to believe that he had an ever-worsening condition brought on by antibiotic use and not yet understood by the medical field. He changed his diet and avoided foods that might be treated with antibiotics (e.g., certain meats). He also avoided exercise for fear that he would overtax his already vulnerable body. He was constantly keeping track of the floaters he was experiencing and often took his blood pressure and heart rate as a form of checking his body. His parents had also arranged for him to see several physicians – the "local experts" on drug side effects.

Case Formulation

Brandon's therapist used the biopsychosocial framework to generate a specific formulation of Brandon's particular health-anxiety symptoms (Figure 9.2) and to derive a specific treatment plan. As depicted in the figure, Brandon experienced floaters and body sensations of concern – which were medically unexplained and most likely caused by factors such as body noise, life stress, or minor and residual symptoms of his previous infection. He interpreted these sensations, however, as side effects of prior antibiotic usage that would be chronic and eventually lead to a deterioration of his health. This in turn led to anxiety, which maintained the problem (a) by exacerbating the physical sensations (e.g.,

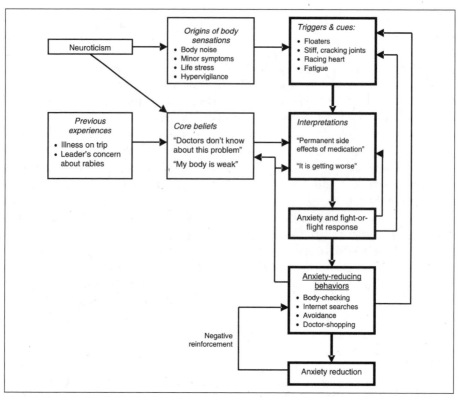

Figure 9.2. Brandon's individualized case formulation.

racing heart, fatigue) and attention (hypervigilance) toward them, and (b) by producing emotional reasoning wherein Brandon perceived the fact that he was anxious as evidence that something was indeed wrong. His hypervigilance to floaters and body sensations provided him with additional data which seemed to confirm his fears.

Brandon's safety behaviors were conceptualized as natural responses to anxiety aimed at reducing distress and leading to some degree of certainty about the nature of his symptoms. However, these behaviors backfired in a number of ways:
- First, body-checking led Brandon to notice *all* of the changes in his body, which also caused greater vigilance.
- Second, his internet searches and medical exams always left some degree of ambiguity about the actual nature of the symptoms, sustaining core beliefs that physicians didn't know very much about his particular problem.
- Third, avoidance prevented Brandon from disconfirming his beliefs that his body was weak, and that the side effects were permanent and getting worse. Unfortunately, however, because they resulted in temporary relief, these maladaptive anxiety-reducing behaviors had become habitual.

Brandon was thus stuck in a self-perpetuating vicious cycle that was gradually becoming stringer and stronger.

Treatment Planning

Using the information in Table 9.1 as a guide, Brandon's therapist devised a treatment plan by matching the formulation components to the appropriate treatment techniques. Psychoeducation was used to teach Brandon about the biopsychosocial model of health anxiety, specifically about the possible origins of medically unexplained body sensations, the effects of anxious thinking, and the maladaptive effects of anxiety-reducing behaviors. Verbal cognitive therapy techniques were used to help Brandon identify and challenge anxiogenic beliefs, attitudes, and interpretations about health, illness, and body symptoms. These beliefs were to be replaced with more realistic cognitions based on the medical evidence and the psychoeducational modules.

Situational, imaginal, and interoceptive exposure were also planned in the service of modifying dysfunctional cognitions and weakening the associations between triggers and inappropriate anxiety. Brandon should practice confronting situations, sensations, doubts, and images that provoke anxiety while simultaneously refraining from anxiety-reducing behaviors (i.e., response prevention) until the had anxiety subsided on its own. Such experiences would teach Brandon that (a) anxiety is temporary, (b) safety behaviors and signals are not necessary to reduce anxiety, (c) he could exercise and eat various foods without putting his body at risk, and (d) safety behaviors and signals are not necessary to prevent medical disasters.

In short, exposure and response prevention would lead to extinction of health anxiety and urges to use anxiety-reducing behaviors. In turn, Brandon would experience fewer physical sensations (because of reduced anxiety), be less preoccupied and attentive to nonthreatening body sensations (because of reduced hypervigilance), and be able to act in ways consistent with his good health. The following chapters illustrate the implementation of the various treatment techniques that are helpful in reducing health-anxiety symptoms.

10

Psychoeducation

Psychoeducation involves the didactic presentation of information to the patients regarding their problem(s) and how they can be treated. Its aim is to improve patients' knowledge and understanding of the problem and provide a credible rationale for the techniques to be used in therapy. As reviewed in Chapter 5, research shows that educational approaches are associated with good short- and long-term outcome for health anxiety. Accordingly, it is a major element of the treatment program outlined in this book.

The present chapter provides the clinician with four psychoeducational modules which we refer to as (a) threatening thinking, (b) fight-or-flight response, (c) safety behavior, (d) body noise and body vigilance – the origins of medically unexplained body sensations.

Patient handouts are also included (see Appendix) so that information presented by the therapist can be reviewed between appointments. Because of the way the four modules flow together conceptually to "tell a story," we recommend that all the material in this chapter be covered within a single session. This might take more than the typical 60 minutes allotted for many therapy appointments, so we also suggest setting aside 90 to 120 minutes for this particular meeting.

Finally, we feel it is beneficial to introduce educational concepts at the very beginning of treatment. This helps to further correct misconceptions, reinforce the conceptual model from which treatment is derived, and provide a rationale for the techniques used in treatment. The therapist will, however, find him- or herself frequently returning to this information throughout the course of treatment.

Gauging The Patient's Perspective

Recall that many patients with health anxiety perceive their doctors as having "written them off" without having fully listened to their complaints. Thus, we begin by asking the patient whether any questions remain from the previous visit, and whether there might be anything further to add to the functional assessment. Next, if not yet expressed, we ask patients for *their* understanding of the unexplained symptoms, the causes, and how they feel about doctors' impressions and the results of lab tests previously conducted. To show consideration for the patient's perspective, the therapist suggests treating this viewpoint as one *possible* explanation for the problem that should neither be ruled out nor accepted unconditionally without exploring other hypotheses. Brandon, whom we introduced in Chapter 9, provided the following summary of his problem and how he believed it should be treated:

> "I really think the antibiotics I took did some sort of damage to my body. I never had floaters before, and I never noticed my joints cracking, my heart racing, and feeling as tired as I have since I took those drugs. I think the doctor I saw in Central America didn't know what he was doing, and my home doctor didn't realize what was going on when I was sick last summer. Between the two of them, they ended up prescribing too much antibiotics. Now, I think my body is becoming weaker and weaker. The other thing is that most doctors don't know what I know about the side effects of antibiotics. I have done a lot of research on the web about this. All the doctors say is that side effects and long-term damage are very rare, and that my tests come out negative. But I know better. I understand that I am anxious about all of this – and that probably has something to do with it. But, I don't see how treating me for an anxiety disorder is going to make my symptoms go away. I mean, these are *real* changes that have happened to me. What I need is a doctor who understands what's happened and can tell me that I really am sick."

The following dialog then ensued:

Therapist: I can tell you feel strongly about this. Therefore, what I'm going to ask you to do might seem difficult. For the purpose of moving forward, though, I'd like us to consider your explanation as one *possible* way of understanding the problem. This means that, for now, we're going to try to suspend judgment about whether it's right or wrong, but instead treat it as one possibility among many. Given that your lab tests and several doctors' opinions don't completely match with your explanation, would you be willing to at least consider that there might be other ways of understanding the problem that you might not have thought of yet?

Patient: Well, I think I know my own body, and I think that I'm right. But, I can see where it might be worth looking at other alternatives as well.

Therapist: Good for you. I think it's smart to be open-minded about this. And remember, we're not discounting your theory; we're simply going to look at it critically and also examine some different perspectives to see what fits best.

From here, we begin by presenting educational information about the role of thoughts and attitudes in producing emotions.

Module 1: Threatening Thinking

In most cases, the patient's primary concern involves catastrophic explanations of one or more physical signs, sensations, or bodily perturbations. Accordingly, it is best to begin with a discussion of these physical sensations and the thoughts that go through the patient's mind. Often, patients have not stopped to consider the distinction between *physical symptoms* and the *meanings* ascribed to them. This module helps the patient learn (a) differences between the body sensation and cognitive appraisals, and (b) the role that appraisals play in emotional responses.

Monitoring Body Sensations and Threatening Thoughts

Handout 10.1(see Appendix), the "Body Symptom Monitoring Form,"includes space for listing troublesome body sensations and how they may be appraised. The patient records some of his or her recent body sensations on the form and is then asked to reiterate the thoughts that come to mind when these symptoms are noticed. If necessary, the therapist should assist the patient with articulating catastrophic thoughts and predictions about the meaning of these symptoms. For example, "I have MS," "The doctors will never figure out what's wrong with me," or "If I don't get help immediately I will die." Highly catastrophic, dire, and farfetched thoughts should be elicited by the therapist since the very idea is to demonstrate that negative, alarming thoughts lead to feelings of anxiety (as we will see further below). At this point, however, these thoughts are not to be challenged; rather, the therapist simply assesses what cognitions are present. The form can be introduced as a "new" way of keeping track of symptoms, which the patient should continue after the session.

The Cognitive Model of Emotion

At this point, the patient is introduced to the cognitive model of emotion (e.g., Beck, 1976) and taught to recognize the effects of threatening thinking. We use the "A-B-C" framework, wherein "A" is an *activating event or stimulus* (i.e., *antecedent*), "B" is a set of *beliefs or interpretations* about "A," and "C" represents the emotional or behavioral *consequence* of "B." The causal relationship between catastrophic thinking and emotional reactions (i.e., the "B-C connection") is the key to understanding how health anxiety arises. The dialog below illustrates how a therapist might introduce the cognitive model. We begin with an example that is not related to health concerns and therefore not emotionally charged for the patient. This way, the patient's grasp of the concept will not be influenced by strong emotional reactivity or defensiveness.

Therapist: Let's talk about how our thoughts influence our emotions. For example, let's say you and a friend planned to meet for dinner at 7:00 p.m., but it is now 7:30 p.m. and your friend still hasn't shown up. If the first thing that goes through your mind is that your friend ditched you and found someone more fun to hang out with instead, how would you feel?

Patient: Down, depressed, sad.

Therapist: Sure – I would probably feel the same way. How about if the first thing that went though your mind was that your friend was being late on purpose just to jerk your chain?

Patient: Then I'd feel angry.

Therapist: Sure. And, what if you said to yourself that your friend is probably on her way and has a good reason for running late that she'll tell you all about when she arrives? What would you feel then?

Patient: I'd probably just feel normal. Maybe a little annoyed, though.

Therapist: And what if you told yourself that your friend was late because she had been hurt in a terrible car accident on the way to your house?

Patient: I'd feel worried.

Therapist: Yeah. Do you see that? Something interesting is happening. The circumstances are the same – your friend is late without calling to say where she is. But, how we *feel* depends on how we *interpret* the situation. When we have the thought that something awful has happened, we become worried; when we think the person is doing something to jerk our chain, we become angry. Do you see how your thoughts and interpretations of the situation make a difference in how you feel?

Patient: Yeah. Depending on how I interpret the situation, I will feel differently.

Therapist: That's exactly right. So, since the only thing that has changed is your *interpretation* of the situation, we can say that your interpretations in fact *cause* your feelings: Your thoughts provoke your feelings. Does that make sense?

After demonstrating the cognitive model of a situation that is not emotionally charged, the next step is to apply it to a health-anxiety-relevant situation, as shown in the next dialog:

Therapist: Now, let's explore how your thoughts provoke feelings about your medical symptoms. You wrote down that when you feel a joint cracking or when you feel lethargic, the first thoughts that come to mind are that you are seriously ill, getting sicker, and that you'll never get the right help. What kinds of feelings do you think these sorts of thoughts provoke?

Patient: Worry, stressing out.

Therapist: Exactly. Anyone who views their health that way would feel worried. I know I would! So, it's not surprising that when *you* think about your body symptoms in this way, you, too, feel worried. Do you see how it is your *interpretation* of your symptoms as being very dangerous that leads you to feel more emotional and worried?

Patient: Yes, but I really think that's what's happening to me.

Therapist: I know you do. We're simply examining what's going on – not deciding whether you are right or wrong. Your feelings and emotions are very strong because of how much you really believe they are true. Do you see what I mean?

Module 2: The Fight-or-Flight Response

The second module involves teaching the patient about the nature and experience of anxiety, fear, worry, and stress. As mentioned, many individuals with health anxiety rebuff the suggestion that they have a problem with anxiety; but this is often based on a misunderstanding of anxiety as simply a psychological *disturbance*. This educational module serves to normalize the experience of anxiety (worry, fear, stress) and to help the patient to more accurately understand how anxiety plays a part in the problem at hand. We accomplish this by teaching the patient that anxiety is a normal and adaptive response to perceived threat, and that it involves three levels of response (physiological, cognitive, and behavioral), all with the purpose of protecting the organism.

What is Anxiety?

To understand the patient's perspective, we typically begin by asking for his or her own definition of anxiety. This can lead to a discussion highlighting how anxiety is an adaptive response to perceived (real or imagined) threat originally designed to protect us from danger and therefore essential to our survival. For example:

Therapist: When you think about a definition of anxiety, what comes to mind?

Patient: I don't know . . . going crazy, out of control, a mental disorder.

Therapist: Do you think anxiety can be good?

Patient: No, it's bad. It's like being crazy.

Therapist: OK. What do you think would happen, though, if you had an important job interview and you experienced absolutely no anxiety at all?

Patient: I see what you mean. I wouldn't take it seriously enough and wouldn't be prepared. I might say the wrong thing or be too casual.

Therapist: So, are you saying anxiety can be a good thing?

Patient: I guess it can, sometimes.

Therapist: So, what is the purpose of anxiety?

Patient: I guess a small amount helps you cope with situations.

Therapist: Right. The overall purpose of anxiety is to protect you from danger. Anxiety is a response to perceived threat that alerts you and helps you prepare to take action. Now, it's a response to *perceived* threat, which means that *actual* danger doesn't need to be present. You might correctly perceive that danger is present, such as when you are crossing a busy street or being chased by a bear. But, sometimes we interpret a situation as dangerous when the level of threat is actually low. Regardless, if we *perceive* threat, we experience anxiety. The important point here is that anxiety – in and of itself – is not abnormal or "crazy." Rather, it serves to protect you and is important for survival. Does this make sense?

Patient: Hmm. I never thought of it that way; but I see what you mean.

Next, we ask the patient to identify what happens when one becomes anxious. These responses are written on a whiteboard or easel and arranged in columns of physiological, cognitive, and behavioral responses, respectively (although we do not title the columns at this point since we later ask the *patient* to identify why we arranged the symptoms in this way). Table 10.1 shows an example of what a completed anxiety symptom chart might look like with typical patient responses. If patients cannot come up with examples for each of the columns, we help them by providing hints (e.g., "what happens to your breathing?" or "What would you do if you were afraid that the building you were in was on fire?") or suggestions from the functional analysis.

Table 10.1. Symptoms of anxiety typically identified by patients

Body sensations	Anxious thoughts	Anxious behaviors
Racing/pounding heart Sweating Heavy breathing Difficulty catching breath Nausea Diarrhea Lightheaded/dizzy Muscle tension Shaking/trembling Hot flash Cold/shivering	Racing thoughts Preoccupation Thinking the worst Trouble concentrating	Avoidance of the danger Escape/get away from threat Restlessness Fidgeting

When a list of the various symptoms has been generated, the therapist can ask the patient to identify the three categories of symptoms. Then, the patient is taught about the three response systems of anxiety as well as the purpose of each. A sample dialog that conveys the important points to be made appears below:

Therapist: As you can see on the board, I grouped the symptoms of anxiety into three categories. Can you tell me what these categories are?

Patient: Yes, the first is physical symptoms. The middle column has to do with thoughts or mental symptoms. The third one has to do with actions.

Therapist: That's exactly right. Remember, I said before that anxiety involves three components; well, these are the three components. Every time a person (or an animal) becomes anxious, we experience all three of these responses. There is always some sort of physiological response, a mental or "thinking" response, and some sort of behavioral response. Remember, also, anxiety is aimed at keeping you safe and protecting you from harm. We should talk about how each of the three systems work to protect you from harm and keep you safe. Let's begin with the physiological response since it is often the most noticeable. As you mentioned, it involves an increase in the rate and strength of your heart beat, and in the rate and depth of breathing. There is muscle tension, which leads to shaking or trembling, stomach aches, sweating, feeling like you have to go to the bathroom, and fatigue – among other kinds of symptoms. You identified most of these which suggest that you're pretty familiar with them. Another term for all of these physical symptoms is the *fight-or-flight response.* Have you ever heard of this term?

Patient: Yes, I have.

Therapist: Can you tell me what you know about the fight-or-flight response?

Patient: Yeah. Doesn't it make you ready to fight or run away from danger?

Therapist: Exactly. All of the physiological symptoms of anxiety are geared toward helping you to either fight off some sort of a predator or threatening situation, or to get out of harm's way. So when your breathing rate automatically increases, this gets more oxygen into your body. It's important to have more oxygen because this is what the muscles of your body use to make energy so that you can fight or run. Oxygen is burned by the cells in our muscles when energy is produced. Your heart automatically beats faster and harder in order to circulate the oxygen rich blood to the various cells and muscles of the body. If you have to be fighting or fleeing for a long period of time, your body will need plenty of fresh, oxygen-rich blood. All of these symptoms seem scary, but as you can see, they are a built-in mechanism for keeping you alive. Do you know what the purpose of sweating is, and why it is a good thing that we sweat when we perceive threat?

Patient: Doesn't it cool your body down?

Therapist: That's exactly right. It also makes our bodies slippery so that predators would have trouble grabbing us. We also sometimes have the urge to go to the bathroom, or have a stomach ache, when we feel anxious or worried. This is because when we're in fight-or-flight mode, the first priority must be to get us to safety. Digestion is not as important at this point. So, any food that is in your stomach is just going to sit there and not be digested, and your body is also going to try to dump off any waste products sitting around in the body that might weigh you down. Your muscles – especially the large ones in your upper body and your legs – become tense and poised for action during fight-or-flight. While this makes the person or animal ready to take action to protect itself, it can also lead to trembling and shaking. This muscle tension can also lead to body aches and headaches. Finally, because the whole fight-or-flight process requires a lot of energy, it is very common for a person to feel tired, fatigued, and generally exhausted. Remember, though, that all of these symptoms are designed to *protect* you from harm. People often worry that they will faint or lose control, or that experiencing "too much" of the fight-or-flight symptoms will lead to some sort of physical catastrophe. But, as you can hopefully see, nothing could be further from the truth. It wouldn't make any sense for the fight-or-flight response – which is designed to protect us from harm – to lead to some sort of medical catastrophe. I've said a lot; what questions do you have about that?

Patient: I understand. It makes sense.

Therapist: The mental or "thinking" symptoms of anxiety serve a similar purpose. From a survival perspective, it is very useful to automatically become preoccupied things that could pose a threat. If our attention were to drift away, we could more easily be caught off guard by the potential threat. A side effect of this, however, is that our minds race with negative thoughts to keep us focused on the importance of fighting or fleeing; and we might have difficulty taking our mind off of the negative thoughts. In short, we might become preoccupied or "obsessed." Do you have any questions about that?

Patient: No. That makes a lot of sense.

Therapist: Finally, anxiety brings about the urge to perform behaviors that serve a protective function. The first is avoidance: If you know a situation is dangerous, it makes sense to *avoid* it; if you can't avoid a potentially dangerous situation, you'll plan or do whatever you need to do to *escape* from the situation. Escape and avoidance have obvious protective value. Sometimes, however, it is either inappropriate or impossible to avoid *or* escape from situations that pose a perceived threat – think of how you feel when waiting for some sort of important news about your health. When escape or avoidance is not a possibility, the urges to escape can be expressed in the form of restless behavior such as foot tapping, eye blinking, pacing, or fidgeting. Any questions about that?

Patient: No. I understand.

Therapist: Great. So, anxiety is a very natural and adaptive response that all people and animals experience when they perceive some sort of threat. Anxiety protects us from harm. It is not dangerous, and it is also not a disease or some form of mental disorder. It is simply a common reaction to the perception of threat. All of the symptoms that go along with anxiety serve some sort of protective function. Even though anxiety, worry, and stress can involve uncomfortable physical symptoms, it is important to keep in mind that these are not dangerous symptoms. Very much to the contrary, they are designed to keep you alive.

Recall from the biopsychosocial case formulation presented in Chapter 9 that the fight-or-flight response inadvertently maintains health anxiety: At the very moment the patient becomes concerned about body symptoms, *more* (and *more intense*) symptoms suddenly appear – those associated with fight-or-flight – which seems to confirm beliefs that a serious medical problem is present ("It's getting worse!"). Many patients are able to relate to this experience of "intensification," and it is therefore useful for them to have an appropriate explanation. Indeed, the increase in symptoms and intensity are due to the fight-or-flight response – the normal emotional response to threatening thinking – rather than a medical condition. This explanation offers a normalizing view of this vicious cycle and gives the patient a less catastrophic attribution for the experience of intensification. The diagram in Figure 10.1 clearly illustrates this vicious cycle and can be drawn for the patient's benefit.

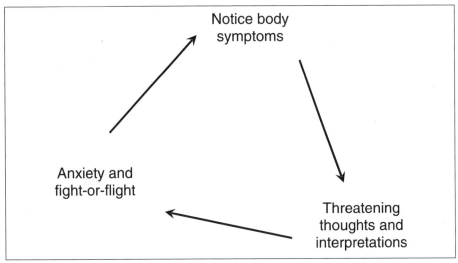

Figure 10.1. Vicious cycle of body sensations, threatening thoughts, the evocation of anxiety, and the fight-or-flight response.

After discussing the anxiety response, you can give Handout 10.2, entitled "The Fight-or-Flight Response," to the patient to review between sessions and to discuss at the next appointment. Because there is a large amount of information, we instruct patients to read the handout daily and to note any questions that come to mind so they can be addressed at the next session.

Module 3: Safety Behavior

As we have discussed, excessive behavioral responses to unrealistic health concerns typically take the form of avoidance, checking (body-checking, or checking with "experts" or expert sources), and reassurance-seeking. One aim of this educational module is to teach the patient how these safety behaviors and safety signals are reinforced by the immediate reduction in affective distress (e.g., anxiety) or discomfort they engender. We explain how these behaviors become habitual responses when in the presence of triggers and health-related cues.

The dialog below illustrates how we introduce the concept of safety behaviors. We begin by explaining how these understandable responses to perceived threat are negatively reinforced. Again, it is important to avoid putting the patient on the defensive. We therefore introduce general concepts before discussing the patient's specific safety behaviors.

Therapist: Now that we've talked a lot about threatening thinking and feelings, it's time we discuss the other side of the coin. What's the *opposite* of threat or danger?

Patient: Safety, I guess.

Therapist: You're absolutely right. People with unexplained medical symptoms tend to engage in actions or perform activities to make them feel safe or protected from illnesses or body symptoms. It makes sense that if you are feeling threatened by symptoms, you would look to develop ways of feeling safer. We call these kinds of behaviors "safety behaviors" because they make you feel safe. Some safety behaviors make good sense: Buckling your set belt when you get into an automobile, for example, reduces the risk of severe injury should you have an accident. This is an example of a true safety aid. Do you see what I mean?

Patient: Yes. I'm with you.

Therapist: Good. When people have problems with unexplained physical symptoms, they also tend to use safety behaviors because they feel like something bad will happen if they don't. Remember, the main characteristic of safety behaviors is that they are designed to either prevent something bad from happening, or they help you to cope with a threat or a physical symptom.

Often, safety behaviors are connected to a specific symptom or to a particular threatening thought. For example, if you feel like your throat is closing in and you think, "I'm going to suffocate," a safety behavior might be to take a drink of water to check that you can still swallow properly. During the last session when we talked in depth about all of your symptoms, you mentioned some behaviors that you have which seem to qualify as safety behaviors. Can you identify what they might be – behaviors that you do to make you feel safer or reduce distress or uncertainty?

Patient: Yeah. I always search the internet for information about my symptoms and the side effects of antibiotics. That makes me feel better to get the information.

Therapist: Good going – that's a perfect example. I noticed a few others, too. One is getting more and more tests from doctors, and another is checking your body for signs of serious conditions – like when you take your pulse. Do you see how these are all done in response to feeling concerned, threatened, and uncertain about your health? They represent attempts to get some definitive explanation or answer that what you are concerned about is true.

Patient: Yes. I see that.

Therapist: Ok. So, tell me about how well these strategies work for you.

Patient: Well, for the moment, they sometimes make me feel better. Like when I look up my symptoms on the internet and they don't match any serious side effects. But, I usually end up worrying about it later and wondering if I looked up the right thing. So, I start searching again and sometimes find something else that scares me about my health.

Therapist: Sure. I see what you mean – and that's a great example of how safety behaviors for unexplained medical symptoms can backfire. They *seem* to work in the short run, so you continue to rely on them when you need relief from distress. But, in the long term, they really don't work: Sooner or later, the physical symptoms and concerns come back, which leads to more safety behaviors. Another problem with safety behaviors for unexplained medical symptoms is that they tend to get worse and more intense with time. Many people might initially use one or two brief safety behaviors; but as concerns with unexplained symptoms progress, they spend more and more time engaged in safety behaviors (which don't work that well, anyway), so that day-to-day functioning becomes impaired.

Next, the patient is taught about ways in which the routine performance of safety behaviors maintains health anxiety. First, many safety behaviors increase awareness of body sensations. For example, body-checking promotes selective attention toward, and preoccupation with, feared sensations that trigger anxiety, such as heart rate, muscle tension, irregularities on or under the skin, gastrointestinal activity, swallowing, breathing, lightheadedness, and so on. Seeking reassurance (e.g., from physicians, relatives, texts, the internet) also leads to an increased focus on bodily sensations, which might simply be part of healthy functioning. The reliance on safety signals (e.g., keeping water, medical equipment, or a cell phone available in case of medical emergencies) also keeps one focused on the body, leading to the increased perception of sensations that could be misinterpreted as significant.

The second general mechanism by which safety behaviors lead to the maintenance of health anxiety is by preventing the disconfirmation of dysfunctional beliefs and threatening misinterpretations of body sensations. For example, when body-checking leads one to detect an ambiguous body sign (e.g., rapid heart rate due probably to anxiety rather than a heart condition), it seems to confirm the belief that a medical condition is present. This is consistent with the clinical observation that some patients report an *increase* in anxiety after body-checking. Excessive reassurance-seeking can also reinforce the threat-related thinking of the health professional to prescribe another test *just to be on the safe side*, or when multiple consultations result in conflicting information leading to greater uncertainty and worry. Safety signals and avoidance also have effects on threatening thinking by preventing the individual from having opportunities to disconfirm such dysfunctional beliefs and interpretations. The patient-therapist dialog continues as follows:

Therapist: Some safety behaviors can actually intensify your physical symptoms. This happens because the safety behaviors lead you to focus more on physical symptoms. For example, by always checking your body, you become very good at being closely attuned to all sorts of symptoms. But this is problematic because then you are noticing more symptoms, which in turn trigger threatening thoughts and concerns. The same with searching the internet and having more doctor appointments: These tend to maintain your focus on your body, by making you pay more and more attention to your symptoms. Do you see what I mean?

Patient: I think so. Yes.

Therapist: Another unfortunate effect of safety behaviors is that they reinforce your threatening thoughts. When you're searching the internet for information, if you find five websites that say your symptoms are nothing to worry about, but then the sixth site hints that maybe you have some serious medical problem, which one do you pay more attention to?

Patient: The one that says I could have a medical condition.

Therapist: Right. That's a normal reaction – people typically keep looking until they confirm their hunches. We humans like to prove ourselves right. But this reinforces the threatening thoughts that produce the fight-or-flight response and can make things even worse. The same thing happens if you check your body over and over or if you have lots of medical tests: The results and feedback you get will likely be a little different on different occasions. Some doctors might speak in different tones, some might spend more or less time with you, and some might recommend other tests *just to be sure*. The tendency will be to err on the side of thinking that this means something is wrong simply because it confirms that you are correct about your symptoms – whether or not the symptoms are really as dangerous as you think. In the end, this strengthens the threatening thoughts that give rise to distress and more symptoms.

A similar discussion of the effects of avoidance follows. Here, we aim to teach patients that avoidance is a very common safety behavior that keeps health-anxious people from getting over their problem since, through avoidance, they are never able to have experiences that disconfirm their dysfunctional beliefs and attitudes.

Therapist: You also mentioned that you avoid certain things, such as exercising – because it might permanently harm your joints; taking antibiotics – because they might make your condition worse; and avoiding certain meats that may have been treated with antibiotics. Just like safety behaviors, avoidance can also backfire. First, avoidance patterns often become worse over time. You might start out avoiding one or two things, but over time, more and more things have to be avoided until it interferes with your functioning. Also like safety behaviors, avoidance leads you to focus more attention on physical symptoms since it keeps your health concerns fresh on your mind. Finally, avoidance prevents you from gathering important evidence about the true nature of your physical symptoms. For example, how can you ever know if you *can* live a normal life, if exercising *will* make you have permanent joint problems, and if eating certain foods *will* make things worse if you constantly avoid all these? You never have the chance to find out what would really happen? Avoidance behavior, like other safety signals, tricks you into thinking that you are preventing things from getting worse, even though you have no proof thereof because you've always been avoiding them. In other words, as long as you continue to avoid these things, you will never *really* have the opportunity to see whether your threatening predictions about your symptoms are accurate or not.

It is useful to graphically depict the maladaptive effects of safety behaviors using a chart similar to that in Figure 10.2. This chart or "map" of the problem now fully accounts for the cognitive and behavioral processes involved in the *maintenance* of health anxiety. But, as many astute patients readily point out, this conceptual model does not yet explain where the frightening body sensations originate from in the first place – or if they are not symptoms of a medical disease. The fourth educational module, presented below, aims to address this question.

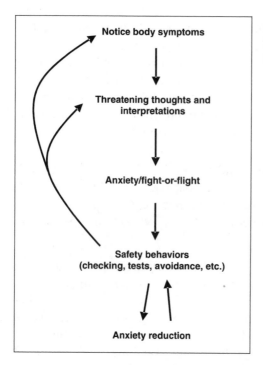

Figure 10.2. Vicious cycle of body sensations, threatening thoughts, the evocation of anxiety, and the fight-or-flight response.

Module 4: Body Noise and Body Vigilance

Origins of Medically Unexplained Complaints

In our clinical work, we find that many patients readily grasp the concepts included in educational Modules 1, 2, and 3. Yet, patients still ask: "If I am not medically ill, why do I even have physical symptoms in the first place?" Notice, first, that this reflects the inaccurate belief that good health means having no body symptoms whatsoever (which is essentially the same as saying that *any* body symptoms are a sign of a *problem*). Module 4 aims to educate patients about the many benign sources and explanations for the bodily sensations and perturbations they experience as well as about the effects of paying excessive attention to body noise.

Handout 10.3, which includes information about sources of symptoms and the effects of focusing attention on one's own body, can be given to the patient to read and discussed during the psychoeducational session. Alternatively, the therapist can summarize the information from the handout during the session and assign the handout for further reading. Either way, the therapist should feel at ease and be able to speak with authority about the information in the handout since it forms an important basis for the treatment of health anxiety. The dialog below illustrates how to introduce the present module. Again, the clinician must be careful not to appear as if he or she is trying to *explain* the patient's medically unexplained symptoms.

Therapist: So, we've covered the role that thoughts and behaviors play in making medically unexplained symptoms worse. But we still need to account for what causes these symptoms in the first place.

Patient: Yeah. Why do I have these problems if as you say I am healthy?

Therapist. Well, there are actually many causes of body symptoms, besides serious medical problems. Remember, though, I am not a physician, so I am not going to try to definitively explain every symptom you have. I don't know for sure what's exactly causing them. But, it might be helpful to at least bear in mind that there are lots of things – many of which *won't show up on medical tests* – that can lead to strange, intense, and even painful symptoms. What do you think about that?

Patient: Well, I suppose it can't hurt to hear about it, but I'm still pretty sure it's a medical problem.

Therapist: Uh huh ... and you might be right. I'm not a physician. I'm not in the position to give you a definitive explanation for your symptoms. But, I do know about different things that can cause the sorts of symptoms you're describing. And I totally agree with you that it's not going to hurt to consider a new alternative. Remember, you said yourself that you're not getting very far assuming that you have a serious problem, right?

Patient: Right.

Therapist: (gives the patient Handout 10.3) I'd like you to read this handout carefully and let me know what thoughts or questions you have as you read it through. When you're done, we can talk about the thoughts you have.

Sources of Body Symptoms

Because the physical concerns and complaints of people with health anxiety are so heterogeneous, it is not feasible within the pages of this book to provide a benign explanation for every possible body sensation. Moreover, providing such information should not even be the goal of psychoeducation (or therapy). Trying too enthusiastically to convince the patient of any particular explanation will likely result in resistance ("yes, but ..."). Instead, the goal is to help the patient understand that there *are* alternatives to his or her conclusion that a serious disease is present. In other words, psychoeducation simply aims to open the patient's mind to different hypotheses about the origin of symptoms. Later in therapy, the patient will conduct tests and collect evidence for these various hypotheses. The therapist should be familiar with the information presented in

Chapter 3, as well as in Handout 10.3, concerning various sources of physical sensations. We summarize the main points below.

Bodily perturbations, sensations, and variations that are not accounted for by medical problems – but that can seem intense, unexpected, and frightening (leading them to be mistaken for signs of illness) – might originate from normal homeostatic processes as the body works to keep a stable and optimal internal environment. Ironically, this is a sign of a healthy body! Sensations can also arise when you change your routine, for example, going to bed much later then usual or engaging in atypical levels of activity (more *or* less than usual). Changes in diet, including the sorts of food, quantity, and even timing of meals can also produce gastrointestinal sensations, changes in alertness, and variations in heart rate. Patients frequently become concerned about colorectal diseases following loose stools that are most likely caused by changes in eating habits such as eating an unusually large (for the patient) meal or consuming more fiber or spices than usual. Finally, patients should be taught about how emotional arousal (e.g., stress resulting from major life changes) and numerous minor medical conditions such as colds, asthma, and allergies can produce bodily symptoms ranging from hives, to a dry, sore throat, to lightheadedness, pounding heart, headaches, and nausea.

Interestingly, most of the aforementioned causes of body sensations will not show up on most medical exams or lab tests because they are by and large considered "normal" processes despite the fact that they produce "symptoms." It might be helpful to explain to patients that medical tests are generally developed so that they produce a positive result only when a condition needing medical treatment is present. Thus, a negative test result (suggesting good health) is not the same as saying that no symptoms are present: It simply indicates that any existing symptoms do not rise to the level of requiring medical attention. This is one way to reconcile the patient's experience of symptoms despite medical feedback suggesting no organic pathology. Of course, there is an organic explanation for every body sensation – it's just that the explanation is not necessarily a serious or urgent one. Importantly, physicians might not consider this state of affairs and are likely to think in all-or-none terms: Either a medical disease is present, or the symptoms are produced by "stress" or "anxiety." Unfortunately, this can come across as rather disparaging to the health-anxious patient, and it must be explained that just as psychologists are not trained as physicians, most physicians do not receive training in the interaction between physical and psychological factors.

Let us emphasize again that the aim of psychoeducation is not to give the patient a definitive explanation for his or her physical complaints. Rather, the therapist is best off trying to raise the patient's awareness of less catastrophic possibilities and propose that they be further examined carefully before concluding that a serious disease is present.

Body Vigilance and Attentional Focus

The tendency to focus attention and thereby become exquisitely sensitive to body sensations and variations (i.e., body vigilance) impacts the detection and perceived intensity of bodily noise. The more an individual scans for and attends to a particular sensation, the more noteworthy it will seem – and the more unpleasant and ominous it will appear. As the person devotes more and more resources to scrutinizing his or her body, he or she also begins to notice and attend to even subtler details of body sensations, and becomes adept at making ever finer sensory discrimination. This is analogous to Eskimos or Inuits who live in the north and can distinguish between many different types of snow based on the types of flakes and water content (e.g., salumaroaq, natatgonaq), whereas those living in more temperate climates pay little attention to these subtle differences and may see only – snow. As people notice subtle differences in their body sensations, they may perceive that new symptoms are emerging, and that general health is further deteriorating. This, of course, leads to increased anxiety, additional sensations (associated with emotional arousal), greater body vigilance, and a self-perpetuating vicious cycle.

The aim of psychoeducation, therefore, is to teach patients that there are real, physiological causes for unexplained body sensations ("symptoms"), although the cause might be benign and not the serious medical condition the patient presumes. When body vigilance and attention are focused on body noise as if these sensations are truly catastrophic, the physiologic experience intensifies, making it seem as if a serious threat to one's health is not only present, but progressing. A case example can illustrate for the patient how body vigilance contributes to body sensations, leading to a grasp of these concepts. The following example might be used:

Case Example

Neil, age 41, awakens to the sound of his alarm clock and quickly springs to his feet. Almost immediately, though, he feels a rush of lightheadedness and blurred vision. He feels faint and thinks he has to hold onto the dresser to keep from falling to the floor. He wonders what could be wrong with him and the first thoughts that come to mind concern the possibility of a stroke. Neil recalls that his father recently suffered a stroke and starts to wonder what it felt like. "Did it feel like this?" he thinks. Within seconds, Neil notices that his heart is now beginning to beat faster and with greater force. He feels as if he cannot get enough air and breaks out in a sweat. "Oh my god, I must be having a stroke!" he says to himself. Neil wakes his wife and has her call

---

an ambulance. His heart is pounding, and it is getting harder and harder to take a deep breath. "I'm going to die," Neil thinks to himself.

Physicians in the emergency room run all sorts of tests, brain scans, and do a complete physical exam on Neil. But everything is normal. Neil is convinced he's had a stroke and cannot believe the doctors when they tell him that his symptoms were "stress related." Although his doctor seems confident that Neil is OK, she gives him a referral to see a neurologist "just to be on the safe side."

Neil is discharged from the hospital a few hours later. But, still fearing the worst, he keeps subjectively monitoring how he is feeling moment by moment. Although he is able to walk and talk normally, some degree of faintness seems to still be present. Over the next several weeks, Neil continues to monitor his sensations and notices that his head seems to feel different now compared to before his initial scare. He has also had occasional episodes of intense dizziness, faintness, strong heart beat, and difficulty breathing, although he never actually loses consciousness.

Neil visits several neurologists, all of whom agree that Neil did not have a stroke. One of these doctors asks Neil if he happened to have just awakened and was getting out of bed when he first noticed his lightheadedness symptoms. Neil recalls that this was indeed the case, and the neurologist explained that this is common. The doctor explained that adults sometimes experience a benign and temporary "spacey" feeling along with a racing heart, faintness, and visual disturbances when getting out of bed in the morning. When Neil quickly stood up out of bed, gravity caused blood to rush from his head, causing the feelings of faintness and dizziness (the body quickly corrects for gravity by increasing blood pressure). Neil interpreted these sensations as indicating a stroke, and this evoked fear and a shot of adrenaline, which triggered the fight-or-flight response, causing an increase in heart and breathing rate, which Neil viewed as confirming his fear of a stroke.

Because Neil remained concerned with his health immediately following his emergency room visit, he continued to monitor his body for more signs of a stroke. This led him to detect even slight variations in heart rate, faintness, and other body noise that are ubiquitous, but that most people ignore or take for granted. Because Neil had skipped breakfast that day because of being rushed to the hospital, his lingering feelings of lightheadedness were probably due in part to low levels of blood sugar. They were also the result of the effects of ongoing worry about his health, which increased his level of physiological arousal. The sense that his body didn't "feel right" after his initial dizziness episode were due to his increased body vigilance, which also began immediately following the initial incident.

Once Neil, who had good insight, understood that the sequence of events was triggered by a benign cause, he felt more comfortable with his doctors' conclusions that he was healthy. This reduced the amount of adrenaline in his system, thereby reducing the episodes of tachycardia (racing heart) and breathlessness. Because he was no longer terrified that something was wrong, he paid less attention to his own body again and reported feeling dizzy or lightheaded much less often.

The clinician can point out the interrelationship of body noise, cognitions, and body vigilance. Noticing strange body sensations triggers thoughts that evoke anxiety and body vigilance, which in turn lead to increased body noise. The cycle is self-perpetuating and gets stronger with each repetition. Patients can be asked if they can think of experiences they've had with this cycle.

Unfortunately, there is no *direct* way to reverse body vigilance. Trying to simply stop paying attention to bodily sensations is not an effective strategy. Instead, as discussed in Chapter 9, treatment aims to reduce body vigilance by correcting how body noise is interpreted. When the patient believes that he or she is probably experiencing benign sensations, it will have the effect of reducing anxiety, which will lead to less vigilance – reversing the vicious cycle described above. Indeed, if one is not anxious about one's body sensations, there is less reason to pay close attention to them (which is probably the way things were for the patient prior to the onset of health anxiety). Psychoeducation, exposure therapy, and cognitive therapy are all aimed at reversing body vigilance in this indirect way.

Providing the Rationale for Treatment

Chapter 9 describes how to develop a treatment plan for health anxiety. During the psychoeducational process, an explanation or rationale is provided for how treatment works to alleviate the problem. The patient is taught that, once he or she is able to consider a less alarming explanation for the unexplained body symptoms, the perception of symptoms subsides because of reduced vigilance and general physiologic arousal. However, the patient must also drop all safety behaviors (e.g., body-checking, reassurance-seeking, doctor-shopping, etc.) and safety signals that prevent the correction of mistaken beliefs and interpretations. This is a gradual process, and the job of the therapist is to foster such changes. In the dialog below, we illustrate how to provide a general rationale for psychological treatment. The chapters that follow include separate rationales for the individual interventions.

Therapist: (Referring to Figure 10.3) As we have talked about today, from this angle,,we can view your problem with unexplained medical symptoms as involving a set of patterns of feeling, thinking, and acting which are very distressing, unproductive, and difficult to stop on your own. The feeling patterns involve noticing unpleasant body sensations; the thinking patterns involve jumping to conclusions that these sensations signify a serious medical problem. When you interpret the body sensations in this way, it leads to even more unwanted feelings (the fight-or-flight response), along with urges to do something about the sensations. As a result, you develop action patterns of going to doctors, searching the internet, checking your body, etc. in order to seek reassurance or get an explanation for your symptoms.

Although the body-checking, reassurance-seeking, and doctor visits are sometimes successful in reducing your health concerns, the relief you get is temporary. These strategies tend to backfire over the long haul since they keep you focused on your body and train you to notice new sensations. They also prevent you from considering new ways of thinking about the sensations. So, over time, you find yourself doing more and more of these maladaptive behaviors to deal with old and new body sensations. Now, you're putting so much time and energy into your health concerns (which ironically is making the body sensations even more intense) that it is disrupting your life.

From a psychological angle, reducing these patterns requires you to change the ways you are thinking and behaving in response to your unexplained symptoms. Once you have a less threatening view of these body sensations, you will no longer experience as much fight-or-flight response, and you will not feel the need to pay such close attention to your body. This reduce your symptoms as well. Similarly, once you stop checking your body, going to doctors, checking the internet, etc., you will decrease your body focus and further reduce the body symptoms. This may be challenging for you because of how strong the existing patterns have become. As your therapist, my job will be to coach you as you learn new skills for managing body sensations. The skills or techniques we use in therapy will fall into three categories: *cognitive therapy*, *exposure*, and *response prevention*. Let me describe each of these:

– *Cognitive therapy* involves identifying the various ways you interpret particular body sensations as well as the various beliefs you have about what it means to be ill or healthy in general. Together, we will carefully explore and examine these beliefs and interpretations to help you correct any inconsistent or problematic thoughts that lead to excessive distress.

– *Exposure therapy* involves gradually confronting situations, thoughts, and body sensations that evoke distress and that you have been avoiding. So, when you are ready, I will help you to gradually face these things so you can learn that you can handle them on your own, and that they are not as dangerous as you might think. For example, you said you avoid books about cancer. So, at some point, such books would make for excellent exposure practices so you can see that the worst thing that happens is that you feel temporarily uncomfortable and perhaps notice some body sensations. During exposure, you can expect to feel anxious at first, but just as with facing any fear, the anxiety subsides if you stick it out and remain in the situation. We'll talk more about exposure when we're ready to begin at some point down the road. It's important that you know we will always plan together for exposures ahead of time. You don't have to worry about being surprised with this. I will always ask you for your thoughts and input.

- Finally, *response prevention* means gradually stopping behaviors like body-checking, going to the internet, and seeking medical tests, explanations, and assurance. Instead, I will teach you skills to help you react to body sensations in healthy ways that do not call attention to the sensations or make them worse. So, I have said a lot just now. How does all of this sound to you?

Patient: Well, I am still a bit skeptical, but I know I should try this. What I've been doing isn't working, so maybe a new plan would do me good. You seem to know what you are talking about.

Therapist: I'm happy to hear that you feel this way. Next time we meet, we'll get started.

Using Psychoeducation During Treatment

Going forward in treatment, the information presented in this chapter can be reiterated when necessary; but we suggest asking the *patient* to recall the information, rather than the therapist presenting it over and over. This allows the patient to hear him-/herself generating statements consistent with change, rather than relying on the therapist. It also helps the patient internalize the information. The handouts in this chapter are also excellent sources of information about physiology that the patient can learn to call on when concerned with body sensations. The therapist should keep an eye out, however, to make sure the patient does not use this information for reassurance-seeking purposes. In the next chapter, we turn to cognitive therapy in which the patient learns skills for identifying, challenging, and correcting dysfunctional, anxiogenic thinking styles.

11

Cognitive Therapy

Cognitive therapy (CT) techniques for health anxiety are concerned with the identification and correction of dysfunctional beliefs about health-relevant internal and external stimuli that, according to the biopsychosocial model, lead to fear and maladaptive responses such as safety behaviors, reassurance-seeking, and avoidance. CT is derived from Beck's (1976) cognitive model of emotion, which, as described in Chapter 3, hypothesizes that emotions occur as a result of how one interprets a situation or stimulus, rather than as a direct result of the stimulus per se. In other words, episodes of health anxiety result not from body sensations as such, but from whether and how the person interprets the sensation as threatening. CT is educational in nature, and it picks up where the psychoeducational modules presented in Chapter 10 leave off. In fact, there is a substantial overlap between CT and psychoeducation. CT basically assumes that if patients were to understand the truth about the physiologic sensations and the low probability of severe illness, they would cease to experience clinical levels of health anxiety. Fear-evoking body noise would then correctly be interpreted as nonthreatening, and safety-seeking behavior such as reassurance-seeking and avoidance would be unnecessary – it would be redundant.

Convincing patients to change dyed-in-the-wool beliefs and long-standing patterns of misinterpreting bodily cues requires providing a more compelling alternative belief or interpretation. Thus, CT focuses on collecting evidence that is *inconsistent* with the patient's disease convictions and *consistent* with the biopsychosocial model. Where health anxiety focuses on specific, immediate, and dire or emergent concerns (i.e., heart failure, suffocation, loss of consciousness, stroke), it may be possible to directly falsify the fears by engineering experiments that provide unmistakable *disconfirming* evidence, for example, trying to provoke a heart attack by running on a treadmill. However, when health anxiety focuses on more general, progressive, or long-term conditions (i.e., cancer, multiple sclerosis), CT strategies that provide evidence for the biopsychosocial model are most suitable. In such instances, the patient benefits from understanding the problem at hand as resulting from selective attention, worry, body-checking, and the intolerance of uncertainty or anxiety.

As reviewed in Chapter 5, research indicates that cognitive techniques are associated with sizable reductions in health concerns, the use of safety-seeking behavior, and illness conviction. Our clinical experience suggests that these techniques also:

– Help build a foundation for a strong therapeutic relationship
– Demonstrate to patients that their cognitions are often subjective, based on faulty reasoning, and influence emotion and behavior
– Improve how the individual monitors his or her cognitions
– Teach specific techniques for evaluating the appropriateness of cognitions
– Modify patients' thinking patterns in ways that broaden their perspective on health, illness, physicians and the medical profession in general, and death
– Provide alternative views (consistent with the biopsychosocial model) to replace relatively narrow and inflexible ones
– Facilitate assessment and prevent premature treatment discontinuation.

This chapter begins with a description of general stylistic issues to be considered when using cognitive interventions for health anxiety. Next, practical CT techniques for facilitating belief change are described. The chapter concludes with discussions about when it is appropriate to use these techniques and some challenges and obstacles in the use of CT.

Stylistic Issues

Collaborative Empiricism

It is an implicit characteristic of CT that the therapist and patient share in the responsibility for the success of treatment. They work together as a team to identify triggers, threatening thoughts and interpretations as well as maladaptive behavioral patterns that maintain health anxiety. This is referred to as *collaborative empiricism* (Beck et al., 1979). At the onset of treatment, the therapist discusses the collaborative nature of the therapy and illustrates how the therapist and patient can take an exploratory approach to the problem. The patient provides the "raw materials" of treatment – body sensations, situations, emotions, thoughts, and behavior – while the therapist provides the structure and education on how to understand and deal with these phenomena.

One reason collaborative empiricism is essential in CT is that the therapist does not know *a priori* whether an individual's cognition is distorted or inappropriate in a given situation. To this end, the *validity* of a cognition refers to how accurately it represents the objective characteristics of a given stimulus or situation. In health anxiety, the focus is often on how validly cognitions represent the patient's health status, risk of illness, and explanation for perceived body symptoms. For example, when a patient attributes foot pain to a rare and serious disease of the circulatory system that has been ruled out by reasonable medical testing, the therapist can coach the patient into thinking of other – less catastrophic – possible causes for the foot pain to refute the conclusion that a serious medical problem is present. Given that patients' experiences of their body sensations are highly subjective, determining an objective reality is often difficult. However, the therapist can assist the patient in ascertaining a reasonable perspective on the physical triggers given the information and circumstances available.

The *utility* of a cognition refers to how functional or adaptive it is in the patient's life and struggle with health concerns. Consider, for example, Bill's rigid beliefs that his physical sensations have a medical basis, but that doctors have not conducted the correct tests because they are simply discounting the problem as "anxiety." A therapist could attempt to examine whether such beliefs are invalid, yet this might prove to be a rather difficult task given the future-oriented nature of the belief and the subjectivity of the patient's perceptions of symptoms and interactions with doctors. Examination of the *utility* of the cognition, however, is more likely to be fruitful. In this case, the therapist explored with Bill the advantages and disadvantages of holding this belief and of continuing to pursue a medical diagnosis given the results of previous medical tests (which were negative). One advantage was that a medical diagnosis and treatment plan might become evident at some point. After reviewing psychoeducational materials, the therapist asked Bill if he could identify possible disadvantages of this belief. Bill noted that (a) going to the doctor led to increased focusing on his physical sensations, and (b) it didn't make him feel any better about the origin or validity of his symptoms.

With these new considerations, it was easier for Bill to view his cognition (and corresponding doctor-shopping behavior) as unhelpful.

The Socratic Style

Whereas psychoeducation is primarily delivered in a didactic (presentational) style, the therapist switches between didactic and Socratic styles when using cognitive interventions. The Socratic style (so named because it was first developed by the Greek philosopher Socrates, although it was later made famous by Plato) employs open-ended questions, reflective listening, and summary statements that are all aimed to help the patient gain a broader and more critical perspective on his or her thoughts and dysfunctional beliefs – and consider more helpful alternative cognitions. As Wells (1997) points out, appropriate open-ended questions include those that open up a particular area of exploration (e.g., "What is it like for you when you notice the floaters in your field of vision?"), shed more light on a point of view (e.g., "How do you interpret the doctor's conclusion that you are not ill?"), or probe for worst-case scenarios (e.g., "What's the worst thing you think would happen if you visited a cancer unit?"). In reflective listening, the therapist echoes what the patient has said with a slight degree of reframing or modification for the sake of clarifying the patient's point of view. This also communicates respect for the patient and for the therapeutic relationship, and can be used to selectively reinforce ideas that the patient expresses (Taylor & Asmundson, 2004). For example:

Patient: I always carry a water bottle with me. It just makes me feel better.
Therapist: So, you feel if you have water with you, it will prevent a medical emergency.

Summary statements further facilitate reflection on the dialog and incorporate follow-up questions, as in this example:

Therapist: So, if you have water with you, it will prevent a medical emergency. How often have you had to depend on the water to save you from something serious? . . . Do you think everyone should carry water with them at all times? . . . What kind of risks are people taking when they leave the house without taking water with them?

It is best for the therapist to display genuine interest and curiosity about the patient's experiences. If the patient feels interrogated, he or she might resist and end up defending the erroneous beliefs.

There is widespread agreement among cognitive-behavioral therapists concerning the importance of using Socratic methods whenever possible. As discussed in Chapter 7 on enhancing motivation, studies from the fields of clinical and social psychology demonstrate that people hold onto beliefs more strongly when the beliefs are self-generated as opposed to when they are spoon-fed to them didactically. Thus, although didactic, psychoeducational procedures are an important treatment component, supplementary discussions of didactic material should be conducted by using Socratic questioning to lead the patient to the desirable conclusions.

Identifying Cognitive Errors

Chapter 10 describes methods for introducing the cognitive model of emotion (the "A-B-C" model). It is useful to reiterate this conceptual model throughout treatment to ensure the patient understands the role that thoughts, beliefs, and interpretations play in determining emotions. In psychoeducation, the emphasis is on simply *understanding* how cognitions influence emotions such as anxiety; in cognitive therapy, we build on the educational material by teaching patients how to *use* this information to manage anxiety.

According to the cognitive model, different emotions are linked to particular types of thinking. As we have discussed, anxiety arises from exaggerated estimates of threat and the likelihood of harm, and beliefs about the inability to cope. Research indicates that problems with health anxiety are specifically associated with various domains of cognitions such as anxiety sensitivity, the tendency to overestimate threat, intolerance of uncertainty, rigid beliefs and definitions about health and illness, faulty assumptions about general health, the distrust of medicine, and dysfunctional beliefs about death and dying. Acquainting patients with the various types of thinking errors helps them become aware of when they are victims of such cognitive patterns, which is a prerequisite to correcting such distortions. Instead of using many of the technical terms given by researchers to describe these belief domains (e.g., anxiety sensitivity), we prefer more practical jargon that will stick with patients. To this end, Handout 11.1 provides a list of faulty thinking patterns in health anxiety. The handout, which can be reviewed in the session, can lead to a discussion of how cognitive distortions play a role in health-anxiety symptoms. Interview data collected during the information-gathering sessions and responses to the self-report measures of cognition administered during assessment may also be used to point out the patient's distinctive patterns of responding to his or her specific cues and triggers.

General Strategies for Correcting Cognitive Errors

Cognitive therapy includes a set of techniques for challenging and modifying thinking errors that lead to emotional distress and maladaptive behavior. In this section, we describe and illustrate a number of commonly used cognitive strategies. In the section thereafter, we present a number of techniques for modifying specific cognitive errors in health anxiety.

Considering Evidence for and Against Threatening Thoughts

One of the most straightforward methods of producing cognitive change is to help the patient examine evidence for and against dysfunctional interpretations, expectations, and assumptions. This method is described extensively by cognitive therapists such as Beck (1976) and Ellis (1994). It is a very useful intervention since patients' thinking errors are, by and large, based on faulty logic and anecdotal data.

Moreover, patients rarely (if at all) take the time to think critically about their dire interpretations of body sensations, overly negative assumptions about health and illness, and other sorts of negative predictions. Thus, this exercise provides the patient with a basis for questioning their thinking and generating alternate – and more realistic (and adaptive) – ways of interpreting anxiety-provoking triggers. It can also address faulty beliefs about the inability to cope. The goal of this intervention is therefore to teach the individual to identify, evaluate, and modify erroneous cognitions about health, body sensations, and feedback from doctors that presently create anxiety, and consider new and more adaptive cognitions about health-relevant situations and stimuli.

To begin with, the patient is taught to treat his or her expectations, assumptions, and interpretations as hypotheses, that is, as *possible*, but not forgone conclusions. The therapist and patient then work collaboratively to explore facts from sources such as the patient's past experiences and self-monitoring diaries (e.g., symptoms come and go based on stress level), materials covered in psychoeducational components of treatment (e.g., body noise), and information obtained from other sources (e.g., doctors do not seem concerned about medical illness). The therapist and patient then collaboratively explore answers to thought-provoking questions such as

– "What's the evidence for this assumption?"
– "Is there any evidence that conflicts with this interpretation, expectation, or prediction?"
– "What has happened in the past when I expected this outcome?"
– "Are there any other ways of looking at this situation?"

The "data" collected in considering these questions is then laid out for the patient to consider, and he or she is helped to put the erroneous cognitions "on trial" and to determine whether they are accurate and useful; or whether it is worthwhile generating new and more probable (and more adaptive) assumptions, interpretations, or expectations.

To illustrate, consider Amanda, who went to her doctor because of increased urgency and frequency of urination. A urinalysis of Amanda's urine indicated an increase in red and white blood cells. Her doctor diagnosed the problem as the beginning of a bladder infection and prescribed an antibiotic. Seeking assurance, Amanda, asked her doctor if she thought it could be kidney cancer, to which the doctor replied, "No." Once she got home, however, Amanda found herself worrying that she had asked the doctor specifically about *kidney* cancer, but not *bladder* cancer. At her next therapy session, Amanda, told her therapist she was extremely worried that

a) The doctor made a mistake by diagnosing *only* an infection, and
b) The doctor was thrown off when Amanda mentioned *kidney* cancer and did not bother to check for *bladder* cancer.

Amanda's therapist began by helping Amanda clarify her threatening thought:

> "I have something much worse than a bladder infection – I probably have bladder *cancer*; and I probably threw off the doctor when I mistakenly mentioned *kidney* cancer during my appointment."

Using Handout 11.1, Amanda was able to label this cognition as containing negative interpretations and assumptions about probability and severity. Next, the therapist and Amanda collaboratively explored evidence for and against her interpretation and assumptions. The therapist used Socratic questioning to help Amanda answer questions such as:

– What is the evidence for and against this assumption/interpretation?
– What relevant facts are being overlooked?
– What was the outcome of similar situations, interpretations, or assumptions in the past?

These questions helped Amanda think critically about her threatening assumptions and interpretations, something she had never done. Table 11.1 shows the evidence for and against the threatening thought that Amanda generated. Amanda recorded this information on the *Thought Challenging Form* shown in Handout 11.2.

Amanda and her therapist then scrutinized the available evidence more closely. For example, the therapist asked whether the fact that doctors *sometimes* make mistakes as well as the fact that a strep infection was *once* misdiagnosed

Table 11.1. Amanda's Evidence for and against her threatening thought

Evidence for	Evidence against
– Doctors sometimes make mistakes	– In the past, problems I thought were cancer were cured by medicine and other treatments that wouldn't have cured cancer
– A doctor once diagnosed me with a virus when I really had a strep infection	– I have had many health worries that never turn out to be accurate
– I have a family history of cancer	– Doctors would probably be able to tell an infection from cancer
	– Doctors probably don't get thrown too easily off by comments their patients make
	– Just because I didn't specifically mention bladder cancer doesn't mean the doctor didn't consider this
	– I have no other signs of cancer

constitute strong evidence for the validity of Amanda's present concerns. Similarly, does a history of cancer translate into a 100% risk? Amanda was able to see that even the evidence she generated for her belief was suspect. To deepen her conviction in the evidence against the threatening thought, Amanda's therapist assumed the role of an "interested skeptic" (Salkovskis, 1989; Taylor & Asmundson, 2004), helping Amanda to voice arguments in favor of changing her distorted thinking. For example:

Therapist: You said that, in the past, when you thought you had cancer, your symptoms were cured with medication or other treatments, and sometimes with just letting time pass. These aren't cancer treatments, though. Why is this evidence against cancer?

Patient: Well, it shows how I misinterpret symptoms as being worse than they really are. If an antibiotic makes the problem go away, it probably wasn't cancer.

Therapist: And how is that evidence against your threatening thought?

Patient: It helps me remember how inconsistent and irrational my thinking is when it comes to my health. When I think clearly about what has happened to me before, I see that I'm just falling into the same trap all over again.

Therapist: And is that really enough to convince you?

Patient: Well, it helps. After all, it's more likely that I'm making this mistake again, as opposed to this *finally* being "the big one."

After considering all of the evidence, Amanda generated the following, less threatening alternative cognition to the threatening thought:

> "It is unlikely that I have cancer, and it is probably worth giving the antibiotics a chance to work. As in the past, my symptoms will likely go away in a few days. If they do not, this will help the doctor determine what else might be wrong."

This thought was written in the far right column of the *Thought Challenging Form* (Handout 11.2) and Amanda was instructed to continue practicing thought challenging on her own to learn how to perform this skill as needed "on the fly."

Behavioral Experiments and Data Collection

Behavioral experimentation or empirical hypothesis testing is a key component of CBT for health anxiety. Beck and Emery (1985) suggested that behavioral experiments are designed as mini-tests to examine the validity of thinking errors in order to bring about cognitive change. These exercises can be introduced as early in treatment as is necessary to help the patient gain more evidence for (or against) healthier (or unhealthy) ways of understanding physical "symptoms." As opposed to strictly verbal techniques such as considering evidence, behavioral experiments provide real-life demonstrations of the validity of thoughts and interpretations, and therefore prove the most effective in producing cognitive, behavioral, and emotional changes. Nevertheless, verbal techniques are often needed initially in order to prepare the patient for behavioral experiments. The following example illustrates a behavioral experiment with a patient concerned that he had a "weak heart."

Case Example

Mike, age 35, had hypochondriasis and comorbid panic attacks. He was concerned that a congenital heart defect, which had been successfully treated in infancy, would cause his heart to "give out" if he exercised or exerted himself for more than a few minutes at a time. Numerous cardiologists had told Mike there was nothing for him to worry about with respect to his heart, yet Mike continued to be sedentary and, as a result, he gained weight. After helping Mike identify dysfunctional interpretations, expectations, and assumptions, the therapist taught Mike to closely consider evidence for and against these cognitive errors. When Mike was able to verbally generate more realistic thoughts and beliefs about his health, the therapist suggested conducting the next treatment session at a local health club where Mike would practice walking or jogging on a treadmill for gradually increasing periods of time without breaks, and at increasing speeds, to test his new beliefs and see whether his heart would really give out. After some initial avoidance, Mike agreed. Although he initially experienced palpitations during the exercise (partly because of anxiety and partly because of his being out of shape), he was eventually able to convince himself that he did not need to be so concerned about his heart. He was subsequently instructed to conduct the same experiment each day between sessions and monitor the outcome on a form provided by the therapist (Figure 11.1).

Additional behavioral experiments that can be used to target other specific thinking errors are presented later in this chapter. Indeed, such exercises should be tailored to the patient's idiosyncratic health concerns and introduced with a clear rationale. Experiments that at once provide (a) disconfirming evidence for the faulty cognition and (b) support for the alternative explanation are the most effective.

Informal Discussions of Cognitive Errors

Although the techniques described above are staples of cognitive therapy, less formal cognitive interventions can also be helpful throughout the course of therapy.

The cognitive-behavioral therapist is familiar with the various cognitive errors and remains on the lookout at all times for those a particular patient is likely to make. Rather than plan and execute a prescribed intervention using charts or worksheets every time a cognitive error arises, the therapist might address such distortions *ad hoc* through informal discussions to help the patient recognize and challenge his or her own distorted thinking patterns. For example, when patients assume danger simply on the basis of anxious feelings (i.e., emotional reasoning), the therapist can help them to consider alternative interpretations without launching into a grand discussion about the nature of emotional reasoning per se. This technique becomes especially useful into the middle and later stages of therapy when patients often become more adept at recognizing their own cognitive errors.

The dialog below illustrates the use of an informal cognitive intervention with a patient, whose health anxiety was focused on one of her eyes.

Patient: I woke up this morning and almost called the ophthalmologist. It was the worst I've felt in a few weeks. I was doing well, but whatever it was that was stuck in my eye is back. I can feel it – when I close my left eye, it doesn't feel the way it should. Look how it's all red, teary, and burning. I really need an appointment.

Therapist: I'm sorry things aren't going well today. I see you are blinking a lot, and touching and rubbing your eye a lot. Have you been doing that all day?

Patient: Yes, it itches a lot and I'm trying to feel what's wrong with it.

Therapist: OK. In light of what your ophthalmologist has told you in the past when you called him about this, perhaps you can think of some possible alternative explanations for why your eye is giving you problems?

Patient: Well, I have been touching it a lot the last few days. Maybe I'm making it worse by messing with it.

Therapist: That's one possibility. Can you think of others?

Patient: The doctor said that some people who wear contact lenses get sores under their eyelids from time to time. So, it could be from that.

Therapist: Right, good. Which kind of thinking trap were you falling into?

Patient: I was making a negative interpretation about something that's probably not as serious as I was thinking.

Therapist: That's right. Do you see how that led you to feel more distressed and caused an urge to call the eye doctor?

Patient: Yes.

Therapist: Good; and I'm glad you didn't call. What would be the pros and cons of calling?

Patient: The pros are that I would get some immediate medical attention and reassurance, but the cons are that it wouldn't solve the problem in the long run. The reassurance only works for a little while.

Therapist: Exactly. Eventually you would have more symptoms that you would feel you'd need to ask about. Plus, calling and going to doctors makes you focus more on your eyes, which is perhaps making the problem worse.

We recommend using a blend of formal and spontaneous cognitive techniques throughout therapy. The following are some guidelines for choosing between formal and informal cognitive strategies:

- Formal interventions are best used when a particular type(s) of thinking error appears to play a prominent role in the individual's health anxiety.
- Patients who actively seek out and value self-help and educational materials often respond well to formal interventions that include self-monitoring and completing worksheets.
- Formal interventions can be used to interrupt and deescalate strong negative emotions.
- Formal interventions are often necessary when the patient is first learning about cognitive therapy and the relationship between thoughts and emotions.
- Formal techniques will be more helpful (at least initially) for individuals who are not psychologically savvy.
- Informal discussions are useful if the therapist wishes to address a cognitive error, but doesn't want to get sidetracked from an important topic being discussed.
- Informal techniques will be more palatable to patients who dislike directives from the therapist, or who harbor ambivalence about therapy.
- An informal intervention may be preferable when an individual has made positive changes, yet has had a lapse and needs to get back on track.

Applying Cognitive Strategies to Particular Thinking Errors

In this section, we discuss the various types of thinking errors in health anxiety (as described in Handout 11.1), as well as the application of specific interventions that can be used to address each type of thinking error.

All-or-Nothing Thinking

All-or-nothing thinking takes an absolutist perspective: The person sees things only in black and white, rather than noticing the shades of gray – demanding absolute perfection. In health anxiety, the most common manifestation of this thinking style is the tendency to believe that one is either completely healthy or ill. In other words, "Good health means being 100% symptom-free," or "Any physical symptom is always a sign of a physical illness." Frequent use of the

words "always," "never," "any," "none," "everyone," and "no one" can be indications of this cognitive distortion. Taking an all-or-nothing perspective, however, overlooks the normalcy of body noise and other types of benign aches,
pains, and bodily perturbations. When the person (inevitably) notices a (benign) body variation, he or she concludes that something *must be wrong*. This
sets in motion the vicious cycle of attending more closely to the body, recognizing benign sensations, and gaining additional "evidence" of ill health.

The persistence of all-or-nothing thinking usually indicates that the patient
has not followed or grasped important concepts from psychoeducation. Thus,
key points from Chapter 10 can be revisited to help patients challenge their
beliefs. Patients can be asked about the concepts of homeostasis, body noise,
and how they think the mind and body influence one another. For example, the
discussion could focus on how psychological stress can induce symptoms such
as headaches and asthma. Patents can then be instructed to list examples of their
own worrisome body sensations (or other "symptoms") and – with the help of
the therapist – examine evidence for and against their belief that these are signs
of an underlying medical illness.

It is also useful to explore with patients the advantages and disadvantages of
all-or-nothing thinking. *Advantages* include this being a rather convenient way
to view the world and make sense of one's health; it also reduces the chance of
overlooking a serious problem if it is present. The major *disadvantage*, however,
is that all-or-nothing thinking inevitably leads to "false alarms" – benign body
sensations and variations being mistaken for actual medical symptoms. This
leads to health worry, frequent trips to the doctor for unexplained symptoms,
strained relations with medical professionals, frequent body-checking, and other maladaptive behaviors (e.g., reassurance-seeking), which serve to maintain
health anxiety.

A behavioral experiment that demonstrates the effect of worry on health anxiety can be used to addresses all-or-nothing thinking. In this exercise, which we
call the "Rumination Experiment," the therapist asks the patient to worry aloud
about an actual predicament (not necessarily related to health anxiety) for several minutes. This reliably evokes changes in mood, increased awareness of bodily sensations, and health-related thoughts. The therapist can then lead a Socratic discussion of the effects of rumination and whether the body sensations that
occurred during the experiment were more likely to be a related to worry or to
a suddenly occurring medical illness. Learning that the presence of at least some
body sensations does not necessarily indicate serious illness can help to modify
rigid all-or-nothing cognitions.

Another experiment targets the rigid belief, "If I don't get to a doctor at the
first sign of trouble, I will develop a serious illness." Here, the patient is instructed to postpone visits or phone calls to medical professionals. When we suggest
this experiment, patients often predict that anxiety will escalate to unbearable

levels because they will not be able to stop obsessing about what might be wrong with them. We recommend patients test this prediction by monitoring their daily levels of health anxiety and preoccupation with symptoms over the course of the week. Very often, patients report that they do not remain preoccupied with their feared symptom(s), and that such symptoms dissipate on their own (probably a function of less body-focused attention). We then work with patients to process the outcome of the experiment and generate more healthy cognitions such as, "My symptoms fade if I do not visit or call the doctor."

Not-so-Great Expectations (Pun Intended)

This thinking pattern involves arriving prematurely at conclusions (usually upsetting ones) and is often the basis for negative predictions about the future. The expectations can concern short-term, tangible negative outcomes (e.g., "Because of my weak circulatory system, I will die in my sleep if I do not elevate my feet") or more vague long-term consequences (e.g., "I have undiagnosed early Alzheimer's disease and my brain is slowly deteriorating"). The strategies we describe here work best for specific, short-term, and falsifiable negative expectations. Techniques for long-term and vague predictions are discussed in later sections.

The most straightforward method for helping patients challenge and modify overly negative expectations is to help them look at evidence for and against their claims. Jose, for example, was medically healthy but believed that his circulatory system was weak. As a result, he thought that if he elevated his head when he slept (i.e., by using a pillow), he would die as not enough blood would get to his brain. Jose had even purchased a bed that tilted so that his head was below his heart when he slept. Jose's therapist helped Jose to challenge his beliefs using the following verbal techniques:

– Jose was asked to clarify specifically what the nature of his illness was and how it would lead to his death. When he was unable to produce a logical "story," the therapist helped Jose to see that his beliefs had gotten the best of him, and that he had no basis for his expectations.
– Jose was asked to examine the evidence for and against his health concerns. Very little evidence supported his belief; however, he also disqualified all of the evidence that did *not* support the belief. For example, when the therapist pointed out that Jose seemed to have no circulatory difficulties while sitting up and standing, Jose argued that his heart and blood vessels worked more efficiently when he was awake than when he was asleep. When questioned about the basis for this assumption, Jose could not identify any valid source. The therapist helped Jose to see how he was discounting information merely because it did not support his belief, rather than based on its validity.

– Keeping in mind that his expectations could be erroneous, Jose was asked to identify the advantages and disadvantages of holding onto his beliefs about his health. The main advantages were that it could be a matter of life and death; disadvantages included its evoking anxiety, strange sleeping habits, constant preoccupation with his body, and continuous monitoring for signs of low blood blow, such as dizziness.

Behavioral experiments for overly negative expectations can be derived directly from the outcome of verbal CT strategies and usually involve the withdrawal of safety-seeking behaviors to determine whether the expectations actually come to pass. Jose and his therapist, for example, decided to conduct a test of Jose's beliefs about dying in his sleep. The experiment involved gradually dropping safety behaviors and was planned collaboratively with the therapist. Essentially, on successive nights, Jose was to decrease the tilt of the bed until it was flat. Finally, a pillow would be added so that Jose's head was actually elevated. After three nights of gradually working through the planned experiment, Jose flattened the bed and used a pillow (as he had done for 30 years before becoming health anxious). He had overcome his health worries.

Negative Interpretations

We have discussed how jumping to conclusions and catastrophically interpreting benign or mild bodily signs and sensations gives rise to health anxiety, body vigilance, and increased attentiveness to the "symptoms" of the feared malady. Verbal CT strategies for challenging such interpretations include examining evidence for and against the faulty and catastrophic beliefs – and then considering *all* of the evidence, rather than only the evidence that seems to confirm the fear-related interpretation (see section on "Disqualifying" further below). Reviewing psychoeducational modules about body noise and benign explanations for noticeable sensations and perturbations provides a basis for identifying less threatening alternative explanations (e.g., "Based on what you have learned, what other explanations could there be?"). Alternatives are considered as hypotheses to be tested out in behavioral experiments as described next.

Silver, Sanders, Morrison, and Cowey (2004) indicate that some feared body sensations can be induced within the treatment session using exaggerations of everyday behaviors. For example, patients who fear that lightheadedness is evidence of a serious brain disorder or stroke can, along with the therapist, practice evoking these sensations by turning their heads back and forth quickly, spinning around in a chair, quickly standing up from a prone or sitting position, or taking deep breaths (i.e., hyperventilating) for a minute or two. This helps

Table 11.2. Procedures for inducing feared body sensations

Feared body sensation	Suggested procedures
Racing heart	– Jog in place
	– Walk/run up and down flights of stairs
Dizziness	– Place head between legs
	– Hyperventilate (60–90 seconds)
	– Spin head back and forth
	– Rapidly get up from a prone or sitting position
Throat sensations	– Tighten a neck tie
	– Try to quickly swallow 5 times in a row
Pain	– Hold arms in the air (with weights) for extended period of time
	– Tense muscles
Gag response	– Brush back of the tongue with a toothbrush
Suffocation	– Hold breath
	– Breathe through a straw
Sweating, flushing	– Jog in place
	– Walk/run up and down flights of stairs

the patient notice that even healthy people experience uncomfortable body sensations. Further, a discussion of how these sensations are produced through normal everyday activity (i.e., the vestibular system quickly adapts to changes in position, but everyone experiences at least *some* momentary sense of imbalance – especially if the person is anxious about and closely monitoring these sensations) will provide an alternative and less threatening hypothesis or interpretation for these feared sensations (e.g., "If getting up out of bed can causes dizziness, perhaps that is why I worry I am having a stroke every morning."). Some additional procedures we use for replicating feared body sensations are included in Table 11.2. The discussion of interoceptive exposure in Chapter 12 also overlaps with this behavioral experiment.

Another behavioral experiment that helps the patient gather evidence against negative interpretations of body noise (and in favor of the biopsychosocial model) is to instruct him or her to switch off between "focusing" and "nonfocusing" days. On focusing days, the patient pays constant attention and closely monitors the feared body sensations. The patient is also allowed to engage in as much body-checking and reassurance-seeking as desired. In contrast, on nonfocusing days, the patient does not monitor body sensations and refrains from responding to them in any way. Instead, they stay occupied with non-health-related activities. In addition to completing the Behavioral Experiment Form (Figure 11.1), the patient records daily levels of anxiety, body sensations, urges to perform safety behaviors (e.g., body-checking, reassurance-seeking), and strength of belief in the negative interpretation using a Likert scale (e.g., from 0–10). The alternating days can continue for a week or two so that consistent results can be obtained. In our experience, patients report that health anxiety, urges to engage in safety behaviors, and conviction in misinterpretations turn up lower on nonfocusing days compared to focusing days. These results can be discussed within the context of the biopsychosocial model. For example:

Therapist: So, it looks like you actually had more symptoms of weakness and trembling on days when you were focusing on your body, compared to when you were trying not to focus or respond to your health concerns. What do you make of that?

Patient: I was surprised. I thought it would be just as bad on both types of days.

Therapist: Right. What do you think it means? If your weakness and trembling feelings were part of multiple sclerosis, as you are concerned they are, would the symptoms go away just by not focusing on your body and going about your daily routine? Maybe you have just discovered a new cure for MS!?

Patient: No, of course not. I guess it means when I pay more attention to the symptoms, it makes them *seem* worse. Now I see what you've been trying to teach me all along.

Therapist: Good for you. Now you have a more realistic and helpful way of thinking about the sensations you notice in your body. They probably are *not* a sign of MS.

Importantly, the patient and therapist should carefully plan this sort of behavioral experiment so that it is carried out during a relatively typical period of time for the patient. Times of high stress (positive or negative) should be avoided since this could increase body noise and confound the experiment. Similarly, it is best not to try this experiment when the patient has planned visits to doctors since this could increase the degree of symptom focus.

Behavioral Experiment Form

Date: _____

Time: _____

Description of the behavioral experiment:

Negative expectation *(What do you fear could happen if you conduct the experiment?)*

What are the chances (likelihood) of something awful occurring? (0–100%): _____%

If this actually occurred, how terrible would it be? (0–100%): _____%

What is the available evidence about the actual likelihood and severity of the threat?

Fear level immediately before beginning the experiment (0–100) _____

Strength of my belief in the expectation immediately before beginning experiment (0–100%) _____%

Fear level immediately after completing experiment (0–100) _____

Strength of my belief in the expectation now that I have completed experiment (0–100%) _____%

What was the outcome of the experiment? (what did I learn?)

After considering the experiment, my revised likelihood estimate is: (0–100%): __ __ __%

After considering the experiment, my revised threat severity is: (0–100%): __ __ __%

Based on this experience, what behavioral experiment should I do next?

Figure 11.1. Behavioral experiment monitoring form.

Intolerance of Uncertainty

"Not knowing for sure whether I have celiac disease is just killing me. As awful as it seems, I would rather be diagnosed with it for sure than go on not knowing if I really have it."

This quote illustrates how intolerance of uncertainty is central to the experience of health anxiety. Many patients consider the *possibility* of an illness (however small) as implying that the illness is *probable*. This possibility-probability confusion leads to the urge to obtain a complete (100%) and unambiguous guarantee of good health (which is usually unobtainable). Even the remote possibility of illness provokes anxiety. Contrast this way of thinking with that of the typical non-health-anxious individual who is able to assume good health unless clearcut and unambiguous illness cues are present. Put another way, people without health anxiety are able to *feel* certain about their health despite the fact that absolute certainty is more or less an illusion.

Health-anxious individuals' intolerance of uncertainty is fairly localized and focused on specific concerns relevant to their specific health concerns, and this provides an opening for cognitive interventions. We recommend using the following demonstration to illustrate the ubiquity of uncertainty in everyday life.

Therapist: I want you to think of someone you care about very much.
Patient: OK – my husband, Steve.
Therapist: Great. Is Steve alive right now at this very moment?
Patient: Sure. Why do you ask?
Therapist: Well, I am interested in how you know *for sure* that he's alive.
Patient: I talked with him on my cell phone while I was out in the waiting room.
Therapist: How long ago was that?
Patient: About half an hour ago.
Therapist: But isn't it possible that something terrible could have happened to him just in the last half-hour? You never know what *could* happen, do you?
Patient: I guess that's true. So, I guess I don't know for *certain* that he's alive. But, I would bet that he is.

This demonstration can lead to a discussion of how it is truly impossible for the patient to be *certain* that her husband is alive *at this very moment* (accidents and medical emergencies are, after all, *possible*). Nevertheless, the patient coped in a healthy way with the uncertainty, basing her judgment on a *probability* as opposed to a possibility or lack of guarantee. Further, there were no frantic attempts to check or gain certainty. Other low probability events that the patient might take for granted on a regular basis can be discussed. Examples include using scissors (a potential source of injury), electrical appliances (a potential source of shock), crossing the street, and even driving to the therapy session. Such a discussion helps patients understand that they know how to manage uncertainties and therefore can learn how to tolerate other low-risk uncertainties, such as those featured in health anxiety.

Some patients describe concerns about medical problems that are slow to onset (e.g., an as yet undiscovered rare and progressive brain disease), or that will not be manifested until some point in the distant future (e.g., "I will become ill in 40 years because of my exposure to pesticides last week"). Thus, it is impossible to obtain certainty for many of the concerns that health-anxious people harbor. This type of uncertainty is fertile grounds for the proliferation of safety behaviors. For example, a younger patient who fears and harbors preoccupations of becoming sick in old age (e.g., developing Alzheimer's) might presently be avoiding certain situations or stimuli (e.g., aluminum, microwave ovens) or performing safety behaviors (e.g., reading about the latest research on the internet), believing such precautions will guarantee that the feared illness will *never* occur. The therapist can engage such patients in a discussion of the effects of safety behaviors. Do safety behaviors and reassurance really reduce "symptoms?" If so, does that mean the symptoms were most likely part of a serious medical condition or were they related to psychological processes? Would the symptoms of a serious disease dissipate solely by seeking reassurance?

It will be fruitless to use CT strategies to try to convince patients with these sorts of long-term illness concerns that the feared illness will *never* occur. First, it is impossible for *anyone* (even the most knowledgeable physician) to guarantee such things. No one can "know the unknowable." Second, trying to come up with reassuring evidence would merely be akin to helping the patient perform safety behaviors. Indeed, patients spend excessive amounts of time and energy trying to figure out for themselves whether they are healthy or ill, often seeking reassurance from persons who cannot give them definitive answers. Unfortunately, many physicians fall into this trap when consulting with health-anxious individuals. They try to provide the *ultimate* guarantee, which backfires since the patient will eventually come up with some reason why the guarantee might not be valid.

So, trying directly to verbally convince patients they are not ill must ultimately backfire. To be effective, CT should focus on acknowledging the presence of body sensations (e.g., "I understand you are experiencing something uncomfortable in your body which you are concerned with and which has not been explained satisfactorily to you") and helping the patient accept that a definitive explanation is simply not possible. Next, the therapist helps the patient generate a less threatening interpretation of feelings of ambiguity and uncertainty (e.g., "Most people experience body symptoms they can't explain. It sounds like you would benefit from learning to respond to such symptoms in a way that won't cause more problems for you"). Learning to accept reasonable (everyday) levels of uncertainty that we all face in life is the overall goal. The dialog below was used to help a patient with fears of hydrocephalus (an abnormal accumulation of cerebrospinal fluid in the ventricles of the brain, gradually leading to severe physical and mental disabilities encephalitis) to recognize that she already knows how to do this:

Therapist: So, you don't know *for sure* whether Steve is alive, but you'd *bet* that he is. What kind of a bet are you making when you tap on your head and notice that it seems to feel like there is water in your head?

Patient: I'm betting it means I have hydrocephalus.

Therapist: Right. And where does that bet lead you?

Patient: I see what you mean. I get anxious and have to check and re-check my head, look up stuff on the internet, and ask doctors for reassurance.

Therapist: And what do doctors tell you?

Patient: That my head is fine. There is no problem with hydrocephalus. But I *could* have it. It really feels like there's water in there. The doctors *could* be wrong.

Therapist: You're right. They could be wrong. But, remember, Steve *could* be dead right now and you *could* be in an accident driving home from our session today. If you apply the same strategy you use in these cases, what might be a more helpful way of looking at the situation with your head?

Patient: I could tell myself that I *probably* don't have a problem; I'm probably obsessing about it so much because I'm always tapping on my head to see if the feeling is there.

Therapist: Exactly – that's very good. So, do I hear you saying that you would be willing to live with some uncertainty? To take the chance that perhaps you are not becoming very ill? To stop trying to be *100%* sure?

Patient: Yes.

Once the patient accepts they must learn to tolerate uncertainty, additional CT as well as exposure and response prevention exercises (see Chapter 12) can be discussed as vehicles for promoting this change. By engaging in these techniques, the patient will learn that uncertainty is managable, and that the negative outcomes he or she is concerned with are *unlikely*, rather than *guaranteed* not to materialize.

If the patient cannot grasp, or doesn't appear to believe, that seeking ultimate reassurance is a doomed strategy, the therapist can demonstrate this in an experiment in which the patient is offered a session of unlimited reassurance – provided they pledge it will last for the entire year (Salkovskis, Warwick, & Deale, 2003). The therapist tries to provide explanations for all of the patient's symptoms, reviews the medical history in detail, searches the internet for be-

Living with uncertainty about my health		
	Short-term	Long-term
Disadvantages	– Might be sick and not know it – More anxiety and worry – I'd be irritable and preoccupied – Less productivity – It's very difficult	– Might not know if I was sick until it's too late
Advantages		– Feeling at peace with my body – No more body-checking – Better relationships with doctors – Notice less symptoms – Better able to accept what doctors are telling me – Less preoccupation – Better work and home functioning

Seeking reassurance and guarantees about my health		
	Short-term	Long-term
Advantages	– Makes me feel better – Better functioning at work and home – It's usually quick and easy	
Disadvantages	– I already know what the doctor or website is going to say	– Reassurance doesn't last too long – It leads to more preoccupation – It bugs other people – Bad relationships with doctors

Figure 11.2. Short- and long-term advantages and disadvantages of tolerating uncertainty and of seeking reassurance.

nign explanations, has a conference call with a physician, etc. This is done until the patient feels (at least somewhat) reassured for the time being. At the subsequent session, it can be assessed how long the reassurance lasted and how successful it was. Most patients will identify that the effects were short-lived. The therapist and patient can then explore why this was the case.

It is also useful to examine with the patient the short- and long-term advantages and disadvantages of learning to live with uncertainty versus those of trying to seek guarantees. Figure 11.2 shows two four-cell tables that illustrate one patient's perceived short- and long-term pros and cons of becoming more comfortable with uncertainty and of seeking assurance. Note that the advantages of living with uncertainty are exclusively *long-term*, while the disadvantages are primarily *short-term*; the opposite is true for seeking reassurance. This can be used to help the patient to better understand

a) The obstacles to learning to live without guarantees, and
b) The benefits of eventually doing so.

Human beings tend to take the quickest path to relief,. so it makes sense that reassurance-seeking behavior has flourished, even though this only leads to trouble in the long-term. We recommend patients keeping for themselves a list of these advantages and disadvantages to refer to when the urge to seek reassurance arises.

Another technique that can help patients resist urges to seek reassurance is the "Life Savings Wager Strategy." Here, the patient is taught to confront him- or herself with the following question when the urge to seek assurances arises: "If I had to bet my life savings on whether or not (for example) the doctor will say that the strange bruise on my leg means I have hemophilia, where would I place my bet?" (Obviously, the patient should insert his or her own health concern.) Much more often than not, the patient takes the correct bet – because he or she usually knows the correct answer. Recall that reassurance-seeking is merely hearing confirmation of what the person already knows, but is not 100% certain of. It is merely a maladaptive anxiety-reducing strategy, rather than a true way of obtaining useful information.

During assessment it is helpful to identify everyone the patient repeatedly asks for reassurance, and how such requests are replied to. The patient can invite those friends and relatives who offer assurances to a treatment session to learn about the maladaptive role of reassurance in the persistence of health anxiety, and to find out about new and healthier responses upon being bombarded with requests for information from the patient. Physicians who offer assurances should also be included – we have done this via conference call. During the session, the patient is first asked to describe what he or she has learned about how reassurance maintains health anxiety. This demonstrates that the patient understands the conceptual model and conveys to the observers that he or she is taking responsibility for overcoming the problem. We then describe how the friends and relatives can help by not giving in to requests for reassurance. We also present and review Handout 11.3, which includes a list of things to say if the patient asks for reassurance. Of course, it should be understood that the patient bears the ultimate responsibility for resisting urges to ask for reassurance in the first place. It is equally important for friends or relatives to reward successful resistance of urges to seek assurance with a plentitude of verbal praise. Handout 11.3 contains examples of such statements. Sometimes, we role play or rehearse situations when it appears that family members might require instruction in dealing with the patient in constructive, helpful ways.

Assumptions About Probability, Severity, and Inability to Cope

People with health anxiety often exaggerate the level of threat associated with their feared illnesses and the cues that trigger these fears. They assume serious diseases are probable even when the risks are objectively low. Such assumptions can take two forms: overestimation of the *probability* of harm ("jumping to conclusions") and overestimation of *severity* ("catastrophizing"). Many patients further assume they would not be able to cope if they were, in fact, diagnosed with a serious illness. These cognitive distortions fuel anxiety since they imply that intolerable illnesses are omnipresent. They also place the patient on high alert, increasing the risk of misinterpreting harmless signs, sensations, and external situations as threatening.

Socratic dialog is recommended for discussing and modifying assumptions about probability, cost, and inability to cope. Once again, the aim of such discussions is not to give the patient a *guarantee* of safety, but to help devise a more valid set of beliefs and interpretations. Once the patient understands the importance of evaluating his or her logic, the therapist can use behavioral experiments (described below) as well as exposure and response prevention techniques (described in Chapter 12) to gather experiential evidence to challenge faulty assumptions.

Therapists should be alert for two phenomena when challenging faulty assumptions and overestimates of threat. First, many anxious patients confuse *probability* estimates with *severity* estimates. That is, they might acknowledge that a feared illness is *unlikely*; yet because the perceived *severity* of having the illness is high (e.g., "It could be fatal"), extreme precautions, avoidance, and safety behaviors seem prudent. For example, one medically healthy individual argued that it was worthwhile for him to have regular full body MRI scans because even though the risk of cancer is low, developing cancer would be deadly, and it is "better to be safe than sorry." Another explained that although she knew the chances of her heart stopping were "one in a million," she *could* be that "one." She therefore avoided sleeping on her left side (safety behavior). Such thinking and behavior indicates the failure to separate the *costs* of a medical problem from the *probability* of having the feared problem. Socratic dialog can be used to help patients separate probability from severity.

The second phenomenon is patients' beliefs that avoidance and safety behaviors have in the past prevented disastrous outcomes from occurring. For example, the patient with cardiac fears previously described told us that believed her heart has not stopped *because* she constantly avoids strenuous activity, pushes on her chest, and sleeps on her left side. Here, the therapist can help the patient to revisit the mechanisms by which safety behaviors serve to maintain overestimates of threat. Health-anxious individuals often believe they have narrowly escaped tragedy because of the performance of avoidant and safety behaviors.

The fear of death is pervasive in health anxiety. Many patients have catastrophic thoughts about death, often believing they will be self-aware if they die. Another faulty assumption underlying the fear of death (and illnesses) is that family members would not be able to cope or would find the patient (or the death) a serious burden. For example, Katrina, a patient in our clinic, voiced the following: "My husband would have no idea how to raise the kids without me. If I died, the Department of Human Services would take custody of my kids, and my husband would squander all of our money." Socratic questioning led the patient to see that, realistically, her kids would be cared for by relatives. However, she continued to catastrophize that this would be overly burdensome, and that family members charged with raising her children would be overwhelmed.

A behavioral experiment was therefore devised in which Katrina polled her husband and immediate family, asking them the following questions:
- Do you think Ginny and Patrick would be taken away from Don (Katrina's husband) and end up as orphans?
- Do you think Don's spending habits would affect the children's welfare?
- Tell me about how your lives would change if I died?

Katrina and her therapist inspected the responses to this poll, which suggested that all of the relatives thought the questions were absurd since her family is very close and would surely stick together and see that the children would be well taken care of in the event of her death. All of the relatives said they would pitch in to see that the children were cared for during the daytime while Don at work. They also indicated that they would help to make sure Don prudently saved money for their children's education. Katrina was able to incorporate what she learned from the responses to these questions and rethink her catastrophic assumptions. She recognized that life would be more difficult for her family if she died, but that they would manage without her. As Silver and colleagues (2004) point out, experiments such as this one that involve asking others about hypothetical situations can backfire if the patient discounts the information that is collected as being merely speculative.

Disqualifying

Patients with health anxiety sometimes use a double standard when evaluating evidence for and against the presence of a serious medical illness. This reasoning bias involves accepting only evidence that *supports* negative beliefs about illnesses and rejecting or discounting evidence that suggests the problem is not serious. For example, after visiting several doctors who told her the chest and neck pains she was experiencing were likely a pulled muscle this patient continued to worry that she had a serious heart problem:

Patient: I really think I have a serious heart problem the doctors are overlooking.

Therapist: Even though all of your doctors have independently told you the same thing – that your heart is healthy and the pain is probably a pulled muscle in your ribcage? They ran lots of careful tests, you know.

Patient: I know, but the doctors didn't seem completely sure. I think they were confused. They didn't look me in the eye; they seemed unsure. They were just trying to put me at ease. One even suggested I get follow-up tests to rule out a few things.

Patients who disqualify can't discuss their health concerns rationally because they use a double standard. Evidence of illness – no matter how weak or irrelevant – is considered compelling, while evidence against illness beliefs – no matter how strong or persuasive – is explained away as beside the point.

Salkovskis et al. (2003) describe a "pie-chart technique" for helping patients increase their range of nonthreatening explanations for otherwise innocuous body sensations. This involves first asking the patient to identify a particular body sensation, such as a headache, that triggers emotional distress. Next, the therapist and patient list all the *possible* causes of this sensation (e.g., eye strain, muscle tension, stress, migraine, inhalation of chemicals, etc.), including the patient's threatening interpretations and assumptions, for example, that his or her headaches are actually a sign of a brain tumor. The patient is then asked to estimate the percentage of headaches attributable to each of the possible causes that have been listed. Each cause is then made into a slice of a pie graph. Importantly, the patient's threatening misinterpretation is saved until last, which means it will account for a very small (thin) slice of the pie. The patient is then asked to further divide this small slice to account for people who have had negative tests for the feared illness. This technique can lead to a discussion about how the patient tends to view the problem very narrowly, discounting lots of less catastrophic possibilities.

Another behavioral experiment that can be used to challenge disqualifications of more benign interpretations of body sensations and negative test results is to survey other people about their body sensations and other health-related experiences. Dara, for example, was worried that, because her doctors spend only a few minutes with her and do not examine her lungs closely, her concerns about respiratory failure are being overlooked and minimized. Dara had taken the medication Risperdal, which lists respiratory failure as a possible side effect *in the elderly* (Dara was only 36). When doctors indicate that Dara's lungs are functioning normally, and that she is not in any danger, she discounts this as invalid since the doctor's conclusion was based only on a brief examination, and "They are probably not familiar with the side-effect profile of every drug."

To help Dara consider alternative, more realistic assumptions, her therapist asked her to conduct an experiment to examine whether other people also be-

lieve that, "If the doctor only visits with you for a short time, he or she will probably miss something important." She casually asked 20 people she knew who were about her age
a) How much they agreed with the above belief, and
b) To explain how they think about it when the doctor only spends a few minutes during a check-up or consultation.

The results indicated that, while most people had in fact experienced doctors who seemed to be in a rush, they generally disagreed with Dara's belief. Furthermore, the polled individuals' thoughts about hurried examinations were generally uncatastrophic and ranged from "I was glad because I couldn't wait to get out of there," "The doctor probably looked at my medical history and saw that things are probably fine," to "I'm pretty young – there's probably nothing wrong for the doctor to worry about." A few of the poll participants even indicated that, like Dara, they had complained of some symptom that the doctor did not seem concerned about. One of these individuals remarked, "Doctors have seen it all. They probably know better than I do when there is a serious problem and whether it's nothing to be alarmed about." Another said, "In today's world of lawsuits, I trust doctors to know what they're doing because they know what could happen if they make a mistake or a misdiagnosis." Dara and her therapist discussed these responses, which helped Dara open her mind to alternatives.

Some patients who discount might even write off evidence gained through behavioral experiments, arguing that the people who took the poll are somehow different or unrepresentative. Here, the patient can be asked how many more people would have to be polled before he or she would consider the results as valid. This can highlight the excessiveness of the patient's belief. For example, if a patient says "Everyone would need to disagree with my belief in order to convince me that I am wrong," one can point out that the patient's beliefs are different from "everyone" else's.

Holding Lofty Standards

Patients with health anxiety might maintain extremely high expectations of medical professionals, believing they *should* be able to pinpoint and explain every bodily sign, sensation, and perturbation. Of course, all body sensations do not require explanations. Nevertheless, when a patient hears a physician remark that a bodily complaint is "probably nothing," it can evoke the urge to seek another opinion from a "more skilled" professional who might be able to offer a more validating explanation for the origin of the complaint.

Holding lofty standards of medical professionals reveals a failure to consider many of the key concepts presented in the psychoeducational modules described in Chapter 10. Therefore, a review of the concept of body noise and the various possible explanations for common vague and innocuous body sensations is required when this core belief is present. This can lead to a discussion of how it is impossible for even the most well-trained and experienced physician to be able to explain *every* bodily perturbation. Similarly, the therapist can review information about the sensitivity of medical tests and how just because someone experiences "symptoms" does not mean that they are significant enough to cause a positive test. The problem with repeated doctor visits and tests is that these end up focusing ever greater attention on the feared body signs, giving them a life of their own. Socratic discussion can be used to complement a didactic presentation of this material and help patients challenge their own thinking patterns.

One useful behavioral experiment involves introducing a delay between noticing symptoms and acting on urges to seek medical consultation (or other forms of reassurance, for that matter). The therapist and patient settle on a period of time during which the patient remains abstinent from consultations on the basis of how long it might take the feared "symptom" to subside. This is usually several days to a week. The patient keeps a calendar and notes when the abstinence period is over. If the body sensations are still present after the experiment is over, he or she is allowed to consult a physician. Most patients report that the feared "symptoms" subside by the time the delay period is over and this can be used as evidence that the physician's assessment is probably correct.

On the basis of faulty beliefs that physicians are highly likely to make errors, some health-anxious individuals "overinform" their providers. A behavioral experiment to help challenge this view of medical providers as incompetent is that the patient, at an upcoming consultation, initially leaves out certain symptom details he or she fears might result in mistakes. This should be planned in advance with the therapist. What often occurs during this experiment is that the physician questions the patient and eventually gathers the information the patient initially left out. In addition, patients typically feel they are being taken seriously, and that the patient-doctor relationship is stronger than when then patient tries to tell the doctor "everything." Moreover, some patients find themselves listening more closely and learning from physicians rather than worrying whether they describe their symptoms in sufficient detail. Silver et al. (2004) suggest using this behavioral experiment later in therapy when the patient might be more open to alternative explanations for feared body signs and sensations.

Intolerance of Anxiety

Health-anxious individuals might present with beliefs that feeling anxious is dangerous because it will lead to loss of functioning, loss of control, or that it will persist forever and spiral to unmanageable levels. Such beliefs present a barrier to successful treatment using exposure techniques and also lead to an increase in bodily sensations. That is, a patient's viewing feeling anxious as a threat will maintain a focus on physiological sensations associated with anxiety, thereby lending apparent support to the belief that something is medically wrong.

When intolerance of anxiety has been identified, therapists can review psychoeducational modules about the physiology of the anxiety/stress response discussed in Chapter 10. Myths and misinterpretations about the harmful effects of anxiety symptoms can be addressed by assessing catastrophic beliefs about harm from long-term anxiety, and by providing corrective information through didactic and Socratic discussion. Therapists can also have the patient describe previous experiences with anxiety to illustrate how such sensations subside over time and fail to result in marked functional disability or loss of control.

Emotional Reasoning

In emotional reasoning the patient uses his or her feelings of anxiety as evidence to support catastrophic thinking. In other words: "If I am anxious, there must be danger." For example, whenever a patient experiences symptoms of a common cold, he or she may become frightened of having contracted AIDS. They then fall prey to emotional reasoning by thinking along these lines: "I'm nervous and afraid, so there must be a good chance that I really do have AIDS. If not, why would I feel so afraid? I'd better go see the doctor."

The problem with emotional reasoning is that feeling anxious is in itself not firm evidence of danger. Health anxiety is the result of a *misinterpretation* of or an exaggerated overestimate of threat, of an objectively low-risk situation or stimulus. Because emotional reasoning can prevent one from realizing the difference between feelings and facts, the patient should be taught to recognize when emotions are being used to validate fears. Some patients articulate that they "know" their health concerns are senseless, but that, when very anxious, they can't resist seeking reassurance. To this end, the therapist can use Socratic dialog to help the patient recognize that the probability of a feared outcome (e.g., serious sickness) remains the same regardless of whether or not one is feeling anxious.

When to Use Cognitive Techniques

We suggest using the cognitive techniques described in this chapter throughout the course of therapy once the patient is socialized to the biopsychosocial model. Because of the importance of rapport-building during the initial sessions, it is probably best to refrain from strongly challenging the patient's dysfunctional beliefs early on in treatment. Instead, Socratic dialog should be used to amplify the patient's ambivalence and help encourage recognition of the inconsistencies in thinking ("I am terribly sick because something doesn't feel right in my body" vs. "Every sensation in my body is not necessarily a sign of illness"). This helps to induce a sense of cognitive dissonance, which can later be resolved through behavioral experiments. Along these lines, patients should be informed that therapy is an open, collaborative process that requires a shared understanding of problem and how it can be reduced.

As we will see in the next chapter, exposure therapy sessions also afford opportunities for informal discussions about mistaken cognitions. Cognitive change can be maximized during exposure by having the patient process – in cognitive terms – the experience of confronting the feared situation. For example, one can discuss the normalcy of uncomfortable body sensations, the futility of trying to achieve certainty about the cause of a sensation, and the costs of avoidance and reassurance-seeking within this context. Strong affect during exposure can also be seen as an opportunity to use cognitive techniques. Emotional patients can be asked to identify the thoughts and images running through their mind at that moment, which can lead to a Socratic dialog addressing mistaken beliefs, assumptions, or interpretations. The therapist can also point out and summarize changes in beliefs during and after the completion of an exposure exercise.

Although not the primary focus of therapy, events outside the context of treatment and issues related to the therapeutic relationship may also evoke strong emotional responses. Here again, the therapist can help the patient identify specific activating events (e.g., break up of a romantic relationship, nearing the end of therapy) and related thoughts, beliefs, and assumptions. Socratic techniques can be used to help the patient challenge identified thinking errors and generate more healthy alternatives.

Challenges and Obstacles

One challenge for clinicians working with health-anxious individuals is refraining from providing reassurance. Therapists should be careful *not* to frame didactic and Socratic discussions in ways that offer the patient a guarantee of good health. Rather, cognitive therapy should suggest alternate ways of thinking about the problem. This means not using cognitive interventions to *prove* or *disprove* explanations for symptoms. Indeed, it is impossible to offer the patient such an ultimate guarantee; this will only lead to temporary distress reduction and increased efforts by the patient to seek assurance. It is helpful to consider that effective cognitive therapy addresses cognitions and behaviors that *maintain* health anxiety, rather than disease explanations (Silver et al., 2004).

Finally, the therapist should keep in mind that it might be extremely frightening for health-anxious individuals to change their thinking and behavioral responses to feared body sensations – these patients often believe their very lives literally hang in the balance. It is no wonder that many health-anxious individuals show "poor insight" into the senselessness of their beliefs. They might quite literally fear for their lives. Therefore, treatment should progress methodically with careful questioning and exploration of beliefs – and with the gentle application of verbal and experimental techniques aimed at collecting information that challenges the faulty beliefs and provides an alternative viewpoint.

12

Exposure Therapy and Response Prevention

Exposure therapy involves a collection of fear-reduction techniques in which the patient gradually confronts fear-evoking stimuli in real life (situational exposure), in the imagination (imaginal exposure), or interoceptively (exposure to feared body sensations). Response prevention, whereby the patient refrains from safety-seeking behaviors such as body-checking and reassurance-seeking, is a necessary accessory to exposure as it prolongs confrontation with the feared stimulus and teaches the patient that anxiety declines even in the absence of safety behaviors. In this chapter we discuss how to plan for and implement these techniques to reduce health anxiety.

Studies of the structure of hypochondriasis (e.g., Hiller, Rief, & Fichter, 2002; Pilowsky, 1967) have identified three dimensions:

a) *Bodily preoccupation* – the fear of unpleasant or unfamiliar bodily sensations;

b) *Disease phobia* – the fear of developing a serious medical condition; and

c) *Disease conviction* – the belief that one has a serious condition despite evidence to the contrary.

Whereas exposure techniques seem to have their most robust effects on the disease phobia symptom dimension (including the phobia of death; Furer & Walker, 2005), they can also be effective in reducing bodily preoccupation and disease conviction. Readers familiar with the exposure treatment of anxiety disorders will note overlaps in how these techniques are applied to the case of health anxiety. In particular, our approach is derived from previous work on the treatment of obsessions and compulsive rituals (e.g., Freeston et al., 1997; Rachman, Hodgson, & Marks, 1971), panic attacks (e.g., Craske & Barlow, 2007), and pervasive worry (i.e., as in generalized anxiety disorder (Ladouceur, Dugas, Freeston, Leger, Gagnon, & Thibodeau, 2000).

Is Exposure a Cognitive, Behavioral, or Cognitive-Behavioral Treatment?

The initial explanations for how exposure reduces anxiety were couched in strictly behavioral terms: With repeated and prolonged exposure, classically conditioned fear responses would gradually diminish by the process of "habit-uation" or "desensitization" (Stampfl & Levis, 1967; Wolpe, 1958). Later theo-ries proposed a cognitive mechanism: Confrontation with fear-evoking stimuli, in the absence of the expected feared consequences, provides the patient with corrective information that disconfirms fear-related cognitions (Foa & Kozak, 1986). Thus, exposure can be used to test predictions about the dangerousness of body sensations and situations as well as the need for safety behaviors. Using exposure with the intention of modifying faulty cognitions does not, however, rob this technique of its behavioral effects (i.e., habituation). In fact, habitua-tion itself provides a major source of cognitive change: Patients learn that their anxiety remains manageable or even subsides over time even if safety behaviors are not performed. In addition to providing ideal conditions for modifying cog-nitions, exposure therapy affects the patient's self-concept. By facing feared sit-uations and stimuli, and by developing healthy coping strategies, the individual is forced to modify negative representations of the self, leading to a sense of confidence that he or she can in fact manage the situation and his or her emo-tions (Tallis, 1995). We feel it is most beneficial for therapists to capitalize on the fact that exposure and response prevention can produce change through both cognitive and behavioral mechanisms.

Introducing Exposure Therapy to the Patient

Exposure therapy allows the health-anxious patient to have experiences in which (a) feared stimuli are confronted without the use of safety-seeking be-haviors, (b) the anxiety associated with these confrontations declines in inten-sity and feared outcomes do not materialize, and (c) the only explanation for the anxiety reduction is that the feared stimuli are not as dangerous as was originally perceived.

These experiences can be accomplished by carefully planning out the expo-sure exercises and using a graduated approach that is driven by a hierarchy, that is, a list of feared stimuli ranging from least- to most-anxiety-inducing. Hierar-chy items must include stimuli that closely match the patient's health anxiety cues. The items are ranked according to the level of distress the patient expects to encounter during the exposure. Before jumping into creating and executing a fear hierarchy, however, the therapist must properly set the stage for exposure by providing a persuasive rationale to the patient for why he or she should con-front fear-evoking cues.

Providing a Rationale

The following is an example of how to introduce exposure therapy as a useful technique for reducing health anxiety:

Therapist: As you recall from our previous meetings, we have identified a number of situations that trigger your becoming very anxious when in fact the actual level of threat is not that high. The approach we use to weaken the connection between these situations and anxiety is to help you confront the situations in a structured and organized way. When you repeatedly confront these situations without escaping or seeking reassurance about them, your anxiety will naturally subside, and you will find that such situations do not provoke as much anxiety. I know this may sound odd, so let's think of another fear with which you might be more familiar: fear of dogs. Let's say I'm very fearful of dogs and avoid being around them. I am afraid of being bitten. How would you suggest I get over my fear of dogs?

Patient: Well, I guess I'd bring you around lots of dogs so you would learn that they're not going to bite you, especially if you're giving them attention they love.

Therapist: Excellent suggestion! That's exactly what we'd do to help my fear of dogs. We'd start by first looking at pictures of dogs, then I might confront a dog in a cage, then I might play with a small, friendly terrier and work my way up to a big dog, like a Great Dane.

Patient: I see what you're getting at. Your fear is one of dogs; mine is anything that reminds me of brain cancer.

Therapist: Exactly! So just like we would gradually expose me to dogs to get over my fear of dogs, we're going to gradually expose you to things that trigger fears of brain cancer: to help you weaken your fear.

Patient: Ok, that makes sense.

The purpose of exposure is not to reassure the patient that feared consequences would never happen; rather, exposure aims to help the patient learn that
a) The risks associated with feared stimuli are *acceptably low* and
b) The anxiety associated with the risks is temporary and tolerable.

A clear rationale that summarizes these points should be provided when beginning to plan for exposure. The therapist should:
- Define exposure and response prevention as techniques designed to weaken maladaptive thinking and behavior patterns in health anxiety.
- Provide a description of *exposure* as involving gradual confrontation with situations, body sensations, and thoughts that evoke health anxiety; and *response prevention* as involving practice with resisting urges to do anything to

escape from these feelings of anxiety, such as body-checking and reassurance-seeking. The anxiety must decline naturally.
- Give specific examples of the types of exposure and response prevention exercises that might be suggested for the patient to practice. These should be based on the patient's idiosyncratic presentation of health anxiety.
- Give a definition of habituation: The basic idea of exposure therapy is that repeatedly confronting feared situations, body sensations, and thoughts helps a person discover that anxiety does not remain at high levels indefinitely. Instead, the distress subsides over time. Since the patient typically escapes from the feared situation before allowing the anxiety to naturally subside (i.e., by using safety behaviors and seeking reassurance), he or she never has the opportunity to see that habituation eventually would have occurred.
- Highlight that exposure also teaches the patient to be capable of managing reasonable levels of uncertainty. Thus, the aim is not to *desensitize* the patient to the issues of illness and death, but rather to *teach* to patient how to face these facts of life without excessive anxiety.

We find it useful to illustrate the concept of habituation using a graph similar to that in Figure 12.1. Looking at the graph, the following points can be highlighted:
- The graph shows what happens with *repeated* and *prolonged* exposure. The first time a feared situation is confronted, discomfort immediately increases and then gradually declines as time passes. At subsequent exposure sessions, the discomfort subsides more quickly because learning has occurred. After several practice sessions, the initial distress level is lower, and it subsides even more quickly because the connection with anxiety has been weakened.
- This pattern only occurs if the exposure exercise is carefully designed to match the patient's fears, and if the patient remains exposed for a long enough time without engaging in any avoidance or safety behaviors to reduce anxiety.
- The patient should expect to feel anxious, especially when starting to confront the feared situation. This distress, however, is temporary; it will eventually subside if the patient remains in the feared situation without employing safety behaviors.
- Three types of exposures will be used: *situational* or in-vivo exposure (real-life stimuli), *interoceptive exposure* (internal body sensations), and *imaginal exposure* (in the imagination).
- These techniques can be very helpful in reducing anxiety, but they require hard work and must be done correctly in order to obtain good results.

Next, the therapist explains how the exposure treatment is tailored to the patient's particular concerns:

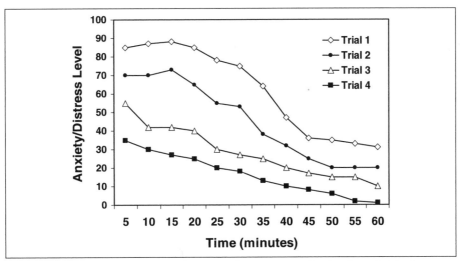

Figure 12.1. Pattern of anxiety reduction (habituation) during repeated and prolonged trials of exposure therapy

- The patient and therapist collaboratively develop lists (hierarchies) of external and internal stimuli that will be ordered according to the level of discomfort each provokes (from less-anxiety-provoking to most-anxiety-provoking).
- Exposure exercises are planned in advance to avoid surprises.
- The therapist provides support and coaching during each exposure task.
- Sometimes, the exposures appear to "push the envelope" of safety or involve doing or thinking about things most people would not ordinarily do or think about on purpose (e.g., write a story about one's own death). The patient must understand the purpose of exposure is not to practice doing what *most people do*: These tasks are designed to weaken health-anxiety symptoms.

Explaining the Role of the Therapist During Exposure

The relationship between patient and therapist in CBT is analogous to that between a student and a teacher or coach. The example below illustrates how one therapist explained her role to a patient:

Therapist: You mentioned you played basketball in high school, right? Well, a good way to think of me is like your basketball coach. Your coach's job was to identify skills needing improvement, like shooting foul shots. He watched you shoot baskets and then gave you specific instructions. You practiced with him, but also practiced these skills on your own over and over to get good at them. If you didn't practice the new techniques, or if you practiced them in a different way than he suggested, you wouldn't develop the skills needed to be a better player. Although the coach wanted you to improve and succeed, he never *forced* you to practice. Rather, *you* ultimately decided how much effort you put into practicing. Treatment for health anxiety goes much the same way. I know how to help you create exercises designed to reduce your health-related concerns. If you practice these exercises the way I show you, chances are you will see improvement. But, if you decide not to practice them as much as you should, or differently than I suggest, chances are you will not improve as much as you would like. I have a great deal of confidence in this technique. But, I cannot force you to do the exercises. What I *will* do is help you see that your feared situations are not as dangerous as you think, and that it is in your best interest to approach rather than to avoid them. If you do the hard work, you will find my coaching and support very helpful. Also, as your coach hopefully did in high school, I will "cheer" you on during the exposure process. We are on the same team against your health anxiety.

Situational Exposure

Building the Hierarchy

In situational exposure, the patient is helped to confront tangible external situations and stimuli that evoke anxiety and distress as well as situations related to illness or death that the patient either avoids or endures with great difficulty and with reliance on safety behaviors and signals. The plan for situational exposure is derived from the functional assessment (see Chapter 8) and with guidance from the patient. The therapist and patient collaboratively generate a list of situations (e.g., talking to a cancer survivor) and stimuli (e.g., book about Lou Gehrig's disease) that trigger health anxiety. These situations should closely match the patient's actual feared stimuli and circumstances, and can be recorded on the Exposure Hierarchy Form shown in Figure 12.2. Situations or stimuli that evoke even the patient's *worst* health-related fears must be included on the hierarchy since failing to confront these reinforces the mistaken idea that such situations really are dangerous.

Below are some examples of the types of situations and stimuli that often appear on situational exposure hierarchies for health anxiety:
- Reading books and newspaper or magazine articles about the feared illness (e.g., a patient who believes he has ALS could read the book *Tuesdays with Morrie*);
- Talking with someone who actually has the feared illness (e.g., someone fearful of having lung cancer could talk with a lung-cancer patient);

Exposure Item	SUDS	Order
1.		
2.		
3.		
4.		
5.		
6.		
7.		
8.		
9.		
10.		
11.		
12.		

Figure 12.2. **Exposure hierarchy form**

- Watching a television show (drama or documentary), movie, or play about someone suffering from the feared illness;
- Reading news stories warning about health threats (e.g., skin cancer, West Nile virus);
- Visiting a local hospital or sitting in a clinic waiting room (e.g., patients worried about HIV or hepatitis C could go the waiting room at the Infectious Diseases Department);

- Attending funerals or visiting a funeral home or cemetery;
- Reading the obituary section of the newspaper;
- Writing one's own obituary;
- Going to the doctor for a check-up, giving oneself a breast or testicular exam (for someone who *avoids* such activities for fear of being diagnosed with a serious problem);
- Going into buildings associated with asbestos;
- Visiting the place where a friend or family member died.

Items on the situational exposure hierarchy list should be detailed enough to advise the patient and therapist of the nature and difficulty of what must be confronted (e.g., reading accounts of having an illness) – yet leave open the option of modifying the specific task(s) in accordance with the patient's particular level of fear (e.g., personal stories of being misdiagnosed, relatives' stories about family members who died unexpectedly). This permits greater flexibility in developing exposures of varying degrees of difficulty as needed.

Once an initial list of situations and stimuli has been generated, the patient assigns a numerical rating of subjective units of discomfort ("SUDS") for each item. The SUDS scale ranges from 0 (*no distress*) to 100 (*maximal distress*), and the therapist can ask: "How anxious would you feel if you confronted _____?" The exposure hierarchy form contains a space for recording the patient's SUDS rating for each item on the list. Next, the therapist and patient together decide on the order in which hierarchy items will be confronted, recording this on the hierarchy form as well. Some considerations for arranging the exposure hierarchy are as follows:

- Begin with low to moderately distressing items (e.g., 40 SUDS or less) to increase the chance of success with initial exercises.
- Use a *graduated* approach in which the exposure items become more distressing, up to the most disturbing items, which are confronted last. Items inadvertently omitted can be added after discussion with the patient.
- Whenever possible, confront each item first under the therapist's supervision and then practice between sessions.

Conducting Exposures

During exposure, the patient confronts the predetermined hierarchy item(s) and remains exposed, without performing safety-seeking behaviors, until the level of distress dissipates. The optimal duration of each exposure session is about 90 minutes. During initial exposures, the therapist may have to shape patients' behavior since most will never have confronted their fears in this way before. It is important to be democratic and show sensitivity so the patient views the therapist as an advocate, rather than as a dictator or taskmaster.

Begin by describing the specifics of the planned exposure task, including how the feared stimulus will be confronted, for how long, and what kinds of safety-seeking behaviors are not permitted during and after the exercise (see the section on response prevention later in this chapter). The *10 Commandments of Exposure* handout (Handout 12.1), which should be reviewed prior to the first exposure, gives the patient an idea of how the exercises will proceed. A brief description of the exercise and an initial SUDS rating should be entered on the Exposure Practice Form (Figure 12.3), which is used to keep track of progress during each exercise.

The following is a representative introduction to a situational exposure task:

Therapist: At our last meeting we agreed that this time you would practice reading stories about glaucoma. So, I brought a handful of personal stories from glaucoma sufferers which I found for you in magazines and on the internet. I also have some scientific articles about glaucoma, as well as some stories

---

Name: _____ Date: _____ Time: _____ Session #: _____

1. Description of the exposure practice:

2. Every _____ minutes during the exposure, rate SUDS from 0 to 100:

3. SUDS when beginning exposure (0–100) _____

SUDS	SUDS	SUDS	SUDS	SUDS
1._____	7._____	13._____	19._____	25._____
2._____	8._____	14._____	20._____	26._____
3._____	9._____	15._____	21._____	27._____
4._____	10._____	16._____	22._____	28._____
5._____	11._____	17._____	23._____	29._____
6._____	12._____	18._____	24._____	30._____

7. What was the outcome of the exposure? What was learned?

8. Comments:

Figure 12.3. Exposure practice form

written by people whose loved ones had glaucoma. We can begin with which-ever you think would be the least distressing to read; but by the end of the session I'd like you to be writing a story about yourself having glaucoma. While you read these stories, I also want you to allow yourself to focus on any disturbing images that may come to mind. That is, I don't want you to push these upsetting thoughts away. The goal is to allow the thoughts to just hang out in your mind. Remember that you will not be allowed to check your eyes or go for any ophthalmology exams. I know this is going to produce anxiety for you, but doing this exposure will help teach you how to successfully man-age thoughts and reminders of glaucoma that you have been going out of your way to avoid. You will see that your distress will subside if you confront these things and allow yourself to become anxious. I will be keeping track of your anxiety level during the exposure by asking you to rate your SUDS level every 5 minutes or so. So, have in mind a number between 1 and 100 to give me. Are you ready?

Troubleshooting

For many patients, success with early exposure exercises predicts success with later, more challenging, ones. If the patient struggles early on, convey sensitivity and understanding that such tasks are highly distressing. Reiterate that this distress, however, is only temporary. The following additional strategies are helpful:
– Model the task prior to instructing the patient to engage.
– Use intermediate exposures that are of greater difficulty than those already conducted, but not as difficult as the planned task. The patient must agree that the intermediate step serves to facilitate eventual exposure to the more difficult item.
– Use cognitive therapy techniques to identify and modify dysfunctional beliefs that are evoking high anxiety or preventing the patient from carrying out ex-posures.
– Review how cognitive change and anxiety reduction has occurred during pre-vious exposures.
– Discuss the importance of learning to take acceptable risks.
– Revisit the importance of learning to tolerate uncertainty.

Imaginal Exposure

As with disorders such as OCD and GAD, thoughts and other mental stimuli play a role in evoking fear and avoidance in health anxiety. For example, a pa-tient might unintentionally see a headline about prostate cancer, which stirs doubts about whether his frequent urination is actually a symptom of this disease. He might also have intrusive images of dying a slow and agonizing death. This problem could be addressed using situational exposure by arranging for the patient to purposely read stories about prostate cancer. Yet, a more systematic way of helping patients confront their often elusive anxiety-provoking thoughts and images is to prepare a script that incorporates these mental stimuli. *Imaginal exposure* entails repeatedly confronting the fear-evoking script until (as with situational exposure) the associated anxiety response is weakened.

There are a number of reasons for including imaginal exposure in the treatment of health anxiety.

- First, this technique helps the patient learn to confront (rather than resist) unpleasant intrusive thoughts (health-related or otherwise) which are ubiquitous – and which become only more intense if they are resisted or suppressed.
- Second, imaginal exposure helps increase tolerance for anxiety by demonstrating to the patient that he or she can manage thoughts about highly distressing material.
- Third, imaginal exposure permits confrontation with doubts about feared illnesses that might not occur until the distant future. For example, "What if I am slowly developing Alzheimer's disease?" In this way imaginal exposure is an excellent tool for helping patients learn to tolerate uncertainties about health-relevant matters.
- A fourth reason for using imaginal exposure is that it helps correct dysfunctional beliefs about senseless (and normally occurring) intrusive thoughts. For example, patients might believe that having thoughts about an illness is an omen that the illness will happen to them. Through repeated and prolonged confrontation with distressing health-related thoughts, patients can learn that such thoughts and images are not significant.

Imaginal Exposure Techniques

In general, the procedures used to implement imaginal exposure are similar to those for situational exposure. Therefore, we focus here on some of the differences. As discussed in Chapter 5, there are three types of imaginal exposure: *primary, secondary*, and *preliminary*. Below, we explain and provide illustrative examples of each type.

Primary Imaginal Exposure

In *primary imaginal exposure* the patient directly confronts anxiety-evoking thoughts or images; this may be spontaneous (e.g., intrusive thoughts of one's own mortality) or cued by external triggers (e.g., doubts about whether one has the rare disease described in a TV documentary). As with situational exposure, a hierarchy of recurring distressing thoughts and images should be developed, arranged in order of SUDS, and recorded on an Exposure Hierarchy Form (Figure 12.2).

During imaginal exposures, the patient is instructed to focus on the distressing cognition and not to engage in any behavioral or emotional avoidance or thought-suppression attempts. To maintain focus, the patient can elaborate on the distressing aspects of the cognition either in writing or by verbalizing it on a tape recorder or other audio-recording device. If the written format is preferred, the patient rereads the thought during the exposure; if a recording has been made, this is repeatedly played back (e.g., via an endless loop tape or a digital audio device set to "repeat") until distress subsides (i.e., reduction in SUDS) as in situational exposure. It is important that imaginal exposure scripts incorporate those specific elements of the scene that provoke the patient's anxiety, for example, the *worst* thing that could happen. To increase vividness, it is also helpful to include real names and places, physical feelings, and emotional reactions in the scene. Inclusion of unimportant details (e.g., setting up the scene and transitions) as well as jokes should be minimized if not directly avoided. The script or scene should also be read or recorded with appropriate emotion.

The example below illustrates how the therapist might introduce and implement primary imaginal exposure.

Therapist: We've talked about your intrusive, distressing images of having terminal cancer. You said that these images often come to mind when you think about the tests you underwent a week ago, and that you try to push the thoughts away or resist them, but that this doesn't work because the thoughts keep returning. You also said the thoughts make you want to ask your family if they think you really have cancer. So, as we have also talked about, today I'm going to help you learn a new and more helpful strategy for dealing with these thoughts. Do you remember what this strategy involves?

Patient: Yes, you said I would have to purposely confront the bad thoughts.

Therapist: That's right. It is actually helpful to practice having these kinds of thoughts on purpose repeatedly, and not engaging in any avoidance or reassurance-seeking. When you practice this, you'll at first experience anxiety, but in time, you'll find that your anxiety will diminish even if you don't push the thought away or ask for assurances. As we have talked about, anxiety naturally subsides if you give it enough time. In the end, you'll weaken the connection between the upsetting images and anxiety. Do you see what I mean?

Patient: Ok, I'm willing to give this a try since nothing else I've done to get rid of the anxiety has worked.

Therapist: Good for you. So, based on what you've told me about these unpleasant thoughts, I'm going to make a recording that will probably induce anxiety in you. I want you to tell me if I'm doing a good job.

(*Into the tape recorder*) You're thinking about the tests you had done because you wanted to make absolutely sure you don't have terminal cancer. You noticed some strange body signs: abnormally shaped bowel movements, occasional dizziness, and other symptoms that you have noticed. You won't know how serious it is, or whether you're actually dying, until the test results come back in some time. And even these results might not be definitive. But, you think you noticed a look on the doctor's face that seemed to suggest she thinks you are very, very ill. You think she looked worried about you but didn't want to say anything until the tests confirmed it. You focus on that idea . . . Your future will probably involve a slow death with terrible pain and anguish . . . You picture yourself wasting away into a skeleton until there's nothing left . . . There's nothing you can do to escape this slow and painful death . . .

OK, how was that? How did I do?

Patient: Oh, gosh. Those are my fears exactly. I'm very anxious right now. My SUDS is about 95.

Therapist: OK. I know this is difficult. Your job is to make friends with this thought. Allow it to hang out in your brain. Remember, the anxiety will come down, but you have to give it time. Meanwhile, just allow yourself to think about these distressing ideas. So, are you ready to focus on the thought? Remember: do not try to push it away. Work on accepting it as a senseless intrusive thought.

The patient then practiced listening to the intrusive thought for the remainder of the session.

As with situational exposure, patients typically evince an immediate increase in anxiety with imaginal exposure, followed by a leveling off and eventual decline in distress. The exposure itself might then last from 10 to 90 minutes and should be terminated when the patient's discomfort has subsided substantially (i.e., reduction in SUDS). Although there is no standard for how much anxiety reduction should occur before termination, a good rule of thumb is at least a 50% reduction. Moreover, the patient should *appear* less distressed and articulate that the thought does not seem as distressing. Some patients might not report the characteristic reduction in SUDS, yet still appear as if they are no longer anxious (e.g., reduction in muscle tension, change in facial expression). We help patients draw the analogy between imaginal exposure and watching a scary movie over and over. When we watch a horror film for the first time we might feel very scared. But if one were to watch the movie 100 times, it would become much less frightening. This is the same mechanism by which imaginal exposure works.

There are pros and cons to consider regarding whether the patient (as opposed to the therapist) should take the lead in writing or recording imaginal exposure scripts. An advantage of having the patient take the lead is that he or she knows best about the details of the particular situation (e.g., which material is most anxiety-evoking) and can therefore produce a more realistic scenario that matches the intrusive thought or image as it is typically experienced. A disadvantage, however, is that the patient might specifically avoid including truly distressing material in the exposure. Thus, the therapist must make sure the scene incorporates the patient's *worst* fears. Another consideration is that a self-generated script might seem more like "thinking" to the patient – especially if the patient is listening to his or her own voice (as opposed to the therapist's) on a tape recorder. If the patient is too fearful of creating the exposure script him- or herself, the therapist might create an initial script with the goal being for the patient to eventually do this him- or herself.

Secondary Imaginal Exposure

This type of imaginal exposure involves focusing on the dreaded consequences of (a) confrontation with feared stimuli or body sensations, or (b) not using safety behaviors or safety signals.

For example, a patient might imagine developing skin cancer from not closely having inspected her skin. Secondary imaginal exposures are therefore conducted in conjunction with situational exposures (i.e., hence the term "secondary"). For instance, the patient with fears of skin cancer might spend a day wearing short sleeves in the sun (situational exposure) and then refrain from checking her skin (response prevention). For imaginal exposure, she might then picture herself inadvertently finding suspicious marks on her skin, going to the doctor, and thinking she has developed terminal cancer. The script for imaginal exposure usually incorporates the situational exposure and lack of reassurance. For example:

> You have been walking around outside without sufficient protection from the sun's ultraviolet light. You think about how a few family members have had moles removed because they were suspicious – the same family members who said they used to sunbathe when they were younger. Now, you're thinking about your own skin. You want to check yourself to make sure there are no new signs of skin cancer. You would like to seek a doctor's reassurance that spending an hour in the sun was not enough to give you a melanoma. The anxiety is becoming more and more intense as you picture what a cancerous mole might look like . . . Maybe you have one, maybe not. Then you happen to notice a strange looking mole on your arm . . . It's multicolored and has a very odd shape to it . . . You can picture it in your mind . . . You can already hear the doctor saying, *"now that looks suspicious"* and looking visibly worried for

you ... You wonder how deep into your skin it goes and whether the cancer has spread. You imagine going to a doctor and him telling you that it is too late – you shouldn't have waited. Now, the cancer has spread out of control and you will die ... All because you were in the sun without protection and didn't check your body ...

Preliminary Imaginal Exposure

This third form of imaginal exposure entails visualizing a confrontation with feared situations and stimuli *before* conducting situational exposure to the items. Such exercises are not usually planned during the hierarchy development phase, but instead are inserted as needed. For example, if a patient is reluctant to engage in a situational exposure to reading a book about having a terminal illness, the therapist might suggest that he or she first *imagine* doing this. Importantly, imagery practice should by used to promote situational exposure, not as a substitute for it.

Interoceptive Exposure

As discussed throughout this book, health anxiety is commonly triggered by essentially innocuous bodily signs, sensations, and perturbations. Systematic exposure to body sensations that provoke health anxiety, known as interoceptive exposure, was initially developed by Barlow and colleagues (e.g., Barlow, Craske, Cerny, & Klosko, 1989) to help patients with panic disorder face innocuous sensations that occur as part of panic attacks. Interoceptive exposure involves intentionally recreating feared body sensations (e.g., spinning to create dizziness) and allowing the patient to learn that (a) these sensations are not dangerous, and (b) the associated anxiety (and indeed the sensations themselves) remits over time if allowed to do so.

Providing a Rationale

It is important to preface interoceptive exposure with a clear rationale, since it might seem strange to the patient to purposely induce the very sensations that trigger anxiety. The following dialog provides a script for how to introduce this technique:

Therapist: As we have been talking about, there are certain body sensations that trigger excessive levels of anxiety for you. The anxiety is excessive because the body sensations do not appear to be dangerous, threatening, or signs of anything serious. Again, the body sensations and your anxiety are *quite real*, but they do not indicate what you are afraid they indicate. It is as if you are frightened that a big tiger is waiting for you around the corner, when it is really only a kitten. The approach we use to weaken excessive anxiety that is associated with body sensations is to help you confront the sensations in a structured and organized way. When you repeatedly confront these feelings without escaping or seeking reassurance about them, you will learn that you are able to control and reduce the feared sensations more than you had thought. You will also learn that you can bring these sensations on at will in a variety of ways. This will help you see that there is no basis for the fear associated with the body sensations. Finally, you will learn more helpful ways of responding to the sensations that do not make you preoccupied with your health.

Planning

As with situational and imaginal exposure, interoceptive exposure requires a comprehensive functional assessment to determine the most appropriate body sensations to be confronted. A hierarchy-driven approach is recommended in which less disturbing sensations are confronted before confronting the most upsetting ones. Planning for interoceptive exposure also requires determining how the feared sensations will be evoked. Procedures for producing many of the commonly feared bodily signs and sensations in health anxiety are presented in the sections below – in the context of two types of interoceptive exposure: primary and secondary.

Interoceptive Exposure Techniques

Primary Interoceptive Exposure

In primary interoceptive exposure, the therapist helps the patient to deliberately provoke feared body sensations in the office using a variety of techniques and maneuvers. The sensation is maintained or repeated during the session until habituation occurs (i.e., reduction in SUDS). One instructs the patient not to engage in any safety behaviors or other activities that would reduce the intensity of the sensation or prevent a feared outcome (e.g., fainting). Instead one encourages the patient to make the sensations as intense as possible. Changes in beliefs about the dangerousness of the sensations are emphasized when discussing the outcome of the exposures.

Table 12.1 shows techniques for inducing commonly feared body sensations during interoceptive exposure. As with situational and imaginal exposures, interoceptive exposures should first be performed in the session with the therapist present. In fact, we encourage the therapist to perform the exposure task along side the patient so that the therapist and patient can compare their physical experiences, and so the therapist can model a calm response to the sensations. Subsequently, the patient is instructed to practice the exercise(s) each day between sessions. Exposure practice forms (Figure 12.3) are used to keep track of SUDS levels both in the session and during homework practice. Cognitive therapy techniques can also be used to identify and modify catastrophic beliefs about the dangerousness of the sensations.

Table 12.1. **Techniques for provoking body sensations during interoceptive exposure**

Technique (instruction)	Body sensation(s)
Hyperventilation (rapid deep breathing for 90 seconds)	Shortness of breath, sense of unreality, tingling, sweating, dizziness, lightheadedness, dry mouth/throat, light sensitivity, chest tightness, racing heart beat, exhaustion
Body tensing (tense muscles in arms, legs, abdomen, neck, face, etc., or do push-ups for 60 seconds)	Muscle tension, sweating, racing heart
Head lifting (place head between legs for 30 seconds, then lift head quickly to normal position; repeat)	Lightheadedness, head rush, disorientation
Swallowing (attempt to swallow 5 times in quick succession)	Throat tightness, lump in throat, breathlessness
Hold breath for as long as possible (at least 60 seconds)	Chest tightness, shortness of breath, smothering sensations
Run in place (lifting knees up to chest; or step up on stairs for 60 seconds)	Shortness of breath, racing heart beat
Staring (stare intensely at a small spot in the corner for 2 minutes)	Sense of unreality
Spinning (either in a standing position or while seated in a revolving chair for 60 seconds)	Dizziness, disorientation
Straw breathing (breathe rapidly through a very thin straw for 60 seconds)	Shortness of breath, chest tightness, smothering sensations
Hot shower (take a hot shower with the door closed)	Weakness, disorientation, hot flash
Gag (use toothbrush to brush the back of the tongue)	Nausea
Caffeine (drink highly caffeinated beverage or take caffeine pills, e.g., NoDoz).	Racing heart, sweating, hot flash

Secondary Interoceptive Exposure

Secondary interoceptive exposure involves confronting feared body sensations by engaging in activities that have been avoided *because they produce the feared sensations.* The possible situations and stimuli for this type of exposure are therefore highly patient-specific and require thorough assessment. Some patients, for example, avoid drinking soda or champagne because of the fear of feeling bloated; others avoid vigorous exercise because they fear heart palpitations, sweating, feeling flushed, or becoming weak. Further examples include avoidance of eating spicy or high-fiber foods (for someone afraid of stomach and lower GI sensations) and jogging outside on a cold morning (for a patient afraid of throat pain, i.e., from the cold air).

As Taylor and Asmundson (2004) point out, the distinction between this form of interoceptive exposure and situational exposure is arbitrary, albeit clinically and conceptually useful. For the most part, the difference lies in the intent and emphasis of the task. Whereas *interoceptive* exposure places the focus on the intense body sensations that are produced, *situational* exposure focuses on confronting fear-evoking situations regardless of whether or not strong body sensations are produced.

Stylistic Considerations During Exposure Sessions

Remarks During Exposure Tasks

Offering appropriate observations, praise, encouragement, and support during exposure maintains the sort of rapport that is necessary for a successful outcome. Ask the patient to tell you what he or she is learning by doing exposures. When exercises are proceeding as planned, the following sorts of comments and open-ended questions are helpful:
- "You're doing great; See how your anxiety level decreases on its own?"
- "It looks like you're much less anxious now compared to when we started the session – and you haven't done any reassurance-seeking. How do you explain that?"
- "This seems like it's getting easier for you. You're weakening the link between your fearful body sensations and anxiety. Good for you!"
- "You see that? You don't need to engage in safety behaviors to reduce your anxiety. The anxiety will decrease on its own if you let it."

If the patient is having difficulty with anxiety during the exercise, convey your understanding of how difficult exposure can be, and that, with time and persistence, the exercises will ultimately become more manageable. Offer the following remarks:

- "Sometimes it takes a while for anxiety to go down. That means that you have to stick with the exposure even though it may be difficult. Eventually, you will begin to feel less distressed; you'll be glad you stuck with it."
- "This time your anxiety didn't decrease by much, but we will keep working at it until it gets easier."

Avoid Providing Reassurance

Patients sometimes query the therapist about the level of risk in doing exposures (e.g., "Are you sure this is safe?" – "Would you do this?"). Avoid providing blanket reassurance that exposure tasks are "harmless," or that the patient is "guaranteed" to be safe. The patient must learn for him- or herself what risks are acceptable. By promising that "everything will be alright," the therapist only strengthens the patient's reassurance-seeking behavior. Rather, it is more effective to help the patient accommodate to uncertainty. Examples of therapeutic responses to questions about the risk of conducing exposure exercises include:

- "I can't guarantee you that you're 100% healthy"
- "I don't know for certain that those body sensations don't mean you have a terminal illness"
- "I can't say for *certain*, but I think the risk is low enough for us to try this exposure without having to be too concerned about your health."

Humor

The use of humor or laughter to lighten the mood during exposures may be appropriate and can be beneficial, although it is not advised in times of extreme distress and especially should not be used as a distraction method. The clinician should follow the patient's lead and ensure that humorous remarks remain relevant to the exposure situation and do not distract from this task.

Response Prevention

This entails voluntarily refraining from safety-seeking behaviors. It means resisting urges to check one's body, look up health and illness-related information in books or the internet, seek medical consultations of all sorts, seek reassurance from family and friends, and engage in other subtle rituals and safety behaviors performed to alleviate health anxiety as identified during the functional assessment. It is vital that response prevention accompany exposure to feared situations, thoughts, and bodily stimuli so the patient can learn that health anxiety and body vigilance subsides naturally, and that safety-seeking is not necessary to prevent feared negative consequences. There is, however, room for flexibility in response prevention. Specific guidelines for the patient to follow should be determined collaboratively. Whereas some patients are able to immediately cease all body-checking, reassurance-seeking, and other safety maneuvers, others require a more gradual approach to stopping these behaviors. Some considerations when planning for response prevention appear below.

- Revisit the educational materials presented in Chapter 10 and emphasize the negative effects of safety behaviors and the rationale for stopping them. Point out that patients are often surprised at how much less attention they pay to their bodies when they successfully engage in response prevention.
- Emphasize that not performing safety behaviors is a difficult choice.
- Define the patient-specific rules for response prevention and record them on the Help with Response Prevention form (Figure 12.4). Give the form to the patient as a guide.
- If relatives or friends are involved in the patient's rituals, encourage their help with refraining from answering reassurance-seeking questions.
- For patients who are initially unable to cease all rituals, consider a gradual approach in which instructions to stop rituals parallel progress up the exposure hierarchy, the goal being complete abstinence midway through treatment.

Specific response-prevention instructions:

Choose not to engage in safety behaviors.

If you are having trouble choosing to resist:

- Remember that the urge is based on a mistaken belief or assumption. You don't *really* need to do *that* to feel better or reduce the chances of being ill.
- Find someone to talk to and ask them to stay with you until the urge passes.
- Leave the situation for a while (if possible) to get away from reminders.
- *If you perform a safety behavior,* immediately record it on a self-monitoring form and discuss it with your therapist. Then, deliberately re-expose yourself to the situation that evoked the safety behavior.

Figure 12.4. Help with response prevention form.

– The patient should record violations of response prevention on Health Concerns Log (see Handout 8.2) so that areas in need of additional attention can be addressed.

Rules for Response Prevention

Below, we outline common response prevention plans and strategies for health anxiety patients:

Body-checking. Patients should not engage in any checking of the body such as taking their pulse, using devices to monitor other vital signs (e.g., blood-sugar levels), or inspecting the skin. Inspecting or scrutinizing body fluids and excreta is also prohibited. For example, bowel movements should be flushed without looking at them.

Reassurance-seeking. Medical appointments for previously evaluated symptoms are off limits. If a new symptom emerges, this should be discussed with the therapist, who should employ cognitive components of treatment to evaluate the evidence for and against the likelihood that this new symptom represents a serious health risk. The aim is not to discourage patients from seeking medical attention when they are in need; rather, to help them make rational, evidence-based decisions about when to seek medical care.

Telephoning medical personnel or "Ask the Nurse" help lines is also off limits, as are internet searches for medical information. If patients must be online for work or school, they should avoid medical websites. Having a partner or relative monitor internet use helps in some cases. The patient is also not permitted to review his or her own medical records.

Patients should not ask for or obtain reassurance about any health matters from friends and family members. This mean no straightforward questioning (e.g., "Do you think my stomach ache is anything to worry about?"), telling others about body sensations (e.g., "I've had this headache for 2 days now . . ."), or discussing symptoms (e.g., "What do you think causes people to get dizzy?"). We suggest asking the *patient* to draft a letter to send to friends and relatives that (a) explains the problem with giving reassurance and (b) provides suggestions for how to respond if asked for reassurance.

For example, "I'm sorry but I can't answer your question because I agreed to help you with treatment. How can I help you manage the anxiety you are feeling in a healthy way?" The therapist can ensure accuracy of the letter and then arrange for the patient to mail it to friends and relatives.

Cleaning/washing. Excessive hand-washing and showering should be off limits for individuals concerned about contracting illnesses. This includes washing with cleaning agents such as hand sanitizers or wetwipes. Creams, make-up, and deodorants are allowed as long as they are not used to reduce contamination fears. Water may be drunk or used when brushing teeth, but not to clean the face or hands. If a washing behavior is performed, the patient should "re-contaminate" him- or herself with the anxiety-provoking contaminant.

Mental analyzing. Patients should not spend time mentally going over what doctors have told them or trying to mentally analyze situations related to their health. This simply leads to preoccupation. Instead of trying to figure out health-related dilemmas, they should purposely imagine being uncertain (as in imaginal exposure, e.g., "maybe I'm sick and maybe I'm not").

Dietary restrictions. Patients may be so convinced that they are suffering from a terminal illness that they may go to great lengths to take dietary supplements, herbs, or other "treatments." They should be discouraged from taking these agents if their use functions to reduce health anxiety. Similarly, adhering to special diets *because of health anxiety* is prohibited.

The therapist should be alert for additional safety behaviors and signals that will require response prevention rules.

Employing a Support Person

If patients encounter difficulty conducting exposure and response prevention tasks independently, it may be useful to designate a "support person" such as a close friend, partner, or other relative to assist with treatment. The support person can attend therapy sessions (at the discretion of the therapist and patient) to receive instructions in how to help. The best support persons are those who are able to be empathetic, yet firm and assertive. Individuals who are overinvolved in the patient's symptoms, or who are overly critical, should be avoided. The support person should attend one or more sessions to become socialized to the treatment approach and to his or her own role. Specifically, this individual functions as an advisor to the patient but does not police all activities. No threats or physical force are to be used to change the patient's behavior; rather, that person should provide encouragement to resist safety behaviors and cope with the temporary anxiety, typically when the patient requests help or needs guidance. Patients should be instructed to call on the support person when they feel they need help.

Integrating Cognitive Therapy

During exposure sessions, cognitive therapy techniques (see Chapter 11) can be used (a) to help set up exposure exercises, (b) during these exercises to help modify dysfunctional cognitions, and (c) following exposure to further facilitate belief change.

When planning and preparing for each exposure, cognitive techniques can identify mistaken beliefs and expectations to be tested during the exercise. The importance of learning to take risks and manage acceptable levels of uncertainty should also be discussed. During exposures, cognitive techniques can be used to promote healthy beliefs about specific feared consequences (e.g., "I have been jogging for 10 minutes and the only thing that's happened is that my anxiety level has decreased. This means my cardiovascular system must be stronger than I'd thought") and about anxiety in general (e.g., "I must confront my fear to prove to myself that these are just harmless body sensations" – "Even if I initially feel anxious, these feelings eventually subside"). After the exposure exercise, Socratic discussion can be used to review the outcome of the intervention, examine evidence for and against the catastrophic fear, and develop more realistic beliefs. What was learned during the exposure? Was it as awful as had been anticipated? Did the feared consequences materialize? If not, how come?

Programmed and Lifestyle Exposure: Encouraging Independence

This chapter has primarily illustrated *programmed exposure*, whereby the patient implements planned exercises under the therapist's direction at specific times and in particular locations. Yet it is also important for patients to engage in *lifestyle exposure*, which means making choices to take advantage of day-to-day opportunities to practice confronting (rather than avoiding) feared stimuli. Encourage the patient to be opportunistic and to view spontaneously arising fear triggers as occasions to practice treatment techniques and work on further reducing their health-anxiety symptoms. Patients can be repeatedly reminded that every time they choose to confront a feared situation without engaging in safety behaviors, health-anxiety symptoms are weakened. And every time the decision is made to avoid a potential lifestyle exposure situation, symptoms are in fact strengthened.

13

Overcoming Common Obstacles and Maintaining Treatment Gains

The first half of this concluding chapter describes a number of barriers to implementing effective cognitive-behavioral treatment of health anxiety (aside from the motivational difficulties described in Chapter 7). We also suggest solutions for overcoming these obstacles. For the most part, potential obstacles belong to two domains: (a) those arising from the patient's behavior and (b) those arising from ways in which the therapist is implementing the various treatment techniques.

The second part of the chapter presents suggestions for how to maintain treatment gains following the termination of therapy.

Overcoming Common Obstacles

Once a patient is engaged, psychological treatment for health anxiety often proceeds smoothly. Rough waters, however, are occasionally encountered, and troubleshooting is sometimes needed. The therapist may have difficulty conceptualizing a particularly complicated symptom presentation; the patient might not properly adhere to treatment instructions; and improvement might be slow despite apparent compliance with all of the treatment components. This first section of the chapter addresses how to troubleshoot some of the common barriers to successful treatment that we have not covered in earlier chapters.

Non-Adherence

The most common obstacle encountered in CBT for anxiety problems – and health anxiety is no exception – is the patient's failure to follow treatment instructions as directed by the therapist. Patients may refuse to engage in behavioral experiments, balk at exposure therapy tasks, or scoff at the suggestion that they stop their safety-seeking behaviors. Because these interventions represent the active ingredients in therapy, noncompliance must be dealt with early on. Luckily, many problems with adherence can be circumvented if the therapist is proactive. Often, adherence problems stem from an incomplete understanding of the biopsychosocial model of health anxiety, or how the model applies to the patient's own symptoms. Second, the rationale for the particular treatment technique must be clear – patients should understand how engaging in difficult and frightening or "risky" therapy exercises will reduce their problems in the long run. These two points underscore the importance of the psychoeducational component of treatment. A third strategy for avoiding adherence problems is to ensure that the patient feels involved in the selection and planning of behavioral experiments, exposure exercises, and the cessation of safety-seeking behaviors.

If a patient is not following through with completing behavioral experiments or exposure tasks, the therapist should gain a clear picture why. Sometimes noncompliance with homework can be addressed with problem-solving (e.g., to make more time available for practicing). It is also important to make sure the therapy task itself is a good match to the patient's health concerns and dysfunctional beliefs. If not, the patient might perceive the exercise as irrelevant. If high levels of anxiety prompt refusal or "shortcuts" (e.g., subtle avoidance or safety strategies) during behavioral experiments and exposure practices, the therapist can review the importance of hypothesis testing and confronting fears as well as the role of avoidance and safety-seeking in maintaining problems with health anxiety. Cognitive strategies (e.g., Socratic dialog) can then be used to identify and address the patient's catastrophic predictions about dangers underlying the reluctance to fully confront the feared stimulus or to drop the safety behavior in question. With an understanding of the purpose of the exercise – and the expectation that anxiety will temporarily increase before it subsides – it is often possible to successfully encourage patients to "invest anxiety now in a calmer future."

Sometimes, therapists are tempted to suspend or postpone planned behavioral experiments and exposure exercises because of the patient's high anxiety. Refining the exposure hierarchy and adding intermediate items are sometimes appropriate therapeutic maneuvers, for example, if patient threatens to discontinue treatment. However, therapists are discouraged from the liberal use of these tactics, even when patients appear quite scared. Habituation *will* occur at some point if the exposure exercise is performed correctly, and postponing only reinforces avoidance patterns and unrealistic beliefs about the dangerousness of objectively low-risk situations. Instead, the therapist should emphasize the patient's control over behavioral experiments and exposures: It is ultimately his or her choice to perform the tasks. Moreover, it is a difficult choice because of the perceived risk. However, this choice has important consequences: Choosing not to complete the exercise as directed is essentially the decision to strengthen health-anxiety symptoms. The therapist can use motivational interviewing techniques (see Chapter 7) to create and amplify the discrepancy between non-adherence and the patient's broader goals and values. When nonadherence is perceived as conflicting with important personal goals (such as self-image, happiness, success), change becomes more likely (Miller & Rollnick, 2002).

Arguments

Arguments can arise over a number of issues in therapy. Patients might protest that they have tried exposure therapy on their own, and that it doesn't work. Chapter 7 outlines strategies for dealing with such arguments. In dealing with arguments over exposure therapy, the therapist can also ask for examples of how the patient has faced his or her fears. If self-exposure has indeed been attempted previously with no positive results, more than likely the patient has incorporated some form of avoidance or safety-seeking into the exercise, thereby making it suboptimal. For example, perhaps the exposure was too brief and the patient left the feared situation before anxiety subsided naturally. Perhaps the patient did not fully engage in the task or used avoidance strategies. Finally, perhaps checking, reassurance-seeking, or other safety behaviors and signals were used to help reduce anxiety during or immediately following the exposure. The therapist should applaud the patient's efforts in attempting exposure and also point out how therapeutic exposure under a clinician's supervision is likely to be more systematic, prolonged, and repeated; and that confronting fears in this way is more likely to be successful (albeit also more difficult).

Sometimes, patients become contentious and look for flaws in the psychoeducational information they are given, rather than processing this information in a positive and helpful way. This can be avoided by using a less didactic style and increasing the use of Socratic dialog so that the belief-altering information is generated directly by the patient. If discussions about body signs and sensations or mistaken beliefs take an argumentative or combative turn, the therapist should summarize the discussion and reach a conclusion that the patient *could* be correct in his or her assertions; but that rather than taking anything for granted, it is important to closely examine the facts or test them out. For example, if a patient strongly states that having *one more* medical test would permanently quell his need for reassurance that he doesn't have a case of MRSA (methicillin-resistant *Staphylococcus aureus* – a highly resistant bacterial infection sometimes known as "the superbug"), this view should be honestly considered; and the ensuing dialog can include questions about past experiences. For example, has the patient ever made the "just-one-more-time" promise before, and if so, what was the outcome? What could be done to find out whether the reassurance-seeking is really necessary? What have doctors said in the past about MRSA, and what does he expect to hear this time? Would it be more helpful to learn how to manage such situations without reassurance? This highlights the importance of maintaining a collaborative patient-therapist relationship.

To reiterate, we strongly advise therapists to refrain from protracted debates with patients over the potential risks involved with doing behavioral experiments and exposure exercises, and ceasing safety behaviors. Not only are such arguments fruitless, they reinforce the patient's patterns of spending too much time focusing on bodily sensations and worrying about risk and uncertainty. Essentially, arguments of this type are nothing more than a verbalizing of the patient's analyzing and reassurance-seeking behaviors. Moreover, when patients perceive that the therapist is frustrated, angry, or trying to coerce them into compliance (e.g., "you can't *make* me do this"), they tend to lose motivation. When a reluctant patient attempts to engage in rational argument about risk and danger, the best course of action for the therapist is to step back and recognize that the decision to engage in treatment is a difficult one. Motivational statements, such as the following, are often persuasive:

- You're right. There is risk involved, but it is not high risk. The goal of treatment is to weaken your perception that these are highly risky situations.
- Remember that in situations like this, it is virtually impossible to have a complete guarantee of safety. No one can reassure you completely – no one is completely sure, themselves.
- It looks like you are having a lot of difficulty deciding to do this exercise. But if you are going to get over your health concerns, you have to confront your uncertainty and find out that the risk is low.
- You are here in treatment for yourself – not for me. So, I won't argue or debate with you. This is entirely your choice. However, I will point out that trying these exercises and enduring the short-term anxiety is likely to help you in the long run. On the other hand, you are the one who has to live with the problem if you choose not to do the therapy.

Terminating Treatment with an Argumentative or Non-Adherent Patient

If, despite much effort to repair such problems – and the use of motivational interviewing techniques – the patient still persists in refusing to cooperate with treatment instructions, it may be appropriate to suspend treatment. For some clinicians, this might mean shifting the focus of therapy to another problem. For others, this might mean ending therapy altogether. If suspension or termination seems inevitable, this process should be handled delicately and in a sensitive (as opposed to a punitive) manner. In most cases, the patient should understand that he or she is welcome to return to treatment at some point in the future if and when he or she is ready and willing to work on the health-anxiety issues according to the therapist's plan. The script below is an example of how we typically discuss nonadherence as indicative of "bad timing." This often works well when needing to terminate treatment.

Therapist: It seems to me that, for whatever reasons, we are not getting very far with therapy. I know this treatment can be very difficult, and I can tell you are having a tough time making the attitudinal changes and doing the exercises that will help you overcome your health concerns. I believe this is why treatment is not – and will not – be as effective for you as it should be. When this happens it means is that now is not the right time for you to be in this kind of therapy. So, it is best that we stop at this point. Maybe at some point in the future it will be a better time for you to consider how psychological treatment can help you, and you will be able to do the exercises you need to do to benefit. I would be happy to work with you at that point.

Excessive Reassurance-Seeking

Some health-anxious individuals approach psychological treatment as they would a medical consultation, believing the therapist will provide that long sought-after "ultimate guarantee" of good health. Such patients might attempt to hijack cognitive interventions by using them to hear from an "expert" (i.e., the therapist) that, for example, the specific "symptom *du jour*" is not a sign of a serious illness, or that short-term anxiety is not dangerous. Whereas efforts to gain assurances are usually straightforward and easily identified (most patients will ask the same questions again and again, though perhaps in different ways), some patients are subtler. Keen judgment is sometimes needed to assess whether the function of questioning truly is reassurance-seeking. Once patients understand the problems associated with reassurance-seeking, it is appropriate to ask about the purpose of suspected questions (e.g., "You've asked me that question a few times today. Are you trying to get me to reassure you about this?"). Other patients seek assurances by stating their concerns over and over hoping for some acknowledgment from the therapist that they are correct. If the therapist hears him- or herself repeating the same information to a patient more than once or twice, or if the patient is repeating ideas more than once or twice, it is a signal to consider whether reassurance-seeking is occurring.

It is easy for the clinician to fall into the trap of offering reassurance. Indeed, it intuitively feels helpful and therapeutic to answer questions, clarify issues, and reduce confusion for patients. The problem with providing assurances, however, is that this robs the patient of the experience of evaluating his or her dysfunctional beliefs. The immediate reduction in distress also reinforces the patient's reassurance-seeking behavior in the presence of the therapist. More-over, during exposure, reassurance-seeking prevents prolonged confrontation (and habituation) to the feared situation, which involves learning to manage feelings of uncertainty. It is therefore important for the therapist to recognize attempts to seek reassurance and avoid the temptation to ease the patient's distress by providing guarantees. Some patients have difficulty resisting urges to seek reassurance even when given instructions not to do so. Excessive and persistent reassurance-seeking must be handled with caution because miscommunications can de-rail therapy. Below we describe some useful ways to address specific types of persistent reassurance-seeking. These techniques have largely been adapted from strategies described for managing reassurance-seeking in other anxiety disorders, such as OCD (e.g., Abramowitz, Franklin, & Cahill, 2003).

"How do you know I'm not medically ill?"

Some patients express the need for certainty in the form of this question. This, of course, cannot be answered satisfactorily since it requires disproving the negative. To address this question, we recommend the therapist first acknowledging that the patient *could* be correct. The next step is to steer the dialog toward a discussion of the ubiquity of uncertainty in everyday life (e.g., "How do I know that I won't get into a deadly accident on my way home from work today?"). Cognitive techniques geared toward resolving intolerance of uncertainty (as discussed in Chapter 11) can also be used.

Requests for Additional Medical Consultations

Repeated and persistent requests for further medical testing, consultations with expert sources of health information, and checking on the internet should be discussed in light of whether or not they will be helpful for moving the patient toward overcoming the need for certainty. What are the pros and cons of an additional consult? A main disadvantage is that this often leads to obtaining incorrect or contradictory information that augments uncertainty and strengthens inaccurate beliefs. For example, patients might read about and misinterpret medical statistics. Individuals with the habit of searching websites for information about medical symptoms should be persuaded to cease and desist from such behavior during treatment since the aim of therapy is to learn to rely on judgments about risk that are derived from real-world evidence.

Asking for Reassurance During Exposure Exercises

When patients desire a guarantee of safety during exposure exercises (e.g., "Are you sure my prostate is not going to become enlarged from sitting on a cold, hard church pew?"), the first inclination may be to put them at ease by reassuring them they are not in any danger. This, however, undermines the goal of living with acceptable levels of risk and uncertainty. On the other hand, patients shouldn't be made to feel as if they are at high risk for negative consequences. Thus, the ideal response uses empathy, focusing on how the exposure task is *designed* to evoke uncertainty and discomfort. Patients learn to reduce their anxiety by remaining in the feared situation without using safety-seeking or reassurance-seeking behaviors. A general rule to keep in mind is that questions about risk in a given situation should be answered only once. Additional queries should be pointed out for the patient and addressed in the following way:

Therapist: I can tell you're feeling uncomfortable and are searching for a guarantee right now. Since I already answered that question, it would not be helpful for you if I answered it again. The best way to deal with your distress and uncertainty is for you to practice tolerating the distress and waiting for it to subside naturally. How can I help you to do that?

We have had broad experience with individuals completely unable (or unwilling) to resist persistent urges to seek reassurance both within and between therapy sessions. Because the repeated assurance-seeking inevitably compromises treatment outcome, therapy had to be suspended in these cases. As addressed above, suspension is the last resort when patients refuse to comply with treatment procedures, and it is imperative that the therapist convey in a caring and sensitive way that discontinuation is recommended when patients are unable to carry out the treatment procedures in ways that would be beneficial.

Common Obstacles with Cognitive Therapy

Therapist's Misuse of Socratic Questioning

Clinicians should be aware of two common mistakes when using Socratic techniques in cognitive therapy: The first concerns engaging in Socratic questioning without previous consideration of the conclusion you wish the patient to reach. It is important that the therapist have in mind a particular way of challenging a dysfunctional belief or assumption, and that Socratic dialog aim at leading the patient toward this challenge. The second mistake concerns excessive use of Socratic questioning, which can make the patient feel defensive. We recommend combining Socratic questioning with reflexive listening and other types of discourse such as summary statements, expressing empathy, and presenting didactic information.

When the Patient Uses Cognitive Therapy for Reassurance

As touched upon, some patients develop the pattern of using psychoeducational material in ritualized ways as reassurance-seeking strategies. For example, one patient with fears of dying unexpectedly and repeatedly read the psychoeducational handouts whenever she felt anxious and used them to reduce anxiety associated with her need for reassurance. Other patients become preoccupied with finding the single "best" way of challenging their dysfunctional beliefs and interpretations, or with identifying the phrase that "most completely" reassures them that they are not seriously ill. The therapist can reduce the chances that cognitive techniques will be used as reassurance-seeking strategies by avoiding the provision of guarantees. For example, rather than teaching patents that their body symptoms "definitely don't mean they are sick," it is better to articulate that the probability of their symptoms indicating the presence of a serious illness, while *acceptably low*, is not zero.

The healthy use of cognitive techniques leads the patient to (a) generate new and adaptive interpretations of body sensations and other health-related stimuli him- or herself, and (b) act appropriately by managing distress and taking "risks" (e.g., during behavioral experiments).

For example, we might teach patient with fears of visiting hospitals to use cognitive challenges to think less catastrophically about the probability of catching illnesses from merely being in the hospital building. Subsequently, that person would be helped to engage in a behavioral experiment or exposure exercise involving visiting a hospital, demonstrating the unlikelihood of becoming ill. Freeston and Ladouceur (1999), on the other hand, have correctly suggested that when patients repeat the same cognitive analyses over and over – or use them in a ritualistic way – it means such material is being effectively used as a safety behavior.

Continued Use of Subtle Safety-Seeking Behaviors

Sometimes, patients fail to show a reduction in health anxiety despite seeming success with cognitive therapy, behavioral experiments, and following repeated trials of well-executed exposure practice. If this occurs, it may be the result of subtle, undetected safety maneuvers (e.g., undetected body-checking) that the patient continues to use to reduce or avoid health worry. Although some individuals *blatantly* use safety behaviors to avoid distress during exposure therapy, others might use them quite innocently and are themselves unaware that they are doing anything to disrupt treatment. For example, one patient continued to subtly count his heart rate during exposure to running in place. This maintained his focus of attention on his heart as well as maintaining his belief that there was a certain heart rate limit over which he could not safely go. The use of safety behaviors, no matter how slight, snarls the process of cognitive change during verbal and behavioral interventions. If this is suspected, the therapist might inquire carefully about any sorts of strategies (behavioral or mental) patients are using to monitor themselves, to reduce anxiety, gain assurance, or prevent harm. Any identified safety maneuvers must, of course, be targeted for eventual elimination.

Unbearable Anxiety Levels during Behavioral Experiments or Exposures

If the patient becomes extremely anxious and emotionally reactive during a behavioral experiment or exposure task, it probably means the specific exercise is too difficult at that particular time. In such cases, the exercise should be stopped, and the therapist should assess the cognitions underlying the intense anxiety. Making sure the patient is involved with the selection of exposures and experiments can often help avoid this problem. Using cognitive techniques to tenderize strongly held dysfunctional beliefs before re-trying the exercise sometimes has also proved useful.

If the patient becomes concerned that the high level of anxiety is a sign that treatment isn't working, the therapist can emphasize that therapy is a process that requires continued practice. Moreover, it can be pointed out that the patient took an important step simply by choosing to enter the feared situation or provoke the feared body sensations at all (something previously avoided). If the patient refuses to tolerate high levels of anxiety, even after an appropriate intermediate (i.e., easier) task has been identified, an alternative consideration is that mood or other affective symptoms are interfering with treatment. For example, interfering with habituation during exposure therapy (e.g., Foa, 1979; Foa et al., 1983). In such cases, strategies to help manage mood symptoms might be incorporated into treatment.

Absence of Anxiety During Exposure

At the other extreme, a patient might report that the planned exposure task evokes very little discomfort. On the one hand, this could be an encouraging sign – perhaps the once-feared situation no longer evokes distress because the patient's fear has been modified through psychoeducation or cognitive therapy. But this will most likely be the case more toward the end of treatment, once the patient has gained confidence with conducting exposures and behavioral experiments. If early exposures evoke little or no distress, it is smart to troubleshoot rather than assume the patient has improved very rapidly. Absence of anxiety during exposure could result if the key anxiety-evoking aspect(s) of the feared situation have not been incorporated into the exposure. This can be assessed and resolved by asking the patient why the exposure did not evoke anxiety, or what would make the situation made more distressing.

A second possibility is that the patient has in some way nullified the exposure or experiment by engaging in distraction (emotional or behavioral avoidance) or safety-seeking behavior. For example, a patient with fears of fainting and getting lost due to feelings of dizziness conducted a behavioral experiment that included making herself feel dizzy and then driving through her town. During the exercise, however, she insisted on having her cellular telephone charged and easily accessible "just in case." This maneuver served to reduce her anxiety because she figured she could call for help is she felt faint or got lost (even though both were unlikely). If the use of avoidance or safety-seeking behaviors is suspected during exposures or behavioral experiments, the therapist should carefully assess for their presence (e.g., "Is there anything you are doing that might make the exposure less distressing?"). The use of such strategies may indicate a problem understanding or accepting the rationale for exposure or the behavioral experiment. Additional time spent with psychoeducation might be necessary. Also, alternatively, the selected task may simply be too frightening, so that a less distressing one should be considered before attempting the targeted exercise at a later time.

Therapist Discomfort with Exposure Exercises

It is common for therapists new to the use of cognitive-behavioral treatments to feel trepidation in asking patients with anxiety problems to purposely confront stimuli that will evoke further anxiety and distress, as in exposure and behavioral experiments. Perhaps these exercises seem unnecessarily painful. If such consternation sets in, one might consider the following:

Research has firmly established that systematic, prolonged, and repeated confrontation with feared stimuli is the treatment of choice for pathological fear and anxiety; without it, patients have little hope of improving. The distress that is evoked during exposure and behavioral experiments is only temporary and diminishes with time, as does the pathological fear itself.

Exposure therapy and behavioral experiments involving confrontation with feared stimuli demand little more of the patient then what they are already doing (albeit they try to avoid these stimuli). Cognitive-behavioral therapy simply asks that the patient confront feared stimuli in ways that will teach them their fears are unfounded and their safety behaviors unnecessary.

There is no evidence that it is dangerous or harmful to evoke anxiety. Anxiety is the body's natural response to perceived threat. At worst, the patient experiences temporary discomfort, which he or she must choose for him/herself if anxiety symptoms are to be brought under control.

It is clear that the patient's habitual responses to anxiety triggers, such as avoidance, safety-seeking behaviors, and compulsive reassurance-seeking, serve only to maintain (if not intensify) health anxiety. Exposure therapy helps patients develop more healthy and adaptive responses to these triggers.

The distress evoked during therapeutic exposure is temporary; and when it does decrease, patients are left with important knowledge about situations and thoughts they once believed were dangerous – and about their own ability to manage their own subjective distress.

Amelioration of health anxiety by exposure will not cause "symptom substitution" of additional problems. There is no empirical evidence that pathological fear and anxiety – or compulsive reassurance-seeking – are caused by unconscious conflicts that persist until they are resolved.

Although exposure and many behavioral experiments require that the therapist purposely help the patient become anxious, when the rationale for using these techniques is made clear – and the treatment plan has been established collaboratively between therapist and patient – the intervention engenders a warm and supportive working relationship which further authenticates the patient's courage and progress.

After Treatment Ends

Considering Future Plans

As treatment begins to wind down, it will be important to address the patient's social and occupational plans. If they have stopped working because of health anxiety, do they have a plan for restarting? Are there potential stressors and other barriers to assuming a "normal" life, such as family turmoil, lack of social support, or residual disability? In some cases, successful treatment leaves formerly debilitated patients with excessive amounts of "downtime" that was formerly taken up with health-related preoccupation and behaviors. The final therapy sessions should involve discussions of how such time can be managed, including the possible referral to social-service agencies or an occupational therapist. Volunteer work is often an excellent suggestion for easing the patient into a workday schedule. The volunteer work, which should be carefully chosen so that it is a rewarding activity for the patient, can be increased gradually as necessary until the goal of a full day is reached.

Preparing for Stressors

Patients should be informed that even in the best case scenario, they can and should *expect* to experience bumps in the road with residual health-anxiety symptoms. Most often, these will occur during times of increased life stress, such as in the midst of occupational or family conflict, following a death or serious illness in the family, job changes, and around the time of childbirth. Thus, patients can be assisted with identifying "high-risk" periods during which they should be ready to apply the techniques learned in therapy, if excessive health concerns or safety behaviors become more numerous or distressing.

Maintaining Improvement

Although even the most successfully treated patients commonly experience occasional anxiety symptoms after the end of treatment, the tools to keep problems with health anxiety under control are in place. Here, we describe a brief protocol for health-anxiety patients who have completed an adequate trial of psychological treatment, yet require "booster sessions" to help with maintenance. This program is based on protocols described previously by Öst (1989), Hiss, Foa, and Kozak (1994), and McKay (1997) for various anxiety disorders. In general, the program emphasizes practicing the skills learned during the active therapy period, namely, cognitive therapy, exposure, and response prevention. The use of stress-management techniques, as described by Taylor and Asmundson (2004), can also be helpful, although we do not elaborate on these strategies here. Follow-up therapy sessions can be initiated directly upon completion of the standard treatment program as described in the previous chapters (i.e., as a *maintenance* program), or incorporated into follow-up sessions for patients who begin to experience a return of symptoms at some later point. The maintenance program should incorporate the following components:
- Identifying "high-risk" situations and the relationship between stress and health anxiety
- Practicing evidence-based thinking
- Practicing a lifestyle of confronting, rather than avoiding, feared stimuli

– Preventing *lapses* from becoming *relapses*
– Maintaining social support.

High-Risk Situations

Even following successful treatment, most patients report that certain situations, external stimuli, and body sensations occasionally still trigger distress and health concern. Situations in which these stimuli are present can be viewed as *high-risk situations*. It is important for patients to plan ahead if confrontation with such triggers is anticipated. This allows the patient to plan for using appropriate coping strategies (i.e., cognitive therapy techniques). Times of increased life stress might, themselves, be high-risk situations. As we have highlighted in numerous places throughout this volume, stress alone can produce uncomfortable body sensations that can trigger health concerns. When life stress is high, one needs to prepare oneself for the possibility of increased body noise and health-related uncertainty. Self-monitoring is a useful tool to help patients identify changes in the frequency of their physical and emotional symptoms.

Practically speaking, once a set of high-risk situations is identified, cognitive techniques can be tailored to the dysfunctional beliefs that arise in these situations, and a brief exposure hierarchy can be developed. The therapist can help the patient confront feared stimuli during the session, and assign homework practice as well. The following analogy of someone learning to play the guitar can be used to convey the importance of continued programmed and lifestyle exposure practice even after formal therapy has ended.

Therapist: Let's say you wanted to learn to play the guitar. So, you decide to take lessons for 6 months. After completing 6 months of lessons, you would still only know the basics of how to play the guitar, and by no means would you be an expert musician. To become a skilled guitarist, you must continue to practice, learning more and more songs to understand different styles of playing, improve your coordination, and progressively refine your playing ability. If you were to stop playing, even after finishing the lessons, your skill level will gradually deteriorate until you would be back to square one. Then if you tried to play, you would find that you didn't know how to any more. The same is true for the skills you learned during treatment of your health anxiety. If you continue to practice confronting rather than avoiding situations and stimuli that make you distressed – and if you continue to practice resisting urges to seek reassurance and engage in other safety behaviors – you will continue to improve your use of these skills, and you would be able to use them no matter what challenging situations came your way. On the other hand, if you return to your old habits of seeking reassurance, you will find that health preoccupation gradually returns, as do those urges to ask for reassurance and check. It's a case of "use it or lose it."

Logical Thinking

Cognitive therapy interventions play an important role in the treatment of health anxiety, and follow-up sessions present an opportunity to reintroduce patients to the use of such strategies for modifying beliefs and assumptions that continue to produce distress. Patients should be encouraged to return to using Handout 11.2 to carefully challenge dysfunctional beliefs that underlie health-related fears and urges to perform safety behaviors. Challenging mistaken cognitions can be used as a springboard to planning behavioral experiments and exposure exercises as discussed next.

Maintaining a Lifestyle of Exposure

As we discuss in Chapter 12, patients must incorporate exposure as a daily habit, in addition to practicing programmed exposure exercises. One important topic to be discussed during follow-up is how to remain motivated to persist with exposure efforts. It is useful to think of motivation in terms of rewards. In other words, *what reward does exposure bring for the patient?* What does the patient stand to gain from deciding to face, rather than avoid, feared situations and stimuli? Avoidance, checking, reassurance-seeking, and safety signals have reward value as well: They bring about an immediate reduction in discomfort. However, in the long run, these safety behaviors preserve dysfunctional cognitions and contribute to the persistence of excessive health anxiety. Although exposure reduces excessive health-related fears in the long term, it results in short-term distress. The hurdle here is that humans are more sensitive to short-term than to long-term effects. Thus, safety-seeking seems (on the surface) like the best decision.

To increase patients' motivation for long-term maintenance, the therapist can help them arrange contingencies so that exposure and abstinence from safety behaviors have short-term reward value, and engaging in avoidance and safety behaviors has negative consequences. Some specific suggestions are as follows:

– Patients can make contracts with themselves such that enjoyable activities (e.g., television, gifts, special meals, trips) can only be done if no safety behaviors are performed for a specific amount of time. Of course, these goals should be realistic and measurable. The idea is for patients to reinforce themselves frequently and not fail very often.

- Patients can make a chart of how often they engage in safety behaviors and keep this available for public viewing, for example, on the refrigerator door at home. Family members will see this and congratulate (reward) the patient on his or her progress. Posting of such forms can also serve as a reminder to the patient to keep working hard.

Neither of these techniques is completely painless, but this is part of reason they work. If avoidance and safety behaviors interfere with improvement, it is better to feel the "pain" now and do something about it than to wait until it is too late. Such strategies also require patients to be honest with themselves about their behavior. If one cheats simply to attain rewards for abstaining from checking or reassurance-seeking, one is merely fooling oneself in the long run. Other techniques for increasing motivation include the following:

- Make a list of the benefits of reducing health anxiety symptoms and the benefits of working hard to prevent them from returning. For example, how will affect academic/job performance, social/dating activities, self-perception?
- List things that the patient can do with greater ease now, compared to the time at the start of the treatment program (e.g., taking a vacation). This encourages patients to reflect on their progress.
- Select a specific short-term goal to work on and identify a short-term reward for accomplishing this goal. As mentioned above, the goal should be realistic and fairly easy to accomplish. The reward should also fit the accomplishment, perhaps something fun that the patient will do or purchase *if and only if* the goal is reached.

The Abstinence Violation Effect

We occasionally work with individuals who attempt to change their behavior by setting very rigid or *absolute* goals, for example, by stating that they should *never search the internet for information about medical symptoms again*. Inevitably, when such reassurance is sought, the person then berates himself or herself for violating a self-imposed, but unrealistically obtainable, standard. At that point, the person decides that since they have already spoiled their plan for complete abstinence, they might as well cancel the plan altogether. This process is called the *abstinence violation effect*, and it is a common phenomenon among those attempting to change any persistent behavioral pattern such as smoking, substance abuse, and overeating. To avoid falling prey to the abstinence violation effect, patients must avoid "black-and-white" or "all-or-none" styles of thinking. One way to counter this type of rigid thinking is to allow for compromises. Patients can be helped to view their life as a continuum wherein most of the time they will be able to manage health anxiety and resist urges to engage in safety-seeking behaviors. However, on occasion, they (as would anyone) will have their difficulties.

Lapse versus Relapse

As the discussion above implies, patients should not be concerned with periodic slips – such *lapses* are inevitable. A lapse can be considered a temporary setback that is identified and dealt with effectively. However, concern is warranted if lapses progress toward *relapse*. Relapse is defined as a return to baseline of health anxiety, preoccupation, avoidance, and safety behaviors. It involves thinking that all the work during therapy was for naught. The distinction between lapse and relapse is an important one: If patients can identify a lapse, self-monitor, and implement the treatment techniques they have learned, they can help themselves overcome the lapse and avoid relapse.

The therapist and patient should work collaboratively to develop a list of specific strategies for managing lapses. Such strategies should draw on what has been learned during treatment. Socratic questioning can be used to help the patient arrive at his or her own solutions. Some useful strategies include the following:
– Consider the difference between lapse and relapse. Expect lapses from time to time ("not a matter of *if*, but *when*").
– Take action to prevent the lapse from becoming a relapse.
– Determine the stimulus that evoked the health concern or safety behaviors, as well as the relevant cognitive distortions.
– Repeatedly confront the situation that evoked the lapse and refrain from safety behaviors.
– Ask for help from a support person or call the therapist.

Continued Social Support

Two types of social support can be important for helping patients maintain their treatment gains: informational support and practical support.

Informational Support

Informational support is the provision of information required to solve a problem. For example, if you are trying to be on time for an appointment but cannot find the street address, you stop and ask someone for directions. This exchange of information (or informational support) occurs informally each day in the form of child-rearing or household hints, for example. Individuals with health anxiety require informational support from experts on this condition and its treatment, such as their therapist. This is why it is important that patients raise questions or concerns they have during treatment. However, now that therapy has ended, patients need to find additional sources of accurate informational support. The therapist should play a role in carefully identifying such resources to ensure they offer information consistent with the biopsychosocial model and cognitive-behavioral approach to treatment. An excellent example of a self-help book for health anxiety is Asmundson and Taylor's (2005) *It's Not All in Your Head*. We suggest a resource such as this as opposed to searching the internet, since many health-anxious patients have difficulty with using the internet as a form of safety-seeking.

Practical Support

Practical support involves receiving help and encouragement from understanding and sympathetic relatives or friends. On an emotional level, this kind of support can enhance the patient's feeling of self-worth and belonging since he or she feels cared for and understood. On a practical level, it helps the patient manage difficult situations (i.e., lapses) by being reminded and assisted with implementing skills learned during therapy. Whereas some patients have ready access to practical support, others are not so lucky. For those who require help with asking for support, the following parameters should be discussed:

- What could the patient's friends and family members do to support efforts in managing health anxiety?
- How should the patient ask others for their support?
- Who are good people to ask and who are not the best people to ask for support?
- Who would be the easiest (and who the most difficult) to ask?

Requests for support should be assertive and specific. It is also important for the patient to let others know when they appreciate their interest and support, and how their support was helpful. This recognition increases the chances of receiving additional support. Role playing such interactions during the therapy session might help hesitant patients to gain confidence in asking for help.

Some Concluding Thoughts

Although many clinicians find the treatment of health anxiety to be a rewarding experience, individual differences in the patient's approach to treatment and willingness to genuinely accept the psychological model (and work from it) often end up being the ultimate predictors of outcome. Nevertheless, even the most compliant patient will encounter difficulties if the various treatment techniques are not executed with precision. Clinicians must remain aware of how the patient is responding to treatment, and how that person is using the therapeutic techniques. In particular, the aim of treatment for health anxiety is not to provide patients with various ways to reassure themselves about health status or the meaning of symptoms. Rather, it is to *learn to manage* the acceptable level of uncertainty and risk that people without health anxiety take for granted in day-to-day life. Cognitive-behavioral therapy is a time-limited form of treatment. The length of treatment (typically 16 to 20 sessions) should be agreed upon and repeatedly evaluated during the course of therapy. The goal of treatment, however, is to teach patients skills they can use on their own for a lifetime.

References

Abramowitz, J.S. (2006). *Understanding and treating obsessive-compulsive disorder: A cognitive-behavioral approach.* Mahwah, NJ: Erlbaum.

Abramowitz, J.S., & Braddock, A.E. (2006). Hypochondriasis: Conceptualization, treatment, and relationship to obsessive-compulsive disorder. *Psychiatric Clinics of North America, 29,* 503–519.

Abramowitz, J.S., Brigidi, B.D., & Foa, E.B. (1999). Health concerns in patients with obsessive-compulsive disorder. *Journal of Anxiety Disorders, 13,* 529–539.

Abramowitz, J.S., & Deacon, B.J. (2005). The OCD spectrum: A closer look at the arguments and the data. In J.S. Abramowitz & A.C. Houts (Eds.), *Concepts and controversies in obsessive-compulsive disorder* (pp. 141–149). New York: Springer-Verlag.

Abramowitz, J.S., Deacon, B.J., & Valentiner, D. (2007). The Short Health Anxiety Inventory in an undergraduate simple: Implications for a cognitive-behavioral model of hypochondriasis. *Cognitive Therapy and Research, 31,* 871–883.

Abramowitz, J.S., Franklin, M.E., & Cahill, S.P. (2003). Approaches to common obstacles in the exposure-based treatment of obsessive-compulsive disorder. *Cognitive and Behavioral Practice, 10,* 14–22.

Abramowitz, J.S., Franklin, M.E., Zoellner, L.A., & DiBernardo, C.L. (2002). Treatment compliance and outcome of cognitive-behavioral therapy for obsessive-compulsive disorder. *Behavior Modification, 26,* 447–463.

Abramowitz, J.S., & Moore, E.L. (2007). An experimental analysis of hypochondriasis. *Behavior Research and Therapy, 45,* 413–424.

Abramowitz, J.S., Olatinji, B., & Deacon, B. (2007). Health anxiety, hypochondriasis, and the anxiety disorders. *Behavior Therapy, 38,* 86–94.

Abramowitz, J.S., Schwartz, S.A., & Whiteside, S.P. (2001). A contemporary conceptual model of hypochondriasis. *Mayo Clinic Proceedings, 77,* 1323–1330.

Airola, P. (1977). *Hypoglycemia: A better approach.* Phoenix: Health Plus.

Alsaadi, T., & Marquez, A. (2005). Psychogenic nonepileptic seizures. *American Family Physician, 72,* 849–856.

Amrhein, P.C., Miller, W.R., Yahne, C.E., Palmer, M., & Fulcher, L. (2003). Client commitment language during Motivational Interviewing predicts drug use outcomes. *Journal of Consulting and Clinical Psychology, 71.* 862–878.

American Psychiatric Association. (2000). *Diagnostic and statistical manual of mental disorders* (4th ed., text revision). Washington DC: Author.

Antony, M.M., Orsillo, S., & Roemer, L. (Eds.). (2001). *Practitioner's guide to empirically based measures of anxiety.* New York: Kluwer.

Aronson, K., Barrett, L., & Quigley, K. (2001). Feeling your body or feeling badly: Evidence for the limited validity of the somatosensory amplification scale as an index of somatic sensitivity. *Journal of Psychosomatic Research, 51,* 387–394.

Asmundson, G., & Norton, R. (1995). Anxiety sensitivity in patients with physically unexplained chronic back pain: A preliminary report. *Behavior Research and Therapy,* *33*, 771–777.

Asmundson, G., & Taylor, S. (2005). *It's not all in your head: How worrying about your health could be making you sick–and what you can do about it.* New York: Guilford.

Asmundson, G., Taylor, S., & Cox, B. (2001). *Health anxiety: Clinical and research perspectives on hypochondriasis and related disorders.* New York: Wiley.

Avia, M.D., Ruiz, M.A., Olivares, M.E., Crespo, M., Guisado, A.B., Sanchez, A. et al. (1996). The meaning of psychological symptoms: Effectiveness of a group intervention with hypochondriacal patients. *Behavior Research and Therapy, 34*, 23–31.

Aydemir, O., Ozmen, E., Kuey, L., Kultur, S., Yesil, M., Postaci, N. et al. (1997). Psychiatric morbidity and depressive symptomatology in patients with permanent pacemakers. *Pacing and Clinical Electrophysiology, 20*, 1628–1632.

Barlow, D.H. (2002). *Anxiety and its disorders* (2nd ed.). New York: Guilford.

Barlow, D.H., Craske, M., Cerny, J., & Klosko, J. (1989). Behavioral treatment of panic disorder. *Behavior Therapy, 30*, 261–282.

Barrios, B.A. (1988). On the changing nature of behavioral assessment. In A.S. Bellack & M. Hersen (Eds.), *Behavioral assessment: A practical handbook* (pp. 3–41). Elmsford, NY: Pergamon.

Barsky, A. (1992). Amplification, somatization, and the somatoform disorders. *Psychosomatics, 33*, 28–34.

Barsky, A.J., & Ahern, D.K. (2004). Cognitive behavior therapy for hypochondriasis: A randomized controlled trial. *The Journal of the American Medical Association, 291*, 1464–1470.

Barsky, A., Ahern, D., Bailey, E., Saintfort, R., Liu, E., & Peekna, H. (2001). Hypochondriacal patients' appraisal of health and physical risks. *American Journal of Psychiatry, 158*, 783–787.

Barsky, A., Barnett, M., & Cleary, P. (1994). Hypochondriasis and panic disorder: Boundary and overlap. *Archives of General Psychiatry, 51*, 918–925.

Barsky, A., Cleary, P., Sarnie, M., & Klerman, G. (1993a). The course of transient hypochondriasis. *American Journal of Psychiatry, 150*, 484–488.

Barsky, A., Cleary, P.D., Wyshak, G., Spitzer, R.L., Williams, J.B.W., & Klerman, G.L. (1992). A structured diagnostic interview for hypochondriasis: A proposed criterion standard. *Journal of Nervous and Mental Disease, 180*, 20–27.

Barsky, A., Coeytaux, R., Sarnie, M., & Cleary, P. (1993b). Hypochondriacal patients' beliefs about good health. *American Journal of Psychiatry, 150*, 1085–1089.

Barsky, A., Fama, J., Bailey, E., & Ahern, D. (1998). A prospective 4- to 5-year study of DSM-III-R hypochondriasis. *Archives of General Psychiatry, 55*, 737–744.

Barsky, A., Goodson, J., Lane, R., & Cleary, P. (1988a). The amplification of somatic symptoms. *Psychosomatic Medicine, 50*, 510–519.

Barsky, A., & Klerman, G. (1983). Overview: Hypochondriasis, bodily complaints, and somatic styles. *American Journal of Psychiatry, 140*, 273–283.

Barsky, A., & Wyshak, G. (1990). Hypochondriasis and somatosensory amplification. *British Journal of Psychiatry, 157*, 404–409.

Barsky, A., Wyshak, G., Klerman, G. (1990a). The somatosensory amplification scale and its relationship to hypochondriasis. *Journal of Psychiatric Research, 24*, 323–334.

Barsky, A., Wyshak, G., Latham, K., & Klerman, G. (1991). Hypochondriacal patients, their physicians, and their medical care. *Journal of General Internal Medicine, 6,* 413–419.

Beck, A.T. (1976). *Cognitive therapy and the emotional disorders.* New York: International University Press.

Beck, A.T., & Emery, G. (1985). *Anxiety disorders and phobias: A cognitive perspective.* New York: Basic Books.

Beck, A.T., Steer, R.A., & Brown, G.K. (1996). *Manual of the Beck Depression Inventory-II.* San Antonio, TX: Psychological Corporation.

Bieling, P.J., & Kuyken, W. (2003). Is cognitive case formulation science or science fiction? *Clinical Psychology: Science and Practice, 10,* 52–69.

Bleichhardt, G., Timmer, B., & Rief, W. (2005). Hypochondriasis among patients with multiple somatoform symptoms: Psychopathology and outcome of a cognitive-behavioral therapy. *Journal of Contemporary Psychotherapy, 35,* 239–249.

Boschen, M.J., & Oei, T.P.S. (in press). A cognitive behavioral case formulation framework for treatment planning in anxiety disorders. *Depression and Anxiety.*

Bouman, T.K. (2002). A community-based psychoeducational group approach to hypochondriasis. *Psychotherapy and Psychosomatics, 71,* 326–332.

Bouman, T.K., & Polman, A. (2007). Group psychoeducation for hypochondriasis: A waitlist-controlled study. Submitted for publication.

Braddock, A.E., & Abramowitz, J.S. (2007, November). *Social anxiety and hyperhidrosis: A survey study.* In A.E. Braddock, (Chair), *Social anxiety within medical problems: Empirical support for cognitive-behavioral conceptualizations and treatment.* Symposium presented at the Annual Conference of the Association for Behavioral and Cognitive Therapies, Philadelphia, PA.

Bravo, I., & Silverman, W. (2001). Anxiety sensitivity, anxiety, and depression in older patients and their relation to hypochondriacal concerns and medical illness. *Aging and Mental Health, 5,* 349–357.

Brown, D., Pryzwansky, W.B., & Schulte, A.C. (2001). *Psychological consultation: Introduction to theory and practice.* New York: Allyn & Bacon.

Brown, T.A., DiNardo, P., & Barlow, D.H. (1994). *Anxiety disorders interview schedule for DSM-IV.* San Antonio, TX: The Psychological Corporation.

Buhr, K., & Dugas, M.J. (2002). The Intolerance of Uncertainty Scale: Psychometric properties of the English version. *Behavior Research and Therapy, 40,* 931–946.

Burns, D. (1980). *Feeling good: The new mood therapy.* New York: Morrow.

Buwalda, F., Bouman, T.K., & van Duijn, M.A.J. (2006). Psychoeducation for hypochondriasis: A comparison of a cognitive-behavioral approach and a problem-solving approach. *Behavior Research and Therapy, 45,* 887–899.

Chalder, T. (1996). Nonepileptic attacks: a cognitive behavioral approach in a single case with a 4-year follow-up. *Clinical Psychology and Psychotherapy, 3,* 291–297.

Chambless, D.L., & Steketee, G. (1999). Expressed emotion and behavior therapy outcome: A prospective study with obsessive-compulsive and agoraphobic outpatients. *Journal of Consulting and Clinical Psychology, 67,* 658–665.

Clark, D.A., & Rhyno, S. (2006). Unwanted intrusive thoughts in nonclinical individuals: Implications for clinical disorders. In. D.A. Clark (Ed.), *Intrusive thoughts in clinical disorders: Theory, research, and treatment* (pp. 1–29). New York: Guilford.

Clark, D.M. (1986). A cognitive approach to panic. *Behavior Research and Therapy, 24*, 461–470.

Clark, D.M., & Fairburn, C.G. (1997). Science and practice of cognitive behavior therapy. Oxford: Oxford University Press.

Clark, D.M., Salkovskis, P.M., Hackmann, A., Wells, A., Fennell, M., Ludgate, J. et al. (1998). Two psychological treatments for hypochondriasis: A randomized controlled trial. *British Journal of Psychiatry, 173*, 218–225.

Clifford, C.A., Murray, R.M., & Fulker, D.W. (1984). Genetic and environmental influences on obsessional traits and symptoms. *Psychological Medicine, 14*, 791–800.

Cloninger, C., Sigvardsson, S., von Korring, A., & Bohman, M. (1984). An adoption study of somatoform disorders. *Archives of General Psychiatry, 41*, 863–871.

Cox, B. (1999). The role of anxiety sensitivity in panic and other disorders. *Program Abstracts of the 19th Annual Conference of the Anxiety Disorders Association of America, 24*, 86.

Cox, B., Borger, S., & Enns, M. (1999). Anxiety sensitivity and emotional disorders: Psychometric studies and their theoretical implications. In S. Taylor (Ed.), *Anxiety sensitivity: Theory, research, and treatment of the fear of anxiety* (pp. 115–148). Mahwah, NJ: Erlbaum.

Craig, T., Boardman, A., Mills, K., Daly-Jones, O., & Drake, H. (1993). The South London somatization study I: Longitudinal course and the influence of early life experiences. *British Journal of Psychiatry, 163*, 579–588.

Craske, M.G., & Barlow, D.H. (2007). *Mastery of your anxiety and panic*. Oxford: Oxford University Press.

Creed, F., & Barsky, A. (2004). A systematic review of the epidemiology of somatization disorder and hypochondriasis. *Journal of Psychosomatic Research, 56*, 391–408.

Deacon, B.J., & Abramowitz, J.S. (2004). Cognitive and behavioral treatments for anxiety disorders: A review of meta-analytic findings. *Journal of Clinical Psychology, 60*, 429–441.

Deiker, T., & Counts, D.K. (1980). Hypnotic paradigm-substitution therapy in a case of hypochondriasis. *American Journal of Clinical Hypnosis, 23*, 122–127.

De Jong, P.J. Haenen, M.A., Schmidt, A., & Mayer, B. (1998). Hypochondriasis: The role of fear-confirming reasoning. *Behavior Research and Therapy, 36*, 65–74.

DiLilla, D., Carey, G., Gottesman, I., & Bouchard, F. (1996). Heritability of MMPI personality indicators of psychopathology in twins reared apart. *Journal of Abnormal Psychology, 105*, 491–499.

Duddu, V., Issac, M., & Chaturvedi, S. (2006). Somatization, somatosensory amplification, attribution styles and illness behavior: A review. *International Review of Psychiatry, 18*, 25–33.

Eisen, J.L., Phillips, K.A., Baer, L., Beer, D.A., Atala, K.D., & Rasmussen, S.A. (1998). The Brown Assessment of Beliefs Scale: Reliability and validity. *American Journal of Psychiatry, 155*, 102–108.

Ellis, A. (1994). *Reason and emotion in psychotherapy*. New York: Lyle Stuart.

Emilien, G., Durlach, C., Lepola, U., & Dinan, T. (2002). *Anxiety disorders: Pathophysiology and pharmacological treatment*. Berlin: Birkhäuser Verlag.

Emmons, K.M., & Rollnick, S. (2001). Motivational interviewing in healthcare settings: Opportunities and limitations. *American Journal of Preventative Medicine, 20*, 68–74.

Engle, D.E., & Arkowitz, H. (2006). *Ambivalence in psychotherapy: Facilitating readiness to change*. New York: Guilford.

Escobar, J. (1995). Transcultural aspects of dissociative and somatoform disorders. *Psychiatric Clinics of North America, 18*, 555–569.

Escobar, J., Rubio-Stipec, M., Canino, G., & Karno, M. (1989). Somatic symptom index (SSI): A new and abridged somatization construct: Prevalence and epidemiology correlates in two large community samples. *Journal of Nervous and Mental Disease, 177*, 140–146.

Fallon, B.A. (1999). Somatoform disorders. In R.E. Feinstein & A.A. Brewer (Eds.), *Primary care psychiatry and behavioral medicine: Brief office treatment and management pathways* (pp. 146–170). New York: Springer-Verlag.

Fallon, B.A. (2001). Pharmacologic strategies for hypochondriasis. In V. Starcevic & D.R. Lipsitt (Eds.), *Hypochondriasis: Modern perspectives on an ancient malady* (pp. 329–351). New York: Oxford University Press.

Fallon, B.A., Javitch, J.A., Hollander, E., & Liebowitz, M.R. (1991). Hypochondriasis and obsessive-compulsive disorder: Overlaps in diagnosis and treatment. *Journal of Clinical Psychiatry, 52*, 457–460.

Fallon, B.A., Liebowitz, M.R., Salman, E., Schneier, F.R., Insino, C., Hollander, E. et al. (1993). Fluoxetine for hypochondriacal patients without major depression. *Journal of Clinical Psychopharmacology, 13*, 438–441.

Fallon, B.A., Quershi, A.I., Schneier, F.R., Sanchez-Lacay, A., Vermes, D., Feinstein, R. et al. (2003). An open trial of fluvoxamine for hypochondriasis. *Psychosomatics, 44*, 298–303.

Fallon, B.A., Schneier, F.R., Marchall, R., Campeas, R., Vermes, D., Goetz, D., & Liebowitz, M.R. (1996). The pharmacotherapy of hypochondriasis. *Psychopharmacology Bulletin, 32*, 607–611.

Fava, G.A., Grandi, S., Rafanelli, C., Fabbri, S., & Cazzaro, M. (2000). Explanatory therapy in hypochondriasis. *Journal of Clinical Psychiatry, 61*, 317–322.

Ferguson, E. (2000). Hypochondriacal concerns and the five-factor model of personality. *Journal of Personality, 68*, 705–724.

Foa, E.B. (1979). Failure in treating obsessive-compulsives. *Behavior Research and Therapy, 17*, 169–176.

Foa, E.B., Abramowitz, J.S., Franklin, M.E., & Kozak, M.J. (1999). Feared consequences, fixity of belief, and treatment outcome in patients with obsessive-compulsive disorder. *Behavior Therapy, 30*, 717–724.

Foa, E.B., Grayson, J.B., Steketee, G.S., Doppelt, H.G., Turner, R.M., & Latimer, P.R. (1983). Success and failure in the behavioral treatment of obsessive-compulsives. *Journal of Consulting and Clinical Psychology, 51*, 287–297.

Foa, E.B., & Kozak, M.J. (1986). Emotional processing of fear: Exposure to corrective information. *Psychological Bulletin, 99*, 20–35.

Foa, E.B., & Kozak, M. (1995). DSM-IV field trial for obsessive-compulsive disorder. *American Journal of Psychiatry, 152*, 90–96.

Follette, W., & Houts, A. (1996). Models of scientific progress and the role of theory in taxonomy development: A case study of the *DSM*. *Journal of Consulting and Clinical Psychology, 64*, 1120–1132.

Follette, W., Naugle, A., & Linnerroth, P. (2000). Functional alternatives to traditional assessment and diagnosis. In M.J. Dougher (Ed.), *Clinical behavior analysis* (pp. 99–125). Reno, NV: Context Press.

Freeston, M.H., Gagnon, F., Ladouceur, R., Thibodeau, N., Letarte, H., & Rheaume, J. (1994). Health-related intrusive thoughts. *Journal of Psychosomatic Research, 38*, 203–215.

Freeston, M.H., & Ladouceur, R. (1999). Exposure and response prevention for obsessive thoughts. *Cognitive and Behavioral Practice, 6*, 362–383.

Freeston, M.H., Ladouceur, R., Gagnon, F., Thibodeau, N., Rheaume, J., Letarte, H. et al. (1997). Cognitive-behavioral treatment of obsessive thoughts: A controlled study. *Journal of Consulting and Clinical Psychology, 65*, 405–413.

Friedman, S. (2001). Cultural issues in the assessment of anxiety disorders. In M.M. Antony, S.M. Orsillo, & L. Roemer (Eds.), *Practitioner's guide to empirically based measures of anxiety* (pp. 37–42). New York: Plenum.

Furer, P., & Walker, J.R. (2005). Treatment of hypochondriasis with exposure. *Journal of Contemporary Psychotherapy, 35*, 251–267.

Furer, P., Walker, J.R., & Freeston, M.H. (2001). Integrated approach to cognitive- behavioral therapy for intense illness worries. In G.J.G. Asmundson, S. Taylor, & B.J. Cox (Eds.), *Health anxiety: Clinical and research perspectives on hypochondriasis and related conditions* (pp. 161–192). New York: Wiley.

Furer, P., Walker, J., & Stein, M. (2007). *Treating health anxiety and fear of death: A practitioner's guide.* New York: Springer-Verlag.

Gatchell, R., Polatin, P., Meyer, T., Garcy, P. (1994). Psychopathology and the rehabilitation of patients with chronic low back pain disability. *Archives of Physical Medicine and Rehabilitation, 75*, 666–670.

Gillespie, N., Zhu, G., Heath, A., Kickie, I., & Martin, N. (2000). The genetic etiology of somatic distress. *Psychological Medicine, 30*, 1051–1061.

Good, B., & Kleinman, A.M. (1985). Culture and anxiety: Cross-cultural evidence for the patterning of anxiety disorders. In A.H. Tuma, J.D. Maser (Eds.), *Anxiety and the anxiety disorders* (pp. 297–323). Hillsdale, NJ: Erlbaum.

Goodman, W.K., Price, L.H., Rasmussen, S.A., Mazure, C., Delgado, P., Heninger, G.R. et al. (1989a). The Yale-Brown Obsessive Compulsive Scale: Validity. *Archives of General Psychiatry, 46*, 1012–1016.

Goodman, W.K., Price, L.H., Rasmussen, S.A., Mazure, C., Fleischmann, R.L., Hill, C.L. et al. (1989b). The Yale-Brown Obsessive Compulsive Scale: Development, use, and reliability. *Archives of General Psychiatry, 46*, 1006–1011.

Gottesman, I. (1962). Differential inheritance of the psychoneuroses. *Eugenics Quarterly, 9*, 223–227.

Gramling, S., Clawson, E., & McDonald, M. (1996). Perceptual and cognitive abnormality model of hypochondriasis: Amplification and physiological reactivity. *Psychosomatic Medicine, 58,* 423–431.

Greeven, A., van Balkom, A., Visser, S., Merkelbach, J., van Rood, Y., van Dyck, R. et al. (2007). Cognitive-behavior therapy and paroxetine in the treatment of hypochondriasis: A randomized controlled trial. *American Journal of Psychiatry, 164,* 91–99.

Grubb, B.P. (2002). The postural tachycardia syndrome: A brief review of etiology, diagnosis, and treatment. *Hellenic Journal of Cardiology, 43,* 47–52.

Gupta, M. (2006). Somatization disorder in dermatology. *International Review of Psychiatry, 18,* 41.

Gureje, O. (2004). What can we learn from a cross-national study of somatic distress? *Journal of Psychosomatic Research, 56,* 409–412.

Gureje, O., Ustun, T., & Simon, G. (1997). The syndrome of hypochondriasis: a cross national study in primary care. *Psychological Medicine, 27,* 1001–1010.

Hadjistavropolous, C., Craig, K., & Hadjistavropolous, T. (1998). Cognitive and behavioral responses to illness information: The role of health anxiety. *Behavior Research and Therapy, 36,* 149–164.

Hadjistavropoulos, H.D., Frombach, I.K., & Asmundson, G.J.G. (1999). Exploratory and confirmatory factor analytic investigations of the Illness Attitudes Scales in a nonclinical sample. *Behavior Research and Therapy, 37,* 671–684.

Hamilton, M. (1960). A rating scale for depression. *Journal of Neurological and Neurosurgical Psychiatry, 18,* 315–319.

Hedlund, J., & Vieweg, B. (1979). The Hamilton Rating Scale for Depression: A comprehensive review. *Journal of Operating Psychiatry, 10,* 149–165.

Hiller, W., Leibbrand, R., Rief, W., & Fichter, M. (2005). Differentiating hypochondriasis from panic disorder. *Journal of Anxiety Disorders, 19,* 29–49.

Hiller, W., Rief. W., & Fichter, M. (2002). Dimensional and categorical approaches to hypochondriasis. *Psychological Medicine, 32,* 707–718.

Hiss, H., Foa, E.B., & Kozak, M.J. (1994). Relapse prevention program for treatment of obsessive-compulsive disorder. *Journal of Consulting and Clinical Psychology, 62,* 801–808.

Hollander, E., Friedberg, J.P., Wasserman, S., Yeh, C., & Iyengar, R. (2005). The case for the OCD spectrum. In J.S. Abramowitz & A.C. Houts (Eds.), *Concepts and controversies in obsessive-compulsive disorder* (pp. 95–118). New York: Springer-Verlag.

House, A. (1989). Hypochondriasis and related disorders: Assessment and management of patients referred for a psychiatric opinion. *General Hospital Psychiatry, 11,* 156–165.

Jawed, S.Y. (1991). A survey of psychiatrically ill Asian children. *British Journal of Psychiatry, 158,* 268–270.

Jonnal, A.H., Gardner, C.O., Prescott, C.A., & Kendler, K.S. (2000). Obsessive and compulsive symptoms in a general population sample of female twins. *American Journal of Medical Genetics, 96,* 791–796.

Kamlana, S.H, & Gray, P. (1988). Fear of AIDS. *British Journal of Psychiatry, 15,* 1291.

Kamphuis, J., & Telch, M. (1998). Assessment of strategies to manage or avoid perceived threats among panic disorder patients: The Texas Safety Maneuvers Scale (TSMS). *Clinical psychology and Psychotherapy, 5,* 177–186.

Kellner, R. (1979). Psychotherapeutic strategies in the treatment of psychophysiologic disorders. *Psychotherapy and Psychosomatics, 32* (Suppl. 4), 91–100.

Kellner, R. (1982). Psychotherapeutic strategies in hypochondriasis: A clinical study. *Acta Psychiatrica Scandinavica, 67,* 69–79.

Kellner, R. (1985). Functional and somatic symptoms and hypochondriasis: A survey of empirical studies. *Archives of General Psychiatry, 42,* 821–833.

Kellner, R. (1986). *Somatization and hypochondriasis.* New York: Praeger-Greenwood.

Kellner, R. (1987). *Abridged manual of the Illness Attitude Scales* (unpublished manual). Albuquerque, NM: Department of Psychiatry, School of Medicine, University of New Mexico.

Kellner, R., Abbott, P., Winslow, W., & Pathak, D. (1987). Fears, beliefs, and attitudes in DSM-III hypochondriasis. *Journal of Nervous and Mental Disease, 175,* 20–25.

Kendler, K., Walters, E., Neale, M., Kessler, R., Heath, A., & Eaves, L. (1995). The structure of the genetic and environmental risk factors for six major psychiatric disorders in women: Phobias, generalized anxiety disorder, panic disorder, bulimia, major depression and alcoholism. *Archives of General Psychiatry, 52,* 374–383.

Kenyon, F.E. (1964). Hypochondriasis: A clinical study. *British Journal of Psychiatry, 110,* 478–488.

Kirmayer, L., Robbins, J., & Paris, J. (1994). Somatoform disorder: Personality and the social matrix of somatic distress. *Journal of Abnormal Psychology, 103,* 125–136.

Kjernisted, K.D., Enns, M.W., & Lander, M. (2002). An open-label clinical trial of nefazodone in hypochondriasis. *Psychosomatics, 43,* 290–294.

Knight, R.O. (1941). Evaluation of the results of psychoanalytic therapy. *American Journal of Psychiatry, 98,* 434–446.

Ladee, G.A. (1966). *Hypochondriacal syndromes.* Amsterdam: Elsevier.

Ladouceur, R., Dugas, M., Freeston, M., Leger, E., Gagnon, F., & Thibodeau, N. (2000). Efficacy of a cognitive-behavioral treatment for generalized anxiety disorder: Evaluation in a controlled clinical trial. *Journal of Consulting and Clinical Psychology, 58,* 957–964.

Lesse, S. (1967). Hypochondriasis and psychosomatic disorders masking depression. *American Journal of Psychotherapy, 21,* 607–620.

Leonhard, K. (1961). On the treatment of ideohypochondriac and sensohypochondriac neuroses. *International Journal of Social Psychiatry, 7,* 123–133.

Lidbeck, J. (1997). Group therapy for somatization disorders in general practice: Effectiveness of a short cognitive-behavioral treatment model. *Acta Psychiatrica Scandinavica, 96,* 14–24.

Lipowsky, Z. (1988). Somatization: The concept and its clinical application. *American Journal of Psychiatry, 45,* 1358–1368.

Lippert, G.P. (1986). Excessive concern about AIDS in two bisexual men. *Canadian Journal of Psychiatry, 31,* 63–65.

Logsdail, S., Lovell, K., Warwick, H., & Marks, I. (1991). Behavioral treatment of AIDS-focused illness phobia. *British Journal of Psychiatry, 159,* 422–425.

Looper, K.J., & Kirmayer, L. (2001). Hypochondriacal concerns in a community population. *Psychological Medicine, 31,* 577–584.

Lucock, M., White, C., Peake, M., & Morley, S. (1998). Biased perception and recall of reassurance in medical patients. *British Journal of Health Psychology, 3,* 237–243.

Lucock, M., & Morley, S. (1996). The health anxiety Questionnaire. *British Journal of Health Psychology, 1,* 137–150.

MacDonald, A., Baker, J., Stewart, S., & Skinner, M. (2000). The effects of alcohol on the response to hyperventilation of participants high and low in anxiety sensitivity. *Alcoholism: Clinical and Experimental Research, 24,* 1656–1665.

MacLeod, A., Haynes, C., & Sensky, T. (1998). Attributions about common bodily sensations: Their associations with hypochondriasis and anxiety. *Psychological Medicine, 28,* 225–228.

Maillouz, J., & Brenner, J. (2002). Somatosensory amplification and its relationship to heartbeat detection ability. *Psychosomatic Medicine, 64,* 353–357.

Marcus, D. (1999). The cognitive-behavioral model of hypochondriasis: Misinformation and triggers. *Journal of Psychosomatic Research, 47,* 79–91.

Marcus, D., & Church, S. (2003). Are dysfunctional beliefs about illness unique to hypochondriasis? *Journal of Psychosomatic Research, 54,* 543–547.

Marks, I. (1987). *Fears, phobias, and rituals. Panic, anxiety, and their disorders.* New York: Oxford University Press.

McKay, D. (1997). A maintenance program for obsessive-compulsive disorder using exposure with response prevention: 2-year follow-up. *Behavior Research and Therapy, 35,* 367–369.

McKay, D., Abramowitz, J., Calamari, J., Kyrios, M., Radomsky, A., Sookman, D. et al. (2004). A critical evaluation of obsessive-compulsive disorder subtypes: symptoms versus mechanisms. *Clinical Psychology Review, 24,* 283–313.

Miller, W.R., & Rollnick, S. (2002). *Motivational interviewing: Preparing people for change* (2nd ed.). New York: Guilford.

Morrison, A. (2001). The interpretation of intrusions in psychosis: An integrative cognitive approach to hallucinations and delusions. *Cognitive and Behavioral psychotherapy, 29,* 257–276.

Neimeyer, R.A. (1994). *Death anxiety handbook: Research, instrumentation, and application.* Washington, DC: Taylor & Francis.

Neimeyer R.A., & Moore, M.K. (1994). Validity and reliability of the Multidimensional Fear of Death Scale. In Neimeyer R.A. (Ed.), *Death anxiety handbook: research, instrumentation, and application* (pp. 103–119). Washington, DC: Taylor & Francis.

Neziroglu, F., McKay, D., & Yaryura-Tobias, J.A. (2000). Overlapping and distinctive features of hypochondriasis and obsessive-compulsive disorder. *Journal of Anxiety Disorders, 14,* 603–614.

Noyes, R. (1999). The relationship of hypochondriasis to anxiety disorders. *General Hospital Psychiatry, 21,* 8–17.

Noyes, R., Carney, C., & Langbehn, D. (2004). Specific phobia of illness: Search for a new subtype. *Journal of Anxiety Disorders, 18,* 531–545.

Noyes, R., Happel, R.L., & Yagla, S.J. (1999). Correlates of hypochondriasis in a non-clinical sample. *Psychosomatics, 40,* 461–469.

Noyes, R., Kathol, R., Fisher, M., Phillips, B., Suelzer, M., & Holt, C. (1993). The validity of DSM-III-R hypochondriasis. *Archives of General Psychiatry, 50,* 961–970.

Noyes, R., Reich, J., Clancy, J., & O'Gorman, T. (1986). Reduction in hypochondriasis with treatment of panic disorder. *British Journal of Psychiatry, 149*, 631–635.

Noyes, R., Watson, B., Letuchy, E., Longley, S., Black, D., Carney, C. et al. (2005). Relationship between hypochondriacal concerns and personality dimensions and traits in a military population. *Journal of Nervous and Mental Disease, 193*, 110–118.

Ohaeri, J.U., & Odejide, O.A. (1994). Somatization symptoms among patients using primary health care facilities in a rural community in Nigeria. *American Journal of Psychiatry, 151*, 728–731.

Olatunji, B., Deacon, B., & Abramowitz, J.S., & Valentiner, D. (2007). Body vigilance in nonclinical and anxiety disorder samples: Structure, correlates, and prediction of health concerns. *Behavior Therapy, 38*, 392–401.

Oosterbaan, D.B., van Balkom, A.J.L.M., van Boeijen, C.A., de Meij, T.G.J., & van Dyck, R. (2001). An open study of paroxetine in hypochondriasis. *Progress in Neuro-Psychopharmacology and Biological Psychiatry, 25*, 1023–1033.

Otto, M., Demopulos, C., McLean, N., Pollack, M., & Fava, M. (1998). Additional findings on the association between anxiety sensitivity and hypochondriacal concerns: Examination of patients with major depression. *Journal of Anxiety Disorders, 12*, 225–232.

Otto, M., Pollack, M., Sachs, G., & Rosenbaum, J. (1992). Hypochondriacal concerns, anxiety sensitivity, and panic disorder. *Journal of Anxiety Disorders, 6*, 93–104.

Pennebaker, J.W. (1982). *The psychology of physical symptoms*. New York: Springer-Verlag.

Pennebaker, J.W., & Watson, D. (1991). The psychology of somatic symptoms. In L.J. Kirmayer & J.M. Robbins (Eds.), *Current concepts of somatization: Research and clinical perspectives* (pp. 21–35). Washington, DC: American Psychiatric Press.

Persing, J., Stuart, S., Noyes, R., & Happel, R. (2000). Hypochondriasis: The patient's perspective. *International Journal of Psychiatry in Medicine, 30*, 329–342.

Pilowsky, I. (1967). Dimensions of hypochondriasis. *British Journal of Psychiatry, 113*, 89–93.

Pilowsky, I., Chapman, R.C., & Bonica, J.J. (1977). Depression, illness behavior, and pain. *Pain, 4*, 183–192.

Pilowsky, I., & Spence, N.D. (1994). *Manual for the Illness Behavior Questionnaire* (unpublished manual, 3rd ed.). Adelaide, Australia: University of Adelaide, Department of Psychiatry.

Rachman, S. (1977). The conditioning theory of fear acquisition: A critical examination. *Behavior Research and Therapy, 15*, 375–387.

Rachman, S. (2002). A cognitive theory of compulsive checking, *Behavior Research and Therapy, 40*, 624–639.

Rachman, S., Hodgson, R., & Marks, I. (1971). The treatment of chronic obsessive-compulsive neurosis. *Behavior Research and Therapy, 9*, 237–247.

Radomsky, A., Gilchrist, P., Dussault, D. (2006). Repeated checking really does cause memory distrust. *Behavior Research and Therapy, 44*, 305–316.

Reiss, S. (1991). Expectancy model of fear, anxiety, and panic. *Clinical Psychology Review, 11*, 141–153.

Reiss, S., & McNally, R.J. (1985). Expectancy model of fear. In S. Reiss & R.R. Bootzin

(Eds.), *Theoretical issues in behavior therapy* (pp. 107–121). San Diego, CA: Academic Press.

Rief, W., Heitmuller, M., Reisberg, K., Ruddel, H. (2006). Why reassurance fails in patients with unexplained symptoms: An experimental investigation of remembered probabilities. *PLOS Medicine, 3,* 1266–1272.

Rief, W., Hiller, W., & Margraf, J. (1998). Cognitive aspects of hypochondriasis and the somatization syndrome. *Journal of Abnormal Psychology, 107,* 587–595.

Robbins, J., & Kirmeyer, I. (1996). Transient and persistent hypochondriacal worry in primary care. *Psychological Medicine, 26,* 575–589.

Rogers, C.R. (1951). *Client-centered counseling.* Boston: Houghton-Mifflin

Romanik, R.L., & Kellner, R. (1985). Case study: Treatment of herpes genitalis phobia and agoraphobia with panic attacks. *Psychotherapy, 22,* 542–546.

Salkovskis, P., & Clark, D.M. (1993). Panic disorder and hypochondriasis. *Advances in Behavior Research and Therapy, 15,* 23–48.

Salkovskis, P., Clark, D.M., & Gelder, M. (1996). Cognition-behavior links in the persistence of panic. *Behavior Research and Therapy, 34,* 453–458.

Salkovskis, P.M., Rimes, K.A., Warwick, H.M., & Clark, D.M. (2002). The Health Anxiety Inventory: Development and validation of scales for the measurement of health anxiety and hypochondriasis. *Psychological Medicine, 32,* 843–853.

Salkovskis, P., & Warwick, H. (1986). Morbid preoccupations, health anxiety and reassurance: A cognitive-behavioral approach to hypochondriasis. *Behavior Research and Therapy, 24,* 597–602.

Salkovskis, P., & Warwick, H. (2001). Meaning, misinterpretation, and medicine: A cognitive-behavioral approach to understanding health anxiety and hypochondriasis. In V. Starcevic & D. Lipsitt (Eds.), *Hypochondriasis: Modern perspectives on an ancient malady* (pp. 202–222). Oxford, UK: Oxford University Press.

Salkovskis, P., Warwick, H., & Deale, A. (2003). Cognitive-behavioral treatment for severe and persistent health anxiety (hypochondriasis). *Brief Treatment and Crisis Intervention, 3,* 353–367.

Savron, G., Fava, G., Grandi, S., Rafanelli, C., Raffi, A., & Belluardo, P. (1996). Hypochondriacal fears and beliefs in obsessive-compulsive disorder. *Acta Psychiatric Scandinavica, 93,* 345–348.

Schmidt, N.B., Lerew, D.R., & Trakowski, J.H. (1997). Body vigilance in panic disorder: Evaluating attention to bodily perturbations. *Journal of Consulting and Clinical Psychology, 65,* 214–220.

Schmidt, A.J.M., Wolfs-Takens, D.J., Oosterlaan, J., & Hout, M.A. (1994). Psychological mechanisms in hypochondriasis: Attention-induced physical symptoms without sensory stimulation. *Psychotherapy and Psychosomatics, 61,* 117–120.

Sheehan, D. (1983). *The anxiety disease.* New York: Scribner.

Sheehan, D., Lecrubier, Y., Harnett-Sheehan, K., Amoriam, P., Janavs, J., Weiller, E. et al. (1998). The Mini International Neuropsychiatric Interview (M.I.N.I.): The development and validation of a structured diagnostic interview. *Journal of Clinical Psychiatry, 59*(Suppl. 20), 22–23.

Silver, A., Sanders, D., Morrison, N., & Cowey, C. (2004). Health anxiety. In J. Bennett-Levy, J, G. Butler, M. Fennell, A. Hackman, M. Mueller, & D. Westbrook (Eds.), *Oxford guide to behavioral experiment in cognitive therapy* (pp. 81–98). Oxford, UK: Oxford University Press.

Smith, G. (1987). Toward more effective recognition and management of somatization disorders. *Journal of family practice,25*, 551–552.

Speckens, A.E.M. (2001). Assessment of hypochondriasis. In V. Starcevic & D.R. Lipsitt (Eds.), *Hypochondriasis: Modern perspectives on an ancient malady* (pp. 246–274). New York: Wiley.

Speckens, A.E.M., Van Hemert, A.M., Spinhoven, P., & Bolk, J. (1996). The diagnostic and prognostic significance of the Whitley Index, the Illness Attitudes Scale, and the Somatisensory Amplification Scale. *Psychological Medicine, 26*, 1085–1090.

Stampfl, T.G., & Levis, D.J. (1967). Essentials of implosive therapy: A learning-based psychodynamic behavioral therapy. *Journal of Abnormal Psychology, 72*, 296–503.

Starcevic, V. (1989). Pathological fear of death, panic attacks, and hypochondriasis. *The American Journal of Psychoanalysis, 49*, 347.

Starcevic, J., Fallon, S., Uhlenhuth, E., & Pathak, D., (1994). Generalized anxiety disorder, worries about illness, and hypochondriacal fears and beliefs. *Psychotherapy and Psychosomatics, 61*, 93–99.

Stein, M., Jang, K., & Livesley, W. (1999). Heritability of anxiety sensitivity: A twin study. *American Journal of Psychiatry, 156*, 246–251.

Stern, R., & Fernandez, M. (1991). Group cognitive and behavioral treatment for hypochondriasis. *British Medical Journal, 303*, 1229–1231.

Stewart, S.H., & Watt, M.C. (2000). Illness Attitude Scale dimensions and their associations with anxiety-related constructs in a nonclinical sample. *Behavior Research and Therapy, 38*, 83–99.

Stewart, S.H., & Watt, M.C. (2001). Assessment of health anxiety. In G.J.G. Asmundson, S. Taylor, & B.J. Cox (Eds.), *Health anxiety: Clinical and research perspectives on hypochondriasis and related conditions* (pp. 95–131). New York: Wiley.

Stone, A.B. (1993). Treatment of hypochondriasis with clomipramine. *Journal of Clinical Psychiatry, 54*, 200–201.

Sue, D.W., & Sue, D. (1999). *Counseling the culturally different* (3rd ed.). New York: Wiley.

Tallis, F. (1995). *Obsessive-compulsive disorder: A neurocognitive and neuropsychological perspective*. New York: Wiley.

Taylor, S. (Ed.). (1999). *Anxiety sensitivity: Theory, research, and treatment of the fear of anxiety*. Mahwah, NJ: Erlbaum.

Taylor, S., & Asmundson, G. (2004). *Treating health anxiety: A cognitive-behavioral approach*. New York: Guilford.

Taylor, S., Asmundson, G., & Coons, M. (2005). Current directions in the treatment of hypochondriasis. *Journal of Cognitive Psychotherapy, 19*, 285–304.

Taylor, S., & Cox, B.J. (1998). Anxiety sensitivity: Multiple dimensions and hierarchic structure. *Behavior Research and Therapy, 36*, 37–51.

Taylor, S. Thordarson, D., Jang, K., & Asmundson, G. (2006). Genetic and environmental origins of health anxiety: A twin study. *World Psychiatry, 5*, 47–50.

Taylor, S., Zvolensky, M., Cox, B., Deacon, B., Heimberg, R., Ledley, D.R. et al. (2007).

Robust dimensions of anxiety sensitivity: Development and initial validation of the Anxiety Sensitivity Index-3 (ASI-3). *Psychological Assessment, 19*, 176–188.

Tolin, D.F., Abramowitz, J.S., Brigidi, B., & Foa, E.B. (2003). Intolerance of uncertainty in obsessive-compulsive disorder. *Journal of Anxiety Disorders, 17*, 233–242.

Torgerson, S. (1986). Genetics of somatoform disorders. *Archives of General Psychiatry, 43*, 502–505.

Visser, S., & Bouman, T.K. (1992). Cognitive-behavioral approaches in the treatment of hypochondriasis: Six single case cross-over studies. *Behavior Research and Therapy, 30*, 301–306.

Visser, S., & Bouman, T.K. (2001). The treatment of hypochondriasis: Exposure plus response prevention vs. cognitive therapy. *Behavior Research and Therapy, 39*, 423–442.

Viswnathan, R., & Paradis, C. (1991). Treatment of cancer phobia with fluoxetine. *American Journal of Psychiatry, 148*, 1090.

Walker, J., Vincent, N., Furer, P., Cox, B., & Kjernisted, K. (1999). Treatment preference in hypochondriasis. *Journal of Behavior Therapy and Experimental Psychiatry, 30*, 251–258.

Warwick, H.M. (1989). A cognitive-behavioral approach to hypochondriasis and health anxiety. *Journal of Psychosomatic Research, 33*, 705–711.

Warwick, H.M. (1995). Assessment of hypochondriasis. *Behavior Research and Therapy, 33*, 845–853.

Warwick, H.M., Clark, D.M., Cobb, A.M., & Salkovskis, P.M. (1996). A controlled trial of cognitive-behavioral treatment of hypochondriasis. *British Journal of Psychiatry, 169*, 189–195.

Warwick, H.M., & Marks, I.M. (1988). Behavioral treatment of illness phobia and hypochondriasis: A pilot study of 17 cases. *British Journal of Psychiatry, 152*, 239–241.

Warwick, H., & Salkovskis, P. (1990). Hypochondriasis. *Behavior Research and Therapy, 28*, 105–117.

Watson, D., & Clark, L.A. (1984). Negative affectivity: The disposition to experience aversive emotional states. *Psychological Bulletin, 96*, 465–490.

Wattar, U., Sorensen, P., Buemann, I., Birket-Smith, M., Salkovskis, P.M., Albertsen, M. et al. (2005). Outcome of cognitive-behavioral treatment for health anxiety (hypochondriasis) in a routine clinical setting. *Behavioral and Cognitive Psychotherapy, 33*, 165–175.

Wells, A. (1997). *Cognitive therapy of anxiety disorders.* New York: Wiley.

Wells A., & Matthews, G. (1994). *Attention and emotion: A clinical perspective.* Hove, UK: Erlbaum.

Wesner, R.B., & Noyes, R. (1991). Imipramine: An effective treatment for illness phobia. *Journal of Affective Disorders, 22*, 43–48.

Wolpe, J. (1958). *Psychotherapy by reciprocal inhibition.* Stanford, CA: Stanford University Press.

Woods, S., Natterson, J., & Silverman, J. (1966). Medical student's disease: Hypochondriasis and medical education. *Journal of Medical Education, 41*, 785–790.

Appendix

– Handouts
– The Y-BOCS Adapted for Health Anxiety
– Brown Assessment of Beliefs Scale (BABS)

Handout 7.1. Change Plan Worksheet

1. I want to begin treatment for medically unexplained symptoms because:

2. My main treatment goals are:
   (a)

   (b)

   (c)

3. I plan to do these things to reach these goals:

4. The *first* steps I plan to take are:

5. Other people can help me by doing the following:

6. I am hopeful that my plan will have the following results:

Handout 8.1. Self-Monitoring of Body Symptoms

Instructions: For one week, note each body symptom that occurs, the time it started and ended, its severity, and the situation in which it occurred. Record this information as soon as the sensation occurs so that this diary is accurate.

Symptom	Time (start/end)	Severity (0–10)	Situation

From: J.S. Abramowitz & A.E. Braddock: *Psychological Treatment of Health Anxiety and Hypochondriasis*   © 2008 Hogrefe & Huber Publishers

Handout 8.2. Daily Monitoring Form

Date: _____   Time began: _____ AM/PM   Time ended _____ AM/PM

Situation _____

Bodily symptom(s) that trigger health concerns _____

_____

_____

Health-related thoughts: _____

_____

_____

Distress Level (circle)								
0	1	2	3	4	5	6	7	8
None		Mild		Moderate		Strong		Extreme

Fight/Flight Symptoms

☐ Trembling	☐ Muscle tension/ache	☐ Restlessness
☐ Fatigue	☐ Difficulty breathing	☐ Racing heart
☐ Sweating	☐ Dry mouth	☐ Dizzy/lightheaded
☐ Nausea/diarrhea	☐ Hot flashes/chills	☐ Frequent urination
☐ Trouble swallowing	☐ Keyed up/on edge	☐ Irritable
☐ Trouble sleeping	☐ Difficulty concentrating	☐ Jumpy/easily startled

Behaviors

☐ Check body	☐ Call doctor	☐ Check medical reference
☐ Visit doctor	☐ Just worry	☐ Check with friend/relative
☐ Distract yourself	☐ Analyze the situation	☐ Discuss the symptoms with someone else
☐ Other		

_____

_____

Handout 8.3. Health Concerns Log

0	1	2	3	4	5	6	7	8	9	10
None		Mild			Moderate		Severe			Extreme

Date	Average anxiety	Average depression	Average intensity of bodily symptoms

From: J.S. Abramowitz & A.E. Braddock: *Psychological Treatment of Health Anxiety and Hypochondriasis*   © 2008 Hogrefe & Huber Publishers

Handout 10.1. Body Symptom Monitoring Form

My body symptoms:	My threatening thoughts:

From: J.S. Abramowitz & A.E. Braddock: *Psychological Treatment of Health Anxiety and Hypochondriasis* © 2008 Hogrefe & Huber Publishers

Handout 10.2. The Fight-or-Flight Response

What is the Fight-or-Flight Response?

When a person perceives that danger is possible, such as when he or she interprets a situation or stimulus in a threatening way, there is an automatic physiological (bodily) response that takes over and helps protect the person from danger. This is called the *fight-or-flight response* because its purpose is to help you either fight or flee from potential danger. When our ancestors lived among other animals out in the wilds, it was important for their survival that, when faced with danger, an automatic "alarm response" would take over causing them to take immediate action (i.e., attack or run). The fight-or-flight response is still an important mechanism, even in today's world. Think of what would happen if a bus was speeding toward you, horn blasting, and you experienced no sense of danger or alarm. You would probably be killed. Luckily, your fight-or-flight response automatically steps in and takes over, making you get safely out of the way. Again, the purpose of this response is to protect you and keep you alive.

When a person perceives danger, the brain sends messages to a part the nervous system called the autonomic nervous system. The autonomic nervous system has two subsections or branches called the *sympathetic nervous system* and the *parasympathetic nervous system*. It is these two branches of the nervous system which are directly involved in controlling the body's energy levels and preparation for action. Very simply, the sympathetic nervous system is the fight-or-flight system that gets the body aroused and ready for action (i.e., fighting or fleeing), and the parasympathetic nervous system returns the body to a normal, nonaroused state.

When activated, the sympathetic nervous system releases a chemical called *adrenalin*. Adrenalin is used as a messenger to continue sympathetic nervous system activity, so that once activity begins, it often continues and increases for some time. However, sympathetic nervous system activity is stopped in two ways. First, the adrenalin is eventually destroyed by other chemicals in the body. Second, eventually, the body "has enough" of the fight-or-flight response and activates the parasympathetic nervous system to restore a relaxed feeling. In other words, the response does not continue forever, nor does it spiral out of control or intensify to "damaging levels." First, the fight-or-flight response is not at all dangerous – it is meant to help you, not harm you. Second, the parasympathetic nervous system is an inbuilt protector which slows down the sympathetic nervous system after a while.

Another important point is that adrenalin takes time to fully exit the blood stream. So, even after your sympathetic nervous system has stopped responding,

From: J.S. Abramowitz & A.E. Braddock: *Psychological Treatment of Health Anxiety and Hypochondriasis*   © 2008 Hogrefe & Huber Publishers

you are likely to feel keyed up or alarmed for some time because the adrenalin is still floating around in your system. This is actually part of the protective mechanism since in the wilds, danger often has a habit of returning. So, it is useful for us to remain in fight-or-flight mode so that we can quickly react if danger returns.

Bodily Symptoms Associated with the Fight-or-Flight Response

The fight-or-flight response is associated with changes in the body that can be intense and that can mimic medical problems. It is therefore important for you to understand what these bodily symptoms and sensations are, and what purposes they serve. Keep in mind that the overall purpose of the fight-or-flight response is to protect you from danger. Its physical symptoms, therefore, are all intended to prepare you to fight of flee. We will next review each type of body symptom.

Breathing Symptoms

During the fight-or-flight response your breathing automatically becomes faster and deeper. This occurs in order to increase the amount of oxygen you take in since the body needs higher levels of oxygen to be able to fight or flee. Oxygen is used by the muscles to make energy for fighting or fleeing danger.

The high rate and depth of breathing sometimes causes harmless but unpleasant symptoms such as breathlessness, feelings of choking or smothering, and pains or tightness in the chest. Also, blood supply to the head may be temporarily decreased. While this is only a small amount and is not at all dangerous, it produces unpleasant (but harmless) symptoms including dizziness, lightheadedness, blurred vision, confusion, feeling of unreality (or, feeling as if you are in a dream state), and hot flushes.

Heart and Cardiovascular Symptoms

In order to efficiently circulate oxygen and nutrients to your muscles for fighting or fleeing, your heart increases its rate and the strength of heartbeat during fight-or-flight. There is also a change in blood-flow patterns, so that blood is taken away from places where it is not needed (by a tightening of the blood vessels) and taken toward places where it is needed more (by dilation of the blood vessels). For example, blood is taken away from the skin, fingers, and toes. This is useful because having less blood flow to these areas means we are less likely to bleed to death if we are cut while fighting or fleeing. As a result of this reaction, however, your skin might turn pale or feel cold, especially your hands and feet. The blood instead goes to large muscles, such as the thighs, heart, and biceps, which need the oxygen for fighting or fleeing.

Other Symptoms

The fight-flight response also increases sweating. Sweat (perspiration) is the body's inbuilt air-conditioning system. When sweat evaporates, it cools the body to prevent it from overheating and thus allows us to continue fighting or fleeing from danger without becoming exhausted from heat.

Your pupils also become dilated (widened) to let in more light during fight-or-flight. This helps people scan the surroundings for danger. It also helps us see better in the dark. However, there may be temporary unpleasant side effects of pupil dilation, such as blurred vision, spots in front of the eyes, or being overly sensitivity to light.

During fight-or-flight, activity in the digestive system also decreases. After all, digesting food is not as important as fighting off danger or fleeing to safety. The energy needed to digest food is therefore used for more immediate survival purposes. A side effect of decreased digestive system activity is a decrease in salivation, which leads to dry or "cotton" mouth. Another side effect is nausea, heavy feelings in the stomach, and sometimes diarrhea.

Muscle groups tense up in preparation for fight-or-flight, and this causes feelings of tension. This tension may occur in the form of trembling or shaking, as well as other medically unexplained symptoms such as body movements, twitching, or eye blinking. It is also common to experience aches and pains (e.g., joint pain, headaches) associated with prolonged fight-or-flight, a direct result of extended periods of muscle tension.

The fight-or-flight response involves activation and arousal of many of the body's systems and large muscle groups. This takes a lot of energy, and therefore people often feel exhausted, drained, and washed out during and after experiencing this type of arousal.

Finally, the fight-or-flight response leads to an increase in alertness and attention. In particular, attention is focused on the source of the perceived threat or danger. This is a very useful effect of the fight-or-flight system because if we didn't pay attention to things that could harm us, we probably wouldn't survive. When it seems like we are preoccupied or unable to take our minds off of something threatening that has caught our attention, it is a natural consequence of this system.

Common Misperceptions of Fight-or-Flight Symptoms

It is easy to misunderstand the symptoms associated with fight-or-flight as those of a serious medical problem. Shortness of breath, twitching, lightheadedness, diarrhea, among other symptoms *can* be signs of more serious conditions. Commonly mistaken ideas and interpretations of the fight-or-flight symptoms include beliefs about losing control, collapsing, cardiac problems, and neurological problems such as having a stroke or fainting. Let's look more closely at each of these conditions:

Losing Control

Some people, when they experience the fight-or-flight response, believe they are going to lose control, become paralyzed, or lose their judgment and begin acting in strange or terrible ways (e.g., hurting people, saying inappropriate things). Or, they may simply have the overwhelming feeling that something bad is going to happen.

From reading this handout, you now know where this feeling comes from: The fight-or-flight response involves the entire body becoming prepared for action, and there is a strong feeling of your needing to escape. However, the fight-or-flight response is not aimed at hurting people who are not a threat, and it will not produce paralysis. Rather, the entire response is designed to get you away from potential danger. People do not "go crazy" or "lose control" when they experience fight-or-flight. In fact, remember that the fight-or-flight system is designed to help you when you are in threatening situations. So, although it might seem like you are confused or disoriented, you are actually able to think faster and react more quickly – you are physically stronger and your reflexes are quicker – than you normally would. This is the same thing that happens when a person is in a real emergency. Think of people who accomplish amazing things (such as lifting extremely heavy objects) and overcome their own intense fears under dire circumstances in order to save themselves or their children.

Heart Conditions

It is easy to mistake the symptoms of fight-or-flight as signs of a serious heart condition since the major symptoms of heart disease are breathlessness, chest pain, as well as palpitations and fainting. However, actual heart disease symptoms are brought on by physical exertion, for example, the harder you exercise, the worse the symptoms become; and symptoms usually go away fairly quickly with rest. This is very different from the fight-or-flight response, which often occurs when you are not exercising or exerting yourself physically. Although the

From: J.S. Abramowitz & A.E. Braddock: *Psychological Treatment of Health Anxiety and Hypochondriasis*   © 2008 Hogrefe & Huber Publishers

fight-or-flight response can intensify with exercise, this is different from the symptoms of heart disease or a heart attack because fight-or-flight symptoms occur equally often at rest.

Even more importantly, heart disease is very easily detected by physicians. It produces a remarkable electrical signal in the heart which is revealed by an electrocardiogram (EKG). In the fight-or-flight response, the only change that shows up on an EKG is an increase in heart rate (sometimes called tachycardia). By itself, tachycardia is not a sign of danger; unless it reaches an extremely high rate such as over 180 beats per minute, which far exceeds the rates that occur during the fight-or-flight response (120–130 beats per minute). Vigorous physical exercise increases your heart rate to around 150 to 180 beats per minute. Your usual heart rate when resting is anywhere from 60 to 85 beats per minute, but this varies from person to person.

Another belief is that "too much" of the fight-or-flight response will weaken the heart and make the person more vulnerable to heart attacks or other dangerous physical conditions in the future. Although there is evidence that long-lasting stress increases the risk of cardiovascular or cerebral diseases as we get older, chronic stress and strain is very different from the fight-or-flight response. As you know by now, fight-or-flight involves short bursts of adrenalin, similar in many ways to what happens during physical exercise. And, of course, we know that exercise-related exertion is very healthy for the body. Although chronically high levels of stress can pose a long-term threat, this risk is minimal compared to the risks associated with poor lifestyle factors such as a poor diet, lack of exercise, smoking, and substance abuse.

Fainting

The fear of fainting is usually based on the mistaken belief that symptoms such as dizziness and lightheadedness mean that one is about to faint. However, the person fails to consider that fight-or-flight arousal is incompatible with fainting. That is, the physical tension (sympathetic nervous system activation) that occurs during fight-or-flight is the exact *opposite* of what happens during fainting spells. Fainting is most likely to occur in people who have low blood pressure, or who respond to stress with major *reductions* in blood pressure. As we know, the fight-or-flight response *increases* heart rate and blood pressure. This is why fainting is extremely rare during fight-or-flight. Another important point is that the fight-or-flight response is designed to *protect* you from harm, so it would make absolutely no sense for nature to develop a response to threat that leads to fainting (which would surely mean the death of the person). Finally, even if you were to faint, consciousness is usually regained within a few seconds. Fainting is simply a way for the body to return to a normal level of functioning.

Handout 10.3. Your Noisy Body

What Is Body Noise and What Causes It?

The human body is in a constant state of flux. Whether we are awake or sleeping, there is always activity in our body – it is always changing. Your heart rate is constantly changing; your body temperature is constantly changing; your level of alertness, visual and auditory acuity, vestibular (balance) system, and even your muscle tension are constantly being adjusted as your body maintains itself. Sometimes we notice these changes and sometimes we do not. The purpose of this handout is to teach you about bodily sensations and variations – or what we'll call *body noise* – and the various explanations for it.

Think of the human body as similar to other complex machines such as computers and automobiles. These machines, even when working properly, often produce strange noises such as clicking, whirring, buzzing, screeching, among other noises. As with such machinery, even a healthy human body produces all sorts of physical symptoms that might be uncomfortable (or even painful), unexpected, and otherwise unwanted. Accordingly, the first aim of this handout is to help you understand that there are numerous explanations for the uncomfortable body sensations you experience.

Homeostasis

One of the most remarkable properties of the human body is *homeostasis*. Homeostasis refers to the process by which the body reacts to changes in the environment in order to maintain its internal balances. The body's reactions include countless dynamic and interconnected mechanisms, some of which might not be noticeable to the person, and others of which – such as feelings of nausea, pain, rapid heartbeat, hot and cold feelings, dizziness, and fatigue – might be quite noticeable.

The control of body temperature in humans is a good example of how homeostasis works. In human beings normal body temperature fluctuates around the value of 98.6°F, but various factors can raise or lower body temperature including exposure to certain environmental conditions (e.g., extreme cold), hormone levels, metabolic rate, and even infections. The body's temperature regulation is controlled by a region in the brain called the hypothalamus. Feedback about body temperature is carried through the bloodstream to the brain and it results in adjustments in breathing and heart rate as well as blood-sugar levels. For instance, when the body becomes overheated, blood-sugar levels decline causing us to feel fatigued so that we reduce our activity to cool off. We

From: J.S. Abramowitz & A.E. Braddock: *Psychological Treatment of Health Anxiety and Hypochondriasis*   © 2008 Hogrefe & Huber Publishers

also perspire, which leads to evaporation and cooling of the skin. Because some of these changes are abrupt and uncomfortable, they can be misinterpreted as signs of a medical condition.

It is impossible to list all of the bodily signs and symptoms associated with homeostasis in this handout (entire books have been written on the subject), and everyone's body functions a little differently. However, when physical symptoms are experienced in the absence of laboratory or diagnostic evidence of a medical illness, a likely explanation is that the unpleasant feelings are probably caused by one or more homeostatic functions.

Shifts in Your Daily Routine

Most of us follow a fairly consistent pattern of daily activities. We go to sleep and wake up at around the same time each day; we go through the same activities when getting prepared for the day and when unwinding before bedtime; we eat our meals around the same time each day; we even go to many of the same places (work, school) on a regular basis. As mentioned above, our bodies are very good at adjusting to these routines. In fact, perhaps our bodies adjust *too* well since it doesn't take much of a change in routine to produce noticeable physical effects, as we discuss below.

Our diet provides a nice illustration of just how sensitive our bodies are to changes in daily routine. The human body adapts to our eating schedule, the kinds of foods we eat, and the quantity of food we eat. So, if we skip a meal, the body's rhythm is thrown off which can produce feelings of tiredness, headaches, changes in blood pressure, heart rate, and breathing rate, and changes in blood-sugar levels, which can make one feel faint. When we try new foods, perhaps those high in fiber or with lots of spices, it can take the stomach by surprise leading to gas, cramps, stomach aches, and changes in the color, smell, and consistency of urine and feces. Finally, eating a lot more (or less) food than we typically do can lead to similar symptoms.

Our muscles and joints also acclimate to our typical activity level and can become strained, which produces pain and tightness, if we are more active than usual or if we use our muscles for activities that we usually perform. For example, if you enjoy playing tennis or softball, yet only play once in a while (or if it's the first game after a long break), you will probably experience soreness or tightness in your arms and chest afterward. This is because your muscles are not used to swinging or throwing since you don't engage in these activities on a regular basis. The same thing happens if you suddenly do heavy lifting that you don't normally do. Many people harmlessly pull muscles in their arms or chest this way and then confuse the pain and tightness for a more serious problem, such as a heart attack.

Sometimes, whether planned or unplanned, we don't get as much sleep as we typically get. This is another example of how the body can produce strange and uncomfortable symptoms that are not indications of a serious medical problem. When we don't get a good night's sleep, we commonly feel weak and lethargic, have trembles, lose our appetite, get a headache, and even experience dizziness, tingling, a racing heart, or have unusual visual experiences (flashes of light). Of course, it is very easy to interpret these signs and sensations as indicating a serious problem, but they are actually ways that our body tells us that we should get more sleep.

Minor Medical Conditions

Many minor ailments can produce very noticeable body changes. For example, even a cold, an allergic reaction, or a small infection can produce tenderness, soreness, swollen lymph nodes, racing heart, shortness of breath, and sneezing and coughing leading to a sore, dry, or scratchy throat. Allergens can also lead to hives, which are red itchy marks on the skin, or welts, which are similar to hives but occur under the skin. Heartburn and acid reflux can produce chest or stomach pain and burning in the throat. Irritable bowel syndrome (IBS) is a benign, yet uncomfortable condition characterized by abdominal pain, bowel cramps and urgency, diarrhea, bloating, constipation, and gas. It is exacerbated by eating certain foods such as tomatoes, spices, red meat, and fatty foods. Although the discomfort associated with IBS is benign, people often misinterpret these symptoms (and also those of hemorrhoids, which can produce pain and bloody stools) for more serious medical problems. Another benign, yet frightening, condition is called "unexplained cutaneous sensory syndrome," which can include skin pain, rash, numbness, and itching. Finally, hyperhidrosis is a harmless condition (yet sometimes embarrassing) in which the person perspires excessively from the hands, face, and other parts of the body.

Orthostatic Intolerance

Orthostatic intolerance refers to how well the body makes the necessary adjustments to counteract gravity. That is, when we stand up from a seated or prone position, our circulatory system needs to work a little harder so that gravity does not pull all of our blood down to our legs and feet. As we age, most everyone experiences normal episodes of orthostatic hypotension in which blood pressure drops as a result of simply moving to a standing position. This might be especially noticeable when getting out of bed in the morning and can involve a number of uncomfortable sensations such as a substantial increase in heart rate, feelings of nausea, vertigo, lightheadedness and faintness (although actually fainting is rare), headaches, and fatigue.

From: J.S. Abramowitz & A.E. Braddock: *Psychological Treatment of Health Anxiety and Hypochondriasis*   © 2008 Hogrefe & Huber Publishers

Health Habits

Certain habits, some of which might be very subtle, can result in uncomfortable body symptoms. For instance, eating and drinking rapidly, chewing gum, and smoking, can cause aerophagia (literally meaning "swallowing air"), a benign condition that produces discomfort and bloating in the stomach and sometimes chronic belching. Breathing heavily can result in feelings of faintness, tingling in the extremities, racing heart, and sweating since the muscles of the chest are working overtime to inhale and exhale.

Mind-Body Connection

It is easy to overlook the mind-body connection as a factor in the production of body symptoms. But all of our emotional reactions (sadness, fear, rage, even excitement and elation) have a physical component. Specifically, emotions are accompanied by activation of the body's sympathetic nervous system and the release of adrenaline (also known as epinephrine). This activity produces a set of perceptible and sometimes intense body changes including (but not limited to) increased heart rate and strength of heart beat, increased speed and depth of breathing, increased muscle tension, dilation of the pupils (which can produce strange visual experiences such as spots or flashes of light), perspiration, dry mouth, decreased activity in the digestive system, and increased urges to use the bathroom. Some emotions, such as disgust, are associated with a reduction in blood pressure and heart rate as well as a reduction in muscle tension.

Although they can seem intense and uncomfortable, these body sensations are harmless. In fact, these reactions are part of the body's natural "fight-or-flight" response. Even prolonged activation of the fight-or-flight response is not dangerous, although this, too, can produce additional frightening body symptoms such as exhaustion and fatigue from the increase in activity within the body, faintness and feelings of unreality from hyperventilation and the body's conversion of oxygen to carbon dioxide, blurred vision and spots from pupil dilation, numbness and tingling in the extremities from blood vessel constriction, breathlessness and feelings of choking or smothering from the increased rate and depth of breathing, aches, pains, tightness, trembling, and twitching from muscle tension, hot or cold flashes from sweating, and nausea and constipation from reduced digestive system activity.

Attention and Body Focus

Any discussion of body symptoms would be incomplete without also covering the importance of paying attention to these symptoms. Attention strongly influences how we experience body symptoms: The more we think about a symptom, the more the symptom will bother us. Therefore, the second aim of this handout is to help you understand how paying close attention to body symptoms actually makes them become more intense.

What Determines Body Focus?

As this handout describes, everyone experiences constant noise in their body. Some people, however, focus intensely on their body, whereas others tend not to. There are three reasons for this: First, some people are simply more focused and attentive than others, perhaps because of their innate personality. So, in addition to being focused on external events, such people are also tuned in to internal bodily events. Second, the degree to which someone is body-focused can be influenced by how much the people around them are talking about and calling attention to body symptoms. For example, if someone is repeatedly asked, "How is your _____ doing today," this will keep them focused on the particular organ or symptom. Similarly, when the media popularizes illnesses such as breast cancer, West Nile virus, or Lyme disease, it causes people to attend more closely to body sensations. Third, focusing on symptoms is influenced by the degree to which the person is concerned with some aspect of their health. Research demonstrates time and again that people who think they might have a medical problem tend to focus and concentrate on – even to the point of "looking for" – the very signs of that problem. This leads them to notice more symptoms, become more concerned, and so on.

How Body Focus and Attention Increase Body Noise

Research consistently shows that when we focus attention on something, we tend to notice it more. In one study, for example, healthy participants who were instructed to deliberately focus on their bodies reported more symptoms than those given instructions to focus elsewhere. In fact, those participants who focused on their bodies reported more painful and bothersome body symptoms. Focusing on a particular symptom gives the symptom a life of its own; the symptom becomes more threatening and disturbing. This in turn makes us focus even more intently on the details and subtleties of the symptoms, making it seem as if we are developing more intense symptoms, which we might interpret as a sign that things are getting worse. Of course, at this point, we don't stop to consider that what we assume are serious medical symptoms might be body noise resulting from a benign cause.

Summary

To summarize the main points of this handout:

- Body symptoms have real physical causes, but not all body symptoms are caused by serious medical problems.

- Symptoms are often the result of the body's tendency to maintain a relatively constant internal state (homeostasis) and can result from changes in daily routine, activity levels, diet, certain health habits, minor ailments, emotional reactions, among other factors.

- How much attention we give to body sensations influences the way we experience these sensations. People who, for whatever reason, are closely attuned to their bodies, notice more sensations and experience them as more intense. When this occurs, the chances increase that these benign body symptoms will be incorrectly interpreted as signs of a more serious medical condition.

Handout 11.1. Common Thinking Patterns in Health Anxiety

1. **All-or-Nothing Thinking:** You look at things in absolute, black-and-white categories, rather than seeing the middle ground. There is no in-between. Any body sensation becomes a sign of a serious health problem. For example, you are either *completely healthy* or *seriously ill,* and *if you do not get to the doctor at the first sign of trouble, it will be too late.* Another example is, *"Detailed tests are the only way to rule out an illness."*

2. **Not-So-Great Expectations:** You make gloom and doom predictions about things that haven't happened yet, as if you are a fortune teller. For example, *"I'm sure I'll find a lump if I check myself," "If I go to the doctor, he/she'll tell me I'm very sick,"* or *"My father died at this age, so I will too"*

3. **Negative Interpretations:** You jump to conclusions and interpret unexplained body sensations as a sign of a serious illness or other medical problem. Anything that seems to feel "not quite right" becomes a serious disease. For example, *"This is not a headache, it's a brain tumor"* or *"The pain in my stomach is a serious illness that no doctors can figure out."*

4. **Intolerance of Uncertainty:** You do not feel satisfied unless you have a complete and agreeable (to you) explanation for the cause and nature of your mysterious body sensations and symptoms. Anything less than a full medical explanation is unacceptable.

5. **Assumptions about:**

   Probability: You take it for granted and overestimate the likelihood of catastrophic outcomes – you assume that a generally unlikely event is much more likely to occur than it really is. For example, the idea that serious illnesses and diseases are very easy to catch and lurking everywhere; that you are more vulnerable than others to a certain illness (perhaps because of family history); or the assumption that because you didn't mention something to the doctor, he or she overlooked the presence of a serious health problem.

   Severity: You overestimate the "awfulness" of feared outcomes and automatically assume that negative events, such as having an illness or dying, would be 101% terrible and certainly more horrific or awful than you could cope with. For example, *"I must look after my health at all times, or I will be a terrible burden on my family,"* and *"Death will be lonely and painful (accompanied by images of oneself being self-aware, buried alive, and eaten by worms)."*

6. **Disqualifying:** You focus only on certain information or facts (usually information that supports your view) but ignore or explain away other facts that are just as relevant (but that do not support your view).

From: J.S. Abramowitz & A.E. Braddock: *Psychological Treatment of Health Anxiety and Hypochondriasis*   © 2008 Hogrefe & Huber Publishers

7. **Lofty Standards:** You hold extremely high expectations of others – usually medical professionals – to be able to understand your body symptoms and give you a definitive explanation or cause for everything you think might be wrong with you. This leads to doctor-shopping and continuing to seek out "the best" doctors to explain the unexplainable, or prevent a serious disease.

8. **Intolerance of Anxiety:** You feel that anxiety or discomfort will persist forever unless you do something to escape. Sometimes the fear is that the anxiety or emotional discomfort will spiral out of control or lead to "going crazy," "losing control," or other harmful medical or physical consequences.

9. **Emotional reasoning:** You assume that something is wrong based simply on the fact that you are feeling concerned about it.

Handout 11.2. Thought Challenging Form

Date: _____ Situation: _____

Threatening Thought and Thinking Pattern	Evidence for this Thought	Evidence Against this Thought	Alternative Thought Based on the Evidence

From: J.S. Abramowitz & A.E. Braddock: *Psychological Treatment of Health Anxiety and Hypochondriasis*   © 2008 Hogrefe & Huber Publishers

Handout 11.3. Helpful Comments

Responding to requests for reassurance:

- It sounds like you are looking for reassurance about that, but remember we agreed it is not helpful for me to answer those kinds of questions.

- Remember that your urge to get reassurance will go down, but only if I don't answer reassurance questions.

- Remember, the anxiety is temporary. It will go down if you give it time.

- Let's go for a little walk and maybe that will help.

- I know it's hard to resist seeking reassurance. What can I do to help you get through this rough time?

- I've tried to do the right thing, but to avoid an argument, I'll tell you what you want to hear. Still, I don't think you're making a good choice here, but I realize it's hard for you. Make sure you discuss this with your therapist. There will be other chances for you to resist reassurance-seeking.

Praising efforts to resist asking for assurance:

- You're doing a great job not asking for reassurance. I'm very proud.

- I've noticed the last few days that you've stopped asking questions about your health. I bet that's been difficult for you. Great job.

From: J.S. Abramowitz & A.E. Braddock: *Psychological Treatment of Health Anxiety and Hypochondriasis*   © 2008 Hogrefe & Huber Publishers

Handout 12.1. The 10 Commandments for Successful Exposure

1. **Exposure practices should be planned, structured, and predictable.** Decide in advance what you will do in the situation and how long you will stay. Plan in advance when you will complete your practice and put it in your schedule. Have a backup plan in case the original one does not work out.

2. **Exposure practices should be repeated frequently and spaced close together.** The more closely spaced the practices, the more fear reduction you are likely to experience. It is a good idea to practice being in the same situation repeatedly until it becomes easier.

3. **Exposure pace can be gradual.** Do not assume that you must do the most difficult thing you can imagine right away, but be sure to choose practices that are nevertheless challenging. The more difficult the items that you practice, the quicker you will learn to be more comfortable. Try to choose practices that are challenging but not so difficult that you will not complete them.

4. **Expect to feel uncomfortable.** It is perfectly normal to feel awful during initial exposure practices. Also, these practices may leave you feeling tired and anxious afterward. With repeated practice, these feelings will decrease. Success should not be judged by how you felt in the situation. Rather, success should be judged by whether you were able to stay in the situation despite feeling awful.

5. **Try not to fight your fear.** Fighting the anxiety will have the effect of increasing your anxious feelings. Instead, just let it happen. The worst thing that is likely to happen is that you will feel temporarily uncomfortable.

6. **Do not use subtle avoidance strategies during exposure.** Complete the practices without the use of distraction, medications, alcohol, leaving early, avoiding eye contact, and other such strategies.

7. **Use exposure practices to test negative predictions about the consequences of facing your fear.** Before beginning an exposure, ask yourself what you are afraid might happen during the practice. Then conduct the exposure practice to test the accuracy of your fearful prediction. Afterwards, think about the evidence you gained from your experience and how it compares to your original fearful prediction.

8. **Rate your fear on scale from 0 to 100.** During exposure practices, it can be helpful to pay attention to how you are feeling and to notice the variables that make your anxiety go up and down during the practice.

9. **Exposure practices should last long enough for a significant reduction in anxiety.** Continue each exposure practice until your anxiety goes down, no matter how much time it takes. A good rule of thumb is to continue an exposure practice until your anxiety rating on the 0–100 scale decreases by at least half (e.g., below 40 if it peaked at 80).

10. **Practices should take place in different settings to generalize learning.** Conducting exposure practices in multiple settings will help bring about a more broad decrease in your anxiety. It is often helpful to conduct exposures with your therapist, at home, and in other settings. It can also be helpful to conduct some exposures by yourself because sometimes the presence of other people can make us feel artificially safe.

Adapted from: Antony, M.M., & Swinson, R.P. (2000). *Phobic disorders and panic in adults: A guide to assessment and treatment.* Washington, DC: American Psychological Association.

Yale-Brown Obsessive Compulsive Severity Scale (Y-BOCS) Adapted for Health Anxiety

TOTAL SCORE (add 1–10) ☐

HEALTH PREOCCUPATIONS list 3:

Time: how much time do your health concerns occupy per day; how frequently do they occur	none	< 1 h / rarely	1–3 h / occasionally	3–8 h / frequently	> 8 h / constantly
	0	1	2	3	4
Interference: How much do health concerns keep you from doing activities (e.g., work / school, social)	none	slight interference	definite, but manageable	substantial interference	unmanageable
	0	1	2	3	4
Distress: How much distress do the health concerns cause you?	none	mild	disturbing but manageable	very disturbing	disabling
	0	1	2	3	4
Resistance: How much effort do you make to resist concerns about your health? How often do you try to turn focus away?	always (100%)	usually	sometimes	rarely	never (0%)
	0	1	2	3	4
Control: How successful are you in stopping intense health concerns? How often can you beat the concerns vs. the concerns beating you?	always (100%)	usually	sometimes	rarely	never (100%)
	0	1	2	3	4

Preoccupation Total ☐

From: J.S. Abramowitz & A.E. Braddock: *Psychological Treatment of Health Anxiety and Hypochondriasis*   © 2008 Hogrefe & Huber Publishers

SAFETY-SEEKING BEHAVIORS list 3:

Time: how much time do you spend checking and seeking information or reassurance per day; how frequently?	none 0	< 1 h / rarely 1	1–3 h / occasionally 2	3–8 h / frequently 3	> 8 h / constantly 4
Interference: How much do these behaviors keep you from doing activities (e.g., work/school, social)?	none 0	slight interference 1	definite, but manageable 2	substantial interference 3	unmanageable 4
Distress: If you were prevented from performing these behaviors, how distressed would you become?	none 0	mild 1	disturbing but manageable 2	very disturbing 3	disabling 4
Resistance: How much effort do you make to resist performing these behaviors? How hard do you try?	always (100%) 0	usually 1	sometimes 2	rarely 3	never (0%) 4
Control: How successful are you in stopping these behaviors yourself?	always (100%) 0	usually 1	sometimes 2	rarely 3	never (100%) 4

Safety Behavior Total ☐

From: J.S. Abramowitz & A.E. Braddock: *Psychological Treatment of Health Anxiety and Hypochondriasis*   © 2008 Hogrefe & Huber Publishers

Brown Assessment of Beliefs Scale

1) Are there certain ideas or beliefs you have that are of significant concern to you **over the past week?** Which one would you rate as being of most concern? (principle belief):

_____

_____

2) Do you have other ideas (thoughts/beliefs) that you are preoccupied with?

_____

_____

For each item, circle the number identifying the response which best characterizes the patient **over the past week**. The patient's specific beliefs can be incorporated into the questions – for example, "How convinced are you of this belief – that touching doorknobs will make you ill?" Optional questions are indicated in parentheses; instructions to the interviewer are *italicized*.

1. Conviction How convinced are you of these ideas/beliefs? Are you certain your ideas/beliefs are accurate? (What do you base your certainty on?)	0. – Completely convinced beliefs are false (0% certainty). 1. – Beliefs are probably not true, or substantial doubt exists. 2. – Beliefs may or may not be true, or unable to decide whether beliefs are true. 3. – Fairly convinced that beliefs are true, but an element of doubt exists. 4. – Completely convinced about the reality of held beliefs (100% certainty).
2. Perception of others' views of beliefs What do you think other people (would) think of your beliefs? [PAUSE] How certain are you that *most* people think your beliefs make sense? *(Interviewer should clarify if necessary that the patient answers this question assuming that others are giving their honest opinion.)*	0. – Completely certain that most people think these beliefs are unrealistic. 1. – Fairly certain that most people think these beliefs are unrealistic. 2. – Others may or may not think the beliefs are unrealistic, or uncertain about others' views concerning these beliefs. 3. – Fairly certain that most people think these beliefs are realistic. 4. – Completely certain that most people think these beliefs are realistic.

From: J.S. Abramowitz & A.E. Braddock: *Psychological Treatment of Health Anxiety and Hypochondriasis*   © 2008 Hogrefe & Huber Publishers

3. Explanation of differing views
You said that (fill in response to item 1) but that (fill in response to item 2). [PAUSE] How do you explain the difference between what you think and what others think about the accuracy of your beliefs? (Who's more likely to be right?)

(Interviewer should not ask this question if responses on item 1 and 2 are the same. In that case, give the same score as in items 1 and 2.)

| |
| 0. – Completely certain that beliefs are unrealistic or absurd (e.g., "my mind is playing tricks on me"). |
| 1. – Fairly certain that beliefs are unrealistic. |
| 2. – Uncertain about why others don't agree– beliefs may be unrealistic or others may be wrong. |
| 3. – Fairly certain that beliefs are true; view of others is less accurate. |
| 4. – Completely certain that beliefs are true; beliefs of others is not accurate. |

4. Fixity of ideas
If I were to question (or challenge) the accuracy of your beliefs, what would your reaction be? [PAUSE] Could I convince you that you're wrong?

(If necessary, supply a nonconfrontational example.)

(Rate on the basis of whether the patient could be convinced, not whether she wishes she could be convinced.)

| |
| 0. – Eager to consider the possibility that the beliefs may be false; demonstrates no reluctance to entertain this possibility. |
| 1. – Easily willing to consider the possibility that beliefs may be false; reluctance to do so is minimal. |
| 2. – Somewhat willing to consider the possibility that beliefs may be false; but moderate resistance is present. |
| 3. – Clearly reluctant to consider the possibility that beliefs may be false; reluctance is significant. |
| 4. – Absolutely refuses to consider the possibility that beliefs may be false – i.e., beliefs are fixed. |

5. Attempts to disprove ideas
How actively do you try to disprove or reject your beliefs? How much effort do you make to convince yourself that your beliefs are false?

(Interviewer should rate attempts patient makes to talk him or herself out of the belief, not attempts to push the thoughts/ideas out of his/her mind or think about something else.)

| |
| 0. – Always involved in trying to disprove beliefs, or not necessary to disprove because beliefs are not true. |
| 1. – Usually tries to disprove beliefs. |
| 2. – Sometimes tries to disprove beliefs. |
| 3. – Occasionally attempts to disprove beliefs. |
| 4. – Makes no attempt to disprove beliefs. |

6. Insight
What do you think has caused you to have these beliefs? [PAUSE] Do they have a psychiatric or psychological cause or are they actually true?

(Interviewer should determine what the patient actually believes, not what she has been told or hopes is true. Psychological etiology should be considered equivalent to psychiatric illness.)

(Recognition that the thoughts are excessive – i.e., taking up too much time – or causing problems for the patient should not be considered equivalent to psychiatric/psychological etiology. Instead, rate patient's awareness that the source/cause of the beliefs is psychiatric/psychological.)

0. – Beliefs definitely have a psychiatric/psychological cause.
1. – Beliefs probably have a psychiatric/psychological cause.
2. – Beliefs possibly have a psychiatric/psychological cause.
3. – Beliefs probably do not have a psychiatric/psychological cause.
4. – Beliefs definitely do not have a psychiatric/psychological cause.

TOTAL BABS SCORE _____ **= SUM OF QUESTIONS 1 THROUGH 6**

ADDITIONAL ITEM *(do not include in total score)*

7. Ideas/delusions of reference
Does it ever seem that people are talking about you or taking special notice of you because of *(fill in belief)*.
OPTIONAL: What about receiving special messages from your environment because of *(fill in belief)*.
(How certain are you of this?)

(This question pertains only to the beliefs being assessed by the BABS interviewer- not if the patient thinks s/he is noticed for a reason unrelated to the beliefs being assessed. Interviewer should NOT base answer on observable actions or compulsions; instead, rate core belief.)

0. – No, others definitely do not take special notice of me.
1. – Others probably do not take special notice of me.
2. – Others may or may not take special notice of me.
3. – Others probably do take special notice of me.
4. – Others definitely do take special notice of me.

Reproduced with permission from Jane Eisen, MD.

From: J.S. Abramowitz & A.E. Braddock: *Psychological Treatment of Health Anxiety and Hypochondriasis*   © 2008 Hogrefe & Huber Publishers

Index*

A

Abstinence violation effect, 271–272

ADIS-IV. *See* Anxiety Disorders Interview Schedule for DSM-IV (ADIS-IV)

Adrenalin, in fight-or-flight response, 296–297

Age of onset, in health anxiety, 38

Agreement with twist, in enhancing motivation and communication, 130

Alertness, fight-or-flight response effects on, 298

All-or-nothing thinking, 307
– cognitive therapy for, 213–215

Amplification, somatosensory, 41–42

Amplified reflection, in enhancing motivation and communication, 129–130

Anthrax symptoms, case example, 63

Anxiety
– absence during exposure, 265–266
– as adaptive response, 13
– in case formulation, 172–173
– described, 13, 185–190, 189f
– health. *See* Health anxiety
– intolerance of, 230, 308
– symptoms of, 186, 186f, 189f
– vicious cycle related to, 189f, 194f

Anxiety Disorders Interview Schedule for DSM-IV (ADIS-IV), 117

Anxiety levels, during behavioral experiments or exposures, 265

Anxiety reduction, 175
– during exposure therapy, 236, 237f

Anxiety sensitivity, 56–57

Anxiety Sensitivity Index--3rd revision (ASI-3), 107–108
– for assessing beliefs, 157

Anxiety symptom chart, example of, 186, 186f

Anxiety-reducing behavior, use of, 173–175

Anxious behaviors, 186f, 189f

Anxious thoughts, 186f, 189f

Appraisal(s), automatic, 23

Argument(s)
– avoidance of, 128–129, 128t
– solutions for overcoming, 259–260

Argumentative patients, terminating treatment with, 260–261

Arousal(s), sympathetic, 48–49

ASI-3. *See* Anxiety Sensitivity Index – 3rd revision (ASI-3)

Asking for assurance, praising efforts to resist, 310

Assessment
– functional, 145–166. *See also* Functional assessment
– initial, 103–121. *See also* Initial assessment
– ongoing, 104

Assumption(s)
– about inability to cope, 225–226
– about probability, 225–226, 307
– about severity, 225–226, 307
– general health, 58–59

Assurance, praising efforts to resist asking for, 310

Attention
– body focus and, 305
– fight-or-flight response effects on, 298
– increase in, 305–306

Attentional focus, body vigilance and, 197–199

Attitude(s), dysfunctional, 148f, 154–158

---

* *Note:* Page numbers followed by an "f" indicate figures; page numbers followed by a "t" indicate tables.

Automatic approach, health anxiety and, 23

Automatic thoughts, threatening, 171

Autonomic nervous system, in fight-or-flight response, 296

Avoidance, 80–81
– passive, 25t, 27–28, 159–160

B

BABS. *See* Brown Assessment of Beliefs Scale (BABS)

BDI-II. *See* Beck Depression Inventory – 2nd ed. (BDI-II)

Beck Depression Inventory – 2nd ed. (BDI-II), 108

Beck's health anxiety, cognitive theory of emotion as applied to, 53f

Behavior(s)
– anxiety-reducing, 173–175
– anxious, 186f, 189f
– checking, 24–26, 25t
– health-anxiety, 24–28, 25t
– maladaptive, 158–164. *See also* Maladaptive behaviors
– passive avoidance, 25t, 27–28
– reassurance-seeking, 24–26, 25t
– safety. *See* Safety behaviors
– safety signals, 25t, 27, 79–80, 158, 162–163
– safety-seeking, 149f. *See* Safety-seeking behaviors
– situational safety, 25t, 27, 79–80

Behavioral experiment monitoring form, 219f

Behavioral experimentation
– in cognitive therapy, 210–211
– unbearable anxiety levels during, 265

Behavioral factors, 74–80
– checking, 24–26, 25t, 77–78, 161–162
– reassurance-seeking, 24–26, 25t, 75–77, 161–162, 253, 261–264
– situational safety behaviors, 25t, 27, 79–80

Behavioral genetics, overview of, 42–43

Behavioral responses, effects on enhancing motivation and communication, 139–140

Belief(s)
– assessment of, 157–158
– catastrophic, 79–80
– death-related, 59–60
– dysfunctional. *See* Dysfunctional beliefs
– in functional assessment, 148f, 154–158
– illness-related, 45
– leading to health anxiety, 52–55, 53f, 54t
– rigid health-related, 58

Benign dermatological symptoms, 51

Benign medical conditions, 49–52
– case example, 49, 51

Bias(es)
– confirmation, 73–74
– memory, 74

Biopsychosocial case formulation, 168–170, 169f

Biopsychosocial factors, in maintenance of health anxiety, 82, 82f

Biopsychosocial model, 131–140
– behavioral responses effects in, 139–140
– body noise in, 134–136
– body vigilance in, 134–136
– dichotomous nature of medical results and diagnoses in, 136–137
– getting foot in door, 132–134
– of health anxiety causes, 46
– of health anxiety development, 64f
– implications of, 64f, 65
– mind-body connection in, 137–139
– psychological treatment rationale in, 141–143, 142t
– rationale for, 141–143, 142t
– treatment implications of, 83–84

Bodily signs, in functional assessment, 147f, 152–153

Body checking, 25t, 26, 77–78. *See also* Checking
– as maladaptive behavior, 160–161

– during response prevention, 253
Body focus
– attention and, 305
– factors determining, 305
– increase in body noise due to, 305–306
Body noise, 46–47, 301–306
– attention effects on, 305–306
– causes of, 301
– described, 301
– in enhancing motivation and communication, 134–136
– health habits and, 304
– homeostasis and, 301–302
– increase in, 305–306
– mind-body connection and, 304
– minor medical conditions and, 303
– orthostatic intolerance and, 303–304
– psychoeducation related to, 194–199
– shifts in daily routine and, 302–303
Body sensations
– anxiety-related, 186f, 189f
– in case formulation, 170–171
– feared, 217, 217t
– during interoceptive exposure, 249, 249t
– monitoring of, 183
Body Symptom Monitoring Form, 295
Body symptoms
– self-monitoring of, 292–293
– sources of, 195–196
Body temperature, control of, 301–302
Body vigilance
– attentional focus and, 197–199
– elevated, 72
– in enhancing motivation and communication, 134–136
– psychoeducation related to, 194–199
Body Vigilance Scale (BVS), 108, 134
Brain tumor, case example, 15
Breathing, fight-or-flight response effects on, 297
Brown Assessment of Beliefs Scale (BABS), 118–119, 314–316
BVS. See Body Vigilance Scale (BVS)

C
Cardiovascular system, fight-or-flight response effects on, 297–298
Case formulation, 167–175
– anxiety in, 172–173
– in anxiety reduction, 175
– anxiety-reducing behavior in, 173–175
– biopsychosocial, 168–170, 169f
– components of, 170–175
– cues in, 170
– fight-or-flight response in, 172–173
– life experiences in, 172
– neuroticism in, 171–172
– observation in, 172
– origins of unexplained body sensations in, 170–171
– overview of, 167–168
– purpose of, 176
– threatening automatic thoughts and interpretations in, 171
– in transmission of health-relevant information, 172
– treatment planning in, 177–179, 178f
– treatment procedures addressing elements in, 176t
– triggers in, 170
Catastrophic beliefs, safety behaviors and safety signals linked to, 79–80
Cause(s), of health anxiety, 41–65
CBHQ. See Cognitions about Body and Health Questionnaire (CBHQ)
CBT. See Cognitive-behavioral therapy (CBT)
Change Plan Worksheet, 291
Change talk, eliciting of, 141–143, 142t
Checking, 77–78. See also Body checking
– compulsive, 161–162
– in health anxiety, 24–26, 25t
Chief complaint, assessment of, 111–112, 112t
Chronic fatigue, case example, 30
Chronic pain, case example, 37
Cleaning/washing, during response prevention, 254
Clinical interview

– areas of difficulty in, 116
– assess chief complaint and history in, 111–112, 112t
– assessment prior to, 105–110
– family issues in, 114–116, 115t
– individual strengths in, 116
– in initial assessment and diagnosis of health anxiety, 110–116, 112t, 115f
– mood assessment in, 112–113
– motivation for treatment in, 116
– open-ended questions in, 112t
– patient history in, 113
– previous treatment in, 114
– social functioning assessment in, 113
Clomipramine, in health anxiety management, 96t
Cognition
– automatic approach and, 23
– doubts, 23–24
– dysfunctional core beliefs, 21–23, 22t
– of health anxiety, 21–24
– images, 23–24
– intrusive thoughts, 23–24
Cognitions about Body and Health Questionnaire (CBHQ), 110
– for assessing beliefs, 157
Cognitive behavioral therapy (CBT), exposure therapy in, 233–234
Cognitive error(s)
– applying cognitive strategies to, 213–230, 217t, 219f, 223f
– correction of, 207–213, 209t. See also Cognitive error correction
– identification of, 206–207
– informal discussions of, 211–213
Cognitive error correction
– behavioral experiments and data collection in, 210–211
– evidence for and against threatening thoughts in, 207–210, 209t
– informal discussions of cognitive errors in, 211–213
– strategies for, 207–213, 209t
Cognitive factors, 71–74
– case example, 72, 73

– confirmation bias, 73–74
– in functional assessment, 148f
– memory bias, 74
– selective attention to threat cues, 71–73
Cognitive model of emotion, 183–185
Cognitive restructuring, 94
Cognitive theory of emotion, as applied to Beck's health anxiety, 53f
Cognitive therapy, 203–232
– for all-or-nothing thinking, 213–215
– assumptions about probability, severity, and inability to cope in, 225–226
– behavioral experiment monitoring form in, 219f
– challenges facing, 231–232
– collaborative empiricism in, 204–205
– correcting cognitive errors in, 207–213, 209t
– described, 203
– disqualifying in, 226–228
– for emotional reasoning, 230
– exposure therapy with, 255
– holding lofty standards – related, 228–229
– identifying cognitive errors in, 206–207
– indications for, 231
– for intolerance of anxiety, 230
– for intolerance of uncertainty, 220–224, 223f
– for negative interpretations, 216–218, 217t, 219f
– for not-so-great expectations, 215–216
– obstacles with, 231–232, 263–265
– patient's use for reassurance, 264
– Socratic style in, 205–206
– stylistic issues in, 204–206
– techniques, 203–232
– for thinking errors, 213–230, 217t, 219f, 223f
Cognitive-behavioral therapy (CBT), 93–95
– arguments related to, 259–260

– asking for reassurance during exposure exercises, 263
– barriers to, 257–267
– ERP vs., 95
– excessive reassurance seeking in,
  261–262
– "How do you know I'm not medically
  ill?" in, 262
– medications vs., 97–98
– nonadherence to, 257–259
– overcoming obstacles, 257–263
– requests for additional medical consultations in, 262
– suggested content of sessions, 100t
– terminating treatment with argumentative or nonadherent patients,
  260–261
Collaborative empiricism
– in cognitive therapy, 204–205
– described, 204
Communication
– agreement with twist in, 130
– avoid arguments in, 128–129, 128t
– avoid lecturing in, 126–127
– biopsychosocial model in, 131–140.
  See also Biopsychosocial model
– conversational styles to avoid in,
  128–129, 128t
– eliciting change talk in, 141–143, 142t
– emphasize patient's control and personal choice in, 130–131
– enhancement of, 122–143
– medicalizing in, 127–128
– psychologizing in, 127–128
– rationale for psychological treatment
  in, 141–143, 142t
– reflect resistance in, 130
– reflective listening in, 125–126, 126t
– roll with resistance in, 129–131
– socialization in, 131
– strategies in, 125–131
Complaint(s)
– chief, 111–112, 112t
– medically unexplained, 194–195
– physical, 29, 30t

Compulsive checking, reassurance-seek-
  ing via, 161–162
Conditions about Body and Health
  Questionnaire (CBHQ)
– in initial assessment, 110
– in maladaptive behavior assessment,
  163
Confirmation bias, 73–74
Consent of patient, in clinical interview,
  117
Consultation(s), patient's requests for
  additional, 262
Control, patient's, 130–131, 299
Cope, inability to, 225–226
Core beliefs, dysfunctional, 21–23, 22t
Cost(s), health anxiety – related, 40
Course, of health anxiety, 38
Cross-cultural issues, health anxiety – related, 39
Cue(s)
– in case formulation, 170
– illness-related, 80–81
– interoceptive, 92
– threat, 71–73
Cultural factors
– in clinical interview, 120
– health anxiety – related, 39

D
Daily monitoring form, 293
Daily routine, shifts in, 302–303
Data collection, in cognitive therapy,
  210–211
Death, beliefs about, 59–60
Death of loved one, 61
Delusion(s), somatic, 31
Depressive symptoms, in clinical inter-
  view, 119
Dermatological symptoms, benign, 51
Diagnosis(es)
– dichotomous nature of, 136–137
– initial assessment and, 103–121. See
  also Initial assessment
Diagnostic and Statistical Manual of Men-
  tal Disorders (DSM-IV-TR)

– hypochondriasis beyond, 16–17
– hypochondriasis in, 14–16, 15t
Diagnostic assessment, functional assessment vs., 145–166
Diagnostic interviews, structured, 116–117
Diet(s), effects of, 47
Dietary restriction, during response prevention, 254
Difficulties of patient, in clinical interview, 116
Digestive system, fight-or-flight response effects on, 298
Disease phobia, 32–33
Disqualifying, 307
– cognitive therapy for, 226–228
Distrust of medicine, 59
Doubt(s), 23–24, 148f, 154
DSM-IV-TR. *See Diagnostic and Statistical Manual of Mental Disorders* (DSM-IV-TR)
Dysfunctional attitudes, identification of, 148f, 154–158
Dysfunctional beliefs
– in case formulation, 171
– domains of, 54t
– in functional assessment, 148f
– historical factors potentially giving rise to, 151–152
– identification of, 148f, 154–158
– origin of, 60–64, 64f

E
Emotion
– cognitive model of, 183–185
– cognitive theory of, 53f
Emotional reasoning, 308
– cognitive therapy for, 230
Empathy, with reflective listening, 125–126, 126t
Empiricism, collaborative, 204–205
Environmental factors, types of, 60–64, 64f
ERP. *See* Exposure and response prevention (ERP)
Etiologic factors, defined, 67

Exercise(s), exposure, 266–267
Expectation(s), not-so-great, 215–216, 307
Experience(s)
– stressful, 61
– traumatic, 61
Explanatory therapy, 86–87
Exposure(s). *See also specific types and* Exposure therapy
– absence of anxiety during, 265–266
– imaginal, 91–92, 242–247
– interoceptive, 92t, 247–250, 249t
– lifestyle, 255
– maintaining lifestyle of, 255, 270
– plan for, 235–236
– programmed, 255
– purpose of, 235
– situational, 238–242, 239f, 241f
– 10 Commandments for successful, 311
– therapist's role during, 237–238
– unbearable anxiety levels during, 265
Exposure and response prevention (ERP), 90–93, 92t
– CBT vs., 95
Exposure exercises, therapists' discomfort with, 266–267
Exposure Hierarchy Form, 238, 239f
Exposure practices, 10 Commandments for successful, 311
Exposure therapy, 233–251
– anxiety reduction during, 236, 237f
– avoid providing reassurance during, 251
– as CBT, 233–234
– cognitive therapy with, 255
– described, 233
– employing support person during, 254
– humor during, 251
– imaginal exposure, 242–247
– interoceptive exposure, 247–250, 249t
– patient introduction to, 234–238, 237t
– programmed and lifestyle exposure, 255
– rationale for, 235–237, 237f
– reassurance-seeking during, 263

– remarks during exposure tasks in, 250–251
– situational exposure, 238–242, 239f, 241f
– stylistic considerations during, 250–251
– therapist's role during, 237–238
External situations, in functional assessment, 148f, 153
External stimuli
– in functional assessment, 148f, 153
– health anxiety precipitated by, 20–21, 21t

F
Fainting, misperceptions related to fight-or-flight response, 299–300
Family issues, in clinical interview, 114–116, 115t
Fatigue, chronic, 30
Fear of Lyme disease, case example, 32
Feared body sensations, procedures for inducing, 217, 217t
Feedback to patient, in clinical interview, 119–120
Fight-or-flight response, 127, 296–300
– adrenalin in, 296–297
– alertness due to, 298
– attention due to, 298
– autonomic nervous system in, 296
– bodily symptoms associated with, 297–298
– breathing symptoms in, 297
– cardiac symptoms in, 297–298
– cardiovascular symptoms in, 297–298
– in case formulation, 172–173
– described, 13, 296–297
– digestive system effects of, 298
– muscle group effects of, 298
– parasympathetic nervous system in, 296
– psychoeducation related to, 185–190, 186f, 189f
– pupil dilation and, 298
– sweating and, 298
– sympathetic nervous system in, 296
Fight-or-flight symptoms, misperceptions of, 299–300
Floater(s), 51
Fluoxetine, in health anxiety management, 96t
Fluvoxamine, in health anxiety management, 96t
Focus, body. See Body focus
Functional assessment, 145–166
– bodily signs assessment in, 147f, 152–153
– cognitive features in, 148f
– components of, 146t
– diagnostic assessment vs., 145–166
– doubts assessment in, 148f, 154
– dysfunctional attitudes identification in, 148f, 154–158
– dysfunctional beliefs identification in, 148f
– external situations assessment in, 148f, 153
– forms for conducting, 147f-149f
– historical factors in, 147f, 151–152
– intrusive ideas assessment in, 148f, 154
– intrusive thoughts assessment in, 148f, 154
– maladaptive behaviors identification in, 158–164
– misinterpretations in, 148f, 154–158
– overview of, 145–150, 146t, 147f-149f
– perturbations assessment in, 147f, 152–153
– practical issues in, 166
– review of recent episodes in, 150–151
– safety-seeking behaviors in, 149f
– self-monitoring in, 164–166
– self-report questionnaires in, 157–158
– sensations assessment in, 147f, 152–153
– triggers in, 147f-148f, 152–154

G
GAD. See Generalized anxiety disorder (GAD)

General health assumptions, 58–59
General population, health anxiety in, 17
Generalized anxiety disorder (GAD), 36
Genetic(s)
– behavioral, 42–43
– of health anxiety, 42–46
Getting foot in door, 132–134

H
Hamilton Rating Scale for Depression
   (HRSD), 119
Health anxiety. *See also specific causes,*
   symptoms, treatment, types
– age of onset of, 38
– Beck's cognitive theory of emotion as
   applied to, 53f
– behaviors related to, 24–28, 25t
– beliefs and interpretations leading to,
   52–55, 53f, 54t
– biopsychosocial model of development of, 64f
– case examples' perspectives on, 1–7
– case formulation in, 167–175
– causes of, 41–65
– clinical conditions characterized by,
   28–37, 30t
– cognitive phenomena in, 21–24
– cognitive therapy for, 203–232
– components of, 18
– costs related to, 40
– course of, 38
– cross-cultural issues related to, 39
– defined, 13–14, 16
– essential features of, 18–28
– exposure therapy for, 233–251
– external stimuli and, 20–21, 21t
– functional assessment in, 145–166
– in general population, 17
– genetics of, 42–46
– heritability of, 42–46
– hypochondriasis vs., 17–18
– initial assessment and diagnosis,
   103–121
– insight in, 28
– internal medicine physician's perspective on, 9
– maintenance factors of, 68–84
– maladaptive, 14
– Mayo Clinics perspectives on, 6–12
– motivation and communication related to, 123–143
– nature of, 13–40
– patients' perspectives on, 1–7
– persistence of, 67–84
– physical sensations triggering and,
   18–19, 19t
– prevalence of, 38, 39
– primary-care physician's perspective
   on, 8
– psychoeducation for, 181–201
– psychologist' perspective on, 9–12
– response prevention in, 251–254, 252f
– thinking patterns in, 307–308
– treatment for, 85–100. *See also* Treat-
   ment(s)
– treatment providers' perspectives on,
   8–12
– triggers of, 18–21, 19t, 21t
Health anxiety cues. *See* Cue(s)
Health assumptions, general, 58–59
Health beliefs. *See* Belief(s)
Health Concerns Log, 293
Health habits, body noise related to, 304
Health worries, case example, 36
Heart, fight-or-flight response effects on,
   297–298
Heart conditions, misperceptions related
   to fight-or-flight response, 299–300
Heritability
– of health anxiety, 42–46
– of illness-related beliefs, 45
High-risk situations, maintaining improvement after therapy in, 269–270
Historical factors
– dysfunctional beliefs resulting from,
   151–152
– in functional assessment, 147f,
   151–152

Holding lofty standards, cognitive therapy for, 228–229
Homeostasis, 47, 301–302
– described, 301
Homeostatic functions, 47
"How do you know I'm not medically ill?", solutions for overcoming, 262
HRSD. *See* Hamilton Rating Scale for Depression (HRSD)
Humor, during exposure therapy, 251
Hypochondriasis
– beyond DSM-IV-TR, 16–17
– case example, 15
– defined, 14, 89
– dimensions of, 233
– DSM-IV-TR criteria for, 14–16, 15t
– health anxiety vs., 17–18
– as OCD, 35
Hypothalamus, 301

I
IAS. *See* Illness Attitudes Scale (IAS)
IBQ. *See* Illness Behavior Questionnaire (IBQ)
IBS. *See* Irritable bowel syndrome (IBS)
Idea(s), intrusive, 148f, 154
Illness Attitudes Scale (IAS), 109
– in maladaptive behavior assessment, 163–164
Illness Behavior Questionnaire (IBQ), 109
Illness phobia, 32–33
Illness-related beliefs, heritability of, 45
Illness-related cues, avoidance of, 80–81
Image(s), 23–24
Imaginal exposure, 91–92, 242–247
– preliminary, 247
– primary, 243–246
– secondary, 246–247
– techniques in, 243–247
Imipramine, in health anxiety management, 96t
Independence, encouraging of, 255
Individual strengths, in clinical interview, 116

Informal discussion, of cognitive errors, 211–213
Informational support, maintaining improvement after therapy in, 272–273
Informational transmission, 63–64, 64f
Initial assessment
– access medical records in, 105
– aims of, 104–105
– ASI-3 in. *See* Anxiety Sensitivity Index – 3rd revision (ASI-3)
– BDI-II in, 108
– BVS in, 108
– CBHQ in, 110
– clinical interview in, 110–116, 112t, 115f. *See also* Clinical interview
– collateral and release of information in, 117
– cultural issues in, 120
– developing therapeutic relationship in, 103–104
– diagnosis and, 103–121
– IAS in, 109
– IBQ in, 109
– importance of ongoing assessment in, 104
– measuring symptom severity in, 117–119. *See also* Symptom severity measurement
– obstacles in, 121
– prior to clinical interview, 105–110
– providing feedback to patient in, 119–120
– referrals in, 120
– SDS in, 110
– self-report measures of symptoms severity in, 105–110
– SHAI in, 106–107
– SSAS in, 110
– structured diagnostic interviews in, 116–117
– WI in, 109
Insight
– in clinical interview, 118–119
– health anxiety and, 28
Internal medicine physician, perspective on health anxiety, 9

Internal stimuli, health anxiety precipitated by, 18–20, 19t
Interoceptive cues, 92
Interoceptive exposure, 92t, 247–250, 249t
– body sensations during, 249, 249t
– planning for, 248
– primary, 248–249, 249t
– rationale for, 247–248
– secondary, 249t, 250
– techniques for, 248–250, 251t
Interpretation(s)
– leading to health anxiety, 52–55, 53f, 54t
– negative, 216–218, 217t, 219f, 307
– threatening, 171
Interview(s)
– clinical, 110–116, 112t, 115f. *See also* Clinical interview
– structured diagnostic, 116–117
Intolerance, orthostatic, 50, 303–304
Intolerance of anxiety, 308
– cognitive therapy for, 230
Intolerance of uncertainty, 57, 307
– cognitive therapy for, 220–224, 223f
Intolerance of Uncertainty Scale (IUS), for assessing beliefs, 157
Intrusive ideas, in functional assessment, 148f, 154
Intrusive thoughts, 23–24
– in functional assessment, 148f, 154
Irritable bowel syndrome (IBS), 49–50
It's Not All in Your Head, 273
IUS. *See* Intolerance of Uncertainty Scale (IUS)

L
Lapse, relapse vs., 272
Learning, observational, 62
Lecturing, avoidance of, 126–127
Life experiences, in case formulation, 172
Lifestyle of exposure, 255
– maintaining improvement after therapy in, 270
Lipoma(s), 51

Listening, reflective, 125–126, 126t
Lofty standards, 308
– cognitive therapy for, 228–229
Logical thinking, in maintaining improvement after therapy in, 270
Losing control, misperceptions related to fight-or-flight response, 299
Lyme disease, fear of, 32

M
Maintaining improvement after therapy, 268–273
– abstinence violation effect and, 271–272
– continued social support in, 272
– in high-risk situations, 269–270
– informational support in, 272–273
– lapse vs. relapse, 272
– logical thinking and, 270
– practical support in, 273
Maintenance factors, 68–84
– behavioral, 74–80
– cognitive, 71–74
– defined, 67
– physiological, 69–71, 70f
Maladaptive behaviors
– body checking, 25t, 26, 77–78, 160–161, 253
– CBHQ in, 163
– IAS in, 163–164
– identification of, 158–164
– passive avoidance, 159–160
– reassurance-seeking via other forms of compulsive checking, 161–162
– safety-seeking behaviors and signals, 162–163
– self-report inventories for, 163–164
– TSMS in, 164
Maladaptive health anxiety, 14
Mayo Clinic, health anxiety perspectives at, 6–12
Medical conditions, benign, 49–52
Medical consultations, patient's requests for additional, 262

Medical diagnoses, dichotomous nature of, 136–137

Medical records, access to, 105

Medical results, dichotomous nature of, 136–137

Medical students' disease, 63–64, 64f

Medicalize, in enhancing motivation and communication, 127–128

Medically unexplained complaints, origins of, 194–195

Medication(s)

– CBT vs., 97–98

– in health anxiety management, 96–98, 96t

Medicine, distrust of, 59

Memory bias, 74

Mental analyzing, during response prevention, 254

Meta-analytic treatment comparison, 98–99, 99t

Mind-body connection

– body noise related to, 304

– in enhancing motivation and communication, 137–139

MINI. See Mini International Neuropsychiatric Interview (MINI)

Mini International Neuropsychiatric Interview (MINI), 17

Minor medical conditions, body noise related to, 303

Misinterpretation(s), in functional assessment, 148f, 154–158

Mood, in clinical interview, 112–113

Motivation for treatment

– in clinical interview, 116

– enhancement of, 122–143

Multidimensional Fear of Death Scale, for assessing beliefs, 158

Muscle(s), fight-or-flight response effects on, 298

N

Nefazodone, in health anxiety management, 96t

Negative interpretations, 307

– cognitive therapy for, 216–218, 217t, 219f

Neuroticism, in case formulation, 171–172

Noise, body. See Body noise

Nonadherence, solutions for overcoming, 257–259

Nonadherent patients, terminating treatment with, 260–261

Nonepileptic seizures, 50–51

Notion(s), 52–55, 53f, 54t

Not-so-great expectations, 307

– cognitive therapy for, 215–216

Nurture, 60–64, 64f

O

Observation(s), in case formulation, 172

Observational learning, 62

Obsession(s), schizophrenia, 35

Obsessive-compulsive disorder (OCD), 34–36

– case example, 35

– common obsessions in, 35

– features of, 34–35

– hypochondriasis as, 35

– schizophrenia obsessions, 35

Obstacle(s), overcoming of, 257–263

OCD. See Obsessive-compulsive disorder (OCD)

Ongoing assessment, importance of, 104

Open-ended questions, in clinical interview, 112t

Orthostatic intolerance, 50

– body noise related to, 303–304

– described, 303

Overestimates of threat, 55–56

P

Pain, chronic, 37

Pain disorder, 37

Panic attacks, somatic sensations during, 33

Panic disorder, 33–34

– case example, 33

Parasympathetic nervous system, in fight-or-flight response, 296
Paroxetine, in health anxiety management, 96t
Partner involvement, in health-anxiety symptoms, 115t
Passive avoidance, 25t, 27–28
– defined, 159
– as maladaptive behavior, 159–160
Patient history
– assessment of, 111–112, 112t
– in clinical interview, 113
Patient's control, emphasis on, 130–131
Persistence, of health anxiety, 67–84
Personal choice, emphasis on, 130–131
Perturbation(s), in functional assessment, 147f, 152–153
Phobia(s)
– disease, 32–33
– illness, 32–33
Physical sensations, health anxiety precipitated by, 18–19, 19t
Physiological factors, 69–71, 70f
– case example, 69
"Play-by-play" descriptions, in functional assessment, 150–151
Postural orthostatic tachycardia syndrome, 50
Practical support, maintaining improvement after therapy in, 273
Preliminary imaginal exposure, 247
Prevalence, of health anxiety, 38, 39
Previous treatment, in clinical interview, 114
Primary imaginal exposure, 243–246
Primary interoceptive exposure, 248–249, 249t
Primary-care physician, perspectives on health anxiety, 8
Probability, assumptions about, 225–226, 307
Programmed exposure, 255
Psychodynamic approaches, 85–86
Psychoeducation, 88–89, 181–201
– anxiety-related, 185–190, 189f

– body noise – related, 194–199
– body vigilance – related, 194–199
– described, 181
– fight-or-flight response – related, 185–190, 186f, 189f
– gauging patient's perspective on, 181–182
– rationale for, 199–201
– safety behavior in, 190–193, 194f
– sources of body symptoms in, 195–196
– for threatening thinking, 183–185
– during treatment, 201
Psychological treatments, 89t, 92t, 95–95
– ERP, 90–93, 92t
– explanatory therapy, 86–87
– imaginal exposure, 91–92
– patient's ambivalence about, 123
– psychodynamic approaches, 85–86
– psychoeducation, 88–89
– rationale for, 141–143, 142t
– transition to, 143
Psychologist, perspective on health anxiety, 9–12
Pupil(s), fight-or-flight response effects on, 298

Q
Question(s), open-ended, 112t
Questioning, Socratic, 263–264
Questionnaire(s), self-report, 157–158

R
Reasoning, emotional, 230, 308
Reassurance
– during exposure therapy, 251
– responses to requests for, 310
Reassurance-seeking, 75–77
– excessive, 261–262
– during exposure exercises, 263
– in health anxiety, 24–26, 25t
– patient's use of cognitive therapy in, 264
– persistent, 75–76
– during response prevention, 253
– responses to, 310

– solutions for overcoming, 261–262
– via other forms of compulsive checking, 161–162
Recent episodes, in functional assessment, 150–151
Referral(s), in clinical interview, 120
Reflect resistance, in enhancing motivation and communication, 130
Reflection, amplified, 129–130
Reflective listening
– empathy with, 125–126, 126t
– in enhancing motivation and communication, 125–126, 126t
Relapse, lapse vs., 272
Relationship(s), therapeutic, 103–104
Relative involvement, in health-anxiety symptoms, 115t
Release of information, in clinical interview, 117
Requests for additional medical consultations, solutions for overcoming, 262
Requests for reassurance, responses to, 310
Resistance
– reflection of, 130
– roll with, 129–131
Response prevention, 251–254, 252f
– body checking during, 253
– cleaning/washing during, 254
– dietary restriction during, 254
– employing support person during, 254
– mental analyzing during, 254
– reassurance-seeking during, 253
– rules for, 253–254
Response prevention form, 252, 252f
Result(s), dichotomous nature of, 136–137
Rigid health-related beliefs, 58
Roll with resistance, in enhancing motivation and communication, 129–131
Rumination syndrome, 49

S
Safety, situational, 25t, 27
Safety behaviors, 25t, 27

– catastrophic beliefs related to, 79–80
– defined, 79, 158
– psychoeducation related to, 190–193, 194f
– situational, 79–80
Safety signals, 25t, 27
– catastrophic beliefs related to, 79–80
– defined, 79, 158
– as maladaptive behavior, 162–163
Safety-seeking behaviors
– continued use of, 264–265
– in functional assessment, 149f
– as maladaptive behavior, 162–163
Schizophrenia obsessions, case example, 35
SCID-IV. See Structured Clinical Interview for DSM-IV-TR (SCID-IV)
SDIH. See Structured Diagnostic Interview for Hypochondriasis (SDIH)
SDS. See Sheehan Disability Scale (SDS)
Secondary imaginal exposure, 246–247
Secondary interoceptive exposure, 249t, 250
Seizure(s), nonepileptic, 50–51
Self-monitoring
– of body symptoms, 292–293
– in functional assessment, 164–166
Self-report inventories, in maladaptive behavior assessment, 163–164
Self-report questionnaire, in assessing cognitions, 157–158
Sensation(s)
– body. See Body sensations
– in functional assessment, 147f, 152–153
– physical, 18–19, 19t
– somatic, 33
Sensitivity, anxiety, 56–57
Severity, assumptions about, 225–226, 307
SHAI. See Short Health Anxiety Inventory (SHAI)
Sheehan Disability Scale (SDS), 110
Short Health Anxiety Inventory (SHAI), 106–107

– for assessing beliefs, 157

Signal(s), safety. *See* Safety signals

Situational exposure, 238–242, 239f, 241f
– building hierarchy in, 238–240, 239f
– conducting exposures in, 240–242, 241f
– troubleshooting in, 242

Situational safety behaviors, 25t, 27, 79–80

Social functioning, in clinical interview, 113

Social support, maintaining improvement after therapy in, 272

Socialization, defined, 131

Socratic questioning, therapist's misuse of, 263–264

Socratic style, in cognitive therapy, 205–206

Somatic delusions
– case example, 31
– health anxiety in, 31

Somatic sensations, during panic attack, 33

Somatization, defined, 29

Somatization disorder
– health anxiety in, 29–30, 30t
– physical complaints in persons with, 29, 30t

Somatosensory amplification, components of, 41–42

Somatosensory Amplification Scale (SSAS), 110

SSAS. *See* Somatosensory Amplification Scale (SSAS)

Stimulus(i)
– external, 20–21, 21t, 148f, 153. *See* External stimuli
– internal, 18–20, 19t

Strength(s), individual, 116

Stressful experiences, 61

Stressor(s), after termination of therapy, 268

Structured Clinical Interview for DSM-IV-TR (SCID-IV), 17

Structured Diagnostic Interview for Hypochondriasis (SDIH), 117

Structured diagnostic interviews, in initial assessment and diagnosis of health anxiety, 116–117

Support
– informational, 272–273
– social, 272

Sweating, fight-or-flight response effects on, 298

Sympathetic arousal, 48–49

Sympathetic nervous system, in fight-or-flight response, 296

Symptom(s), body, 195–196

Symptom severity, self-report measures of, 105–110

Symptom severity measurement
– in clinical interview, 117–119
– depressive symptoms in, 119
– insight in, 118–119
– Y-BOCS in, 118

T

Talk, change, 141–143, 142t

Temperature, body, 301–302

10 Commandments for successful exposures, 311

Termination of treatment, with argumentative or nonadherent patients, 260–261

Texas Safety Maneuver Scale (TSMS), in maladaptive behavior assessment, 164

Thanatophobia, 60

Therapeutic relationship, developing of, 103–104

Therapist(s)
– discomfort with exposure exercises, 266–267
– misuse of Socratic questioning, 263–264
– role during exposure therapy, 237–238

Thinking
– all-or-nothing, 213–215, 307
– logical, 270
– threatening, 183–185

Thinking errors, applying cognitive strategies to, 213–230, 217t, 219f, 223f
Thinking patterns, in health anxiety, 307–308
Thought(s)
– anxious, 186f, 189f
– intrusive, 23–24, 148f, 154
– threatening. *See* Threatening thoughts
Thought Challenging Form, 309
Threat(s), overestimation of, 55–56
Threat cues, selective attention to, 71–73
Threatening automatic thoughts, in case formulation, 171
Threatening thinking, psychoeducation related to, 183–185
Threatening thoughts
– considering evidence for and against, 207–210, 209t
– monitoring of, 183
Tinnitus, case example, 56
Toleration of uncertainty, advantages and disadvantages of, 223, 223f
Transmission, informational, 63–64, 64f
Traumatic experiences, 61
Treatment(s). *See also specific types*
– CBT, 93–95
– ERP, 90–93, 92t
– explanatory therapy, 86–87
– health anxiety – related, 85–100
– imaginal exposure, 91–92
– maintaining gains following termination of, 267–273
– maintaining improvement after, 268–273. *See also* Maintaining improvement after therapy
– meta-analytic treatment comparison of, 98–99, 99t
– motivation for, 116
– pharmacologic, 96–98, 96t
– plans after, 267–268
– preparing for stressors after, 268
– psychodynamic approaches, 85–86
– psychoeducation, 88–89, 201
– psychological, 89t, 92t, 95–95, 123

Treatment planning, 176–179, 176t, 178f
– case example, 177–179, 178f
– case formulation in, 177–179, 178f
Trigger(s)
– in case formulation, 170
– external stimuli as, 20–21, 21t
– in functional assessment, 147f-148f, 152–154
– of health anxiety, 18–21, 19t, 21t
– internal stimuli as, 18–20, 19t
TSMS. *See* Texas Safety Maneuver Scale (TSMS)
Tuesday's with Morrie, 5
Tumor(s), brain, 15
Twin studies, health anxiety phenomena in, 44

U
Unbearable anxiety levels, during behavioral experiments or exposures, 265
Uncertainty
– intolerance of, 57, 220–224, 223f, 307
– toleration of, 223, 223f
Unexplained complaints, from medical standpoint, 194–195

V
Vertigo, 50
Vigilance, body. *See* Body vigilance

W
Washing/cleaning, during response prevention, 254
Whiteley Index (WI), 109
WI. *See* Whiteley Index (WI)
Worry(ies), health-related, 36

Y
Yale-Brown Obsessive Compulsive Scale (Y-BOCS), 118, 312–313
Y-BOCS. *See* Yale-Brown Obsessive Compulsive Scale (Y-BOCS)